EVERYDAY SCIENCE

Real-Life Activities

John M. Scott
illustrated by
David Morin

J. WESTON
WALCH
PUBLISHER
PORTLAND, MAINE

1   2   3   4   5   6   7   8   9   10

ISBN 0-8251-2705-X

Copyright © 1988
J. Weston Walch, Publisher
P. O. Box 658 • Portland, Maine 04104-0658

Printed in the United States of America

CONTENTS

Chapter 6 WHAT IS THE PRESSURE ON YOUR HEAD?
It's the Same Pressure that Blows Airplanes Apart!

Discussion

Chapter 7 WILL THE DAY COME WHEN YOU CAN LIVE IN THE SEA?
How Can You Avoid a Diver's Number One Enemy?

Discussion

Chapter 8 NATURE'S "BELIEVE-IT-OR-NOT" ODDITIES
"Odd Fellows" Prove that Sometimes One Plus One Does Not Equal Two! 123

Discussion

Foreword

Everyday Science: Real-Life Activities is unique. It offers you the results of over 30 years of science teaching by John M. Scott. In the lab, in the lecture room, in articles and books, John Scott has the ability to clothe abstract thought in concrete language.

During the school year Scott taught at Campion High School in Prairie du Chien, Wisconsin. Educators who visited Scott's classes were so impressed by the enthusiasm his teaching generated among his students that in 1959 he was designated the Wisconsin Physics Teacher for that year. In 1967 he was picked as one of the top 40 science teachers in the nation.

At the request of the National Science Foundation, Scott also conducted summer institutes in physics for elementary school teachers and supervisors. It was during these summer sessions at Creighton University in Omaha, Nebraska, that I became acquainted with Scott and his fascinating way of teaching science.

John Scott has the rare combination of traits that mark an ideal teacher: the capacity and diligence to master a subject, and the ability to communicate this knowledge in a stimulating fashion.

The late Dr. Wernher von Braun, the eminent space scientist, cited John Scott for "turning the classroom into a launching pad of exciting new ideas." Scott believes that the minds of students are not "cups to be filled" but "torches to be lit." The job of the teacher is to strike the "spark" that will ignite this torch.

In *Everyday Science: Real-Life Activities*, Scott presents science so everyone may enjoy it, thrill to its discoveries, and come to realize that science is part of the fabric of life.

The unique feature of this book is that it offers many activities in science that can be done with simple equipment and with ordinary household items. No expensive outlay is required for complex demonstration equipment. There are no time-consuming pieces of apparatus to build. Each experiment relates directly to the world around us.

By working the many exciting experiments described in this book, students will acquire a personal, intimate experience of the fundamental laws of nature.

In addition, students will find that *Everyday Science: Real-Life Activities* is a treasure house of scientific facts composed of fascinating stories, cogent examples, novel applications, and "Believe-It-Or-Not" anecdotes which are as exciting and motivational as they are relevant to students' everyday experiences.

Bazil N. Lazure

Physics Professor
Creighton University

To the Reader

Each morning the sun deposits a fresh day on the doorstep, teachers have a golden opportunity to open the shutters of the mind, to let shine the golden light of truth, and to reveal to young people the magic and delight that crowds every minute with mystery and fascination.

The enthusiastic science teacher can turn the classroom into a launching pad of exciting new ideas to boost the minds of the young into orbits of knowledge and inspiration, remembering always that every advance in science, every achievement in technology, every masterpiece of art comes from the mind.

The world breaks like an unceasing surf on the shores of young minds. The longer the island of knowledge, the longer the shore of wonder. The joy of discovery is one of the greatest the human mind can experience.

Endless Adventure

We live in a universe throbbing with wonder, mystery, and adventure. There is no end to the adventures we may have if only we approach life with open eyes and mind.

In teaching students to observe, to think, to draw conclusions, the teacher's greatest stock-in-trade is the natural curiosity of the young. "We have just opened the door into the limitless reaches of the universe," said Dr. Wernher von Braun, the "Father of the Saturn V rocket."

"We can see just far enough ahead to know that man is at the threshold of a momentous era. Here is opportunity, challenge, adventure so tremendous as to exceed anything that has gone before. Here is the tomorrow youth wants to embrace."

Like dart players, teachers can toss needle-sharp questions into the minds of their students to make them come alive. And once students come alive, their minds will erupt energy like uranium atoms in fission.

Questions

The following are samples of some of the many questions found in this book. At the end of each question is listed the page on which the answer may be found.

- How can you reduce your weight without going on a diet? (43)

- When did skiing take off? (47)

- Why is 5 miles per second the "Magic Speed" for astronauts in orbit around planet Earth? (68)

- Did you ever skate on water? (83)

- Do you ever inhale? (90)

- How did a mouse become a "fish"? (107)

- Why do golf balls have dimples? (124)

- Can you float steel on water? (132)

- What is "faster water"? (143)

- Why is it dangerous for you to take a drink of ice-cold soda pop, then bite into a red-hot hot dog? (174)

- Can you make steel burn? (179)

- How can you prove that light is a "dark subject"? (192)

- How can a jug of water set your house on fire? (198)

- What are the three bones in your body that never grow? (229)

- Why can we speak of your "double duty" ears? (240)

- Did you ever eat sunlight for breakfast? (265)

- Can you turn your head into a broadcasting station? (277)

- Can you get electricity from a lemon? (281)

- Do you know why there will be no sunrise tomorrow morning? (292)

Demonstrations

If Confucius had taken time out to observe a demonstration in science, he would no doubt have added, "One demonstration is worth more than a thousand pictures."

The unique feature of this book is that it offers many classroom demonstrations in science that can be done with simple equipment and with ordinary household items. No expensive outlay is required for complex demonstration equipment. There are no time-consuming pieces of apparatus to build, and each experiment directly relates to the world around us.

The busy teacher who has to make the most of what is easily available will, I sincerely hope, find in this book a wealth of information on how to make use of ordinary, everyday objects in presenting demonstrations in science.

We concentrate on demonstrations your students will take delight in doing. In particular, the many applications of science to daily life will help turn the big, wide world around us into a lab for carrying on experiments. Even though all your students may not be junior-grade Einsteins, it does not matter. This book presents science so that everyone may enjoy it, thrill to its discoveries, and come to realize that science is part of the fabric of life.

This book makes science exciting by showing how every aspect of our lives is controlled by science or, rather, is science in action.

—*John M. Scott*

Chapter Topics

Note on Equipment and Safety

All of the activities in this book are designed to be performed safely with inexpensive, readily available materials. Unusual or toxic chemicals are not needed for any activity. Each is labeled as follows:

Home — These activities use supplies often found in the home. They are simple to perform for students and adults. Adults should always be present to help younger people with their investigations.

Supervised Classroom — There is equipment needed for these activities that would normally be available in a school science classroom, or the nature of the activity makes it best suited for a class demonstration. A few require Bunsen burners, or other hot or burning materials. Of course, the absolute rule is that teachers must always closely supervise students working in the laboratory.

No Label — No equipment is needed for these activities. They are simply thinking exercises or involve checking library references.

Chapter 1

NATURE'S TRAFFIC LAWS

They're Enough to Kill You

On the night of April 8th, a red Corvette roared down Highway 18. Its speed was later estimated to be in excess of 100 miles per hour. The police took up the chase. By the time the police car turned the corner and reached the junction of Highway 18, not even the taillights of the speeding car could be seen. They thought that the driver had escaped, and thus succeeded in breaking a traffic regulation.

Nature, however, was "on the job" and insisted on "playing it straight." Just south of town, behind Campion High School, Highway 18 makes a slight curve. The speed of the Corvette, however, was so great that Newton's First Law of Motion took over.

Instead of making it around the curve, the Corvette zoomed straight into a field. An eyewitness said the car shot through the air 450 feet and rolled over 4 times. The shattered body of the driver was found 120 feet from the car. The car was stripped clean of most of its fiberglass body.

The "Highway Killer" that lurks on our expressways is known as Newton's First Law of Motion: "**EVERY BODY PERSISTS IN A STATE OF REST, OR IN UNIFORM MOTION IN A STRAIGHT LINE, UNLESS ACTED UPON BY AN EXTERNAL FORCE.**"

Newton's First Law of Motion has killed more Americans in auto accidents than the total number of Americans killed in World War I, World War II, the Korean War, Vietnam, and all other wars involving the United States.

Your first lesson in safe driving begins long before you sit behind the wheel of the family car. The most essential laws governing safe driving are not the ones enforced by the police. They are the fundamental laws of Nature.

1

The truth is that you can sometimes violate a traffic regulation and escape the consequences. But—and here is the most important fact—you cannot break nature's traffic laws.

Last year approximately 48,000 Americans tried to break nature's traffic laws. They paid the penalty—with their lives. Nature's laws are unrelenting, always in force, always demanding obedience. You do what nature says or pay the penalty—which is swift, sudden, and sure. No questions asked, no trial by jury, no delay.

700 PEOPLE STRETCHED OUT ON ROAD

In order to remind people of the deaths on their highways, 700 citizens of Portland, Oregon, did something very dramatic. They stretched out on a Portland highway to remind everyone that in the previous year 700 people died in car accidents in Oregon. Mobil Oil used a picture of this in a $4 million advertising campaign to promote auto safety. *Life* magazine gave a full page to this overwhelming picture of 700 bodies.

WATCH THAT CURVE!

Do you realize that the only "external force" that enables a car to turn is friction between the tires and road? When the road is covered with ice, there is less friction. The chance of making the turn is decreased and the conclusion is simple: "Cars that wreck themselves going around curves do so because they obey Newton's First Law of Motion!"

A CHILD IS TOP-HEAVY!

During the fall of 1980 a special warning was sounded for parents of young children. An infant is proportioned differently than an adult. This means that small children are top-heavy, usually until the age of five. If these children are not restrained in a car crash, or even a sudden stop, they tend to pitch forward headfirst. Even a minor collision can throw a small child against the car's interior and cause serious injuries.

Holding a child in a parent's arms is not a substitute for a Child Restraint System. Some people think that holding a child in a car protects the child but safety experts disagree. In an accident, a child in a parent's arms can be crushed between the car's interior and the unrestrained parent. Even if the parent is wearing a selt belt, in a 30-mile-per-hour collision a 10-pound child exerts a 300-pound force against the parent's grip. Chances are that even a strong adult won't be able to hold on to a child in such a situation.

SNOWMOBILE BRINGS DEATH

On Monday, December 19, 1983, the Des Moines, Iowa, *Register* carried a news item about two men who were killed riding a snowmobile. The men were traveling at such a high rate of speed that they missed a sharp curve. The snowmobile became airborne, flew about 80 feet in the air, and landed in a deep ravine.

NAVY PILOT SHOOTS HIMSELF DOWN

A Navy pilot who forgot Newton's First Law of Motion shot himself down. This fantastic accident, the first of its type in aviation history, occurred when test pilot Tom Attridge put his Grumman F11F-1 into an 888-mile-per-hour dive and fired two quick bursts over the Atlantic Ocean near Long Island.

The Navy gave the following explanation of the accident: "When a stream of cannon shells spewed from the four guns at the rate of 1000 rounds per minute, or better than 64 rounds for each four-second burst, they were traveling more than 1500 feet faster than the airplane. The shells were traveling forward and also were falling towards the earth. They were following a curved course toward the ocean. The jet meanwhile went into a steeper dive and increased its speed.

"About 2 to 3 miles from the point where the firing began, the plane and shells collided. One shell shattered the bulletproof glass in the jet's windshield. A second shell pierced the engine, which died, causing the jet to crash land in a wood. The 33-year-old pilot was hospitalized with a fractured leg and three broken vertebrae."

DANGER ON YOUR LAWN

Newspapers recently carried this warning: "The boy David of Biblical times is no longer with us, but on many lawns across America are modern mechanized 'Davids' which make use of Newton's First Law of Motion to injure more than 80,000 people every year.

"The 23-inch blade of a common rotary lawn mower can pick up a rock or chunk of metal and hurl it at speeds up to 240 miles per hour. A piece of wire traveling at this speed can penetrate a shoe, and be driven almost completely through the foot, damaging both bone and flesh. Physicians consider rotary mowers one of the most dangerous pieces of machinery their patients use."

CANNONBALL

Hugo Zacchini, billed as the Human Cannonball, is a gentleman who has put

Newton's First Law of Motion to work for many years. Ever since he was 20 years old, Hugo has been sliding into a cannon and getting hurtled out again by a force of compressed air equal to 250 pounds per square inch. Black powder is exploded at the same time, but only for dramatic effect.

As soon as Zacchini slips into the mouth of the cannon, the barrel begins to rise until it stands at an angle of 45°. There is a deafening blast, and Zacchini bursts from the cannon muzzle amid a cloud of theatrical smoke. Traveling at nearly 90 miles per hour, he sails upward with his arms extended like Superman. He narrowly avoids the yellow vinyl banners.

Now he begins his descent over the potted dwarf trees. He lands finally in the middle of a broad nylon net. The net sags like an old bed, nearly swallowing up Zacchini. Then the net shoots him upward like a watermelon seed. He bounces twice before he stops. He has traveled 170 feet.

DEADLY STATISTICS

A government report states that auto accidents are the leading cause of death of America's young people ages 1 to 24.

A study of the circumstances surrounding the death of the 20,279 young people who died in one year on our highways, reveals the following:

Most were male.
Most were drunk or on drugs.
Most were driving too fast.
Most were not using seat belts.
Most were not paying attention.
Most were driving on a Saturday.

DEER, DEER!

The Iowa Department of Transportation informs us that November is Iowa's most dangerous month of the year for traffic accidents involving deer. In 1983 there were 1,700 traffic accidents involving deer. Two persons were killed and 194 injured. The most dangerous time of the day for traffic accidents involving deer is from 6 P.M. until midnight.

PUNCH DRUNK

One of the most tragic and devastating examples of Newton's First Law of Motion is found in boxing. The human brain sits inside the skull like a mound of

Jell-O in a bowl. If a blow is delivered to the head, the bony ridges on the inner surface of the skull may slam into the outer membrane surrounding the brain. This membrane, which carries much of the brain's blood supply, may be torn. Blood then leaks into the space between the skull and the brain, building up brain-damaging pressure. More violent blows can damage the brain tissue itself when the skull smashes against the brain.

Even blows landed by inexperienced, relatively lightweight boxers can be very powerful. Tests at the University of Wisconsin show that a 145-pound amateur boxer produced an average of 600 pounds of pressure with each punch. The results of a punch of this force delivered to the head can be devastating. They include bruising, bleeding, and swelling within the brain, tearing of blood vessels leading to the brain, and damage to brain centers controlling speech, walking, and facial expressions.

Because punches to the head are so quickly effective in disabling an opponent, they are among the most potent and most frequently used weapons in the boxer's arsenal. So it may not be surprising that in a 25-year period more than 400 boxing matches have ended in the death of one of the contestants.

Recently, the Royal College of Physicians in London completed a 7-year study of 224 former professional boxers. The researchers came to the conclusion that the longer a man boxes, the greater the chances of permanent injury to his brain.

WHY IS THE PITCHER'S MOUND HIGHER?

Before he was felled by a stroke in July 1980, Houston Astros pitcher J.R. Richard was considered the best righthander in baseball. This 6-foot 8-inch giant could hurl a baseball at a speed of 98 miles per hour.

But not even J.R. Richard could throw a baseball in a straight line!

Why not? Does not Newton's First Law of Motion state that "a body in motion continues in motion in a straight line"?

It does, but it likewise adds, "unless compelled by an external force to change."

What is the "external force" that makes it impossible for a baseball, a bullet, or an arrow to continue in a straight line?

The answer is gravity. The pull of gravity makes the path of a baseball a parabola, a curve that goes down in a graceful arc.

As the baseball travels the 60½ feet from the pitcher's mound to home plate, it drops 3 to 4 feet. In order to allow for this loss in height, the pitcher's mound is made three to four feet higher than the bottom of the strike zone at home plate.

INERTIA

The tendency of a body at rest to remain at rest—and a body in motion to remain in motion in a straight line—unless acted upon by an external force, is called inertia.

If you are riding in the front seat of a car and the driver suddenly slams on the brakes, your body will continue to move forward unless stopped by an external force—hopefully by the seat belt and shoulder strap—or, unfortunately, by the windshield.

The word "inertia" comes from the Latin word "iners," meaning idle or unskilled. When we say that matter is inert, we mean that it does not have the power to move itself, or, if it is put into motion, it cannot stop itself.

"THE FASTEST MAN ON EARTH"

"The Fastest Man on Earth" is the title held by Lt. Col. J.P. Stapp. He was strapped into the rocket sled Sonic Wind. In just 5 seconds he was accelerated to a speed of 632 miles per hour. The rocket sled was then stopped in 1.4 seconds. Col. Stapp's arms and legs were securely tied to the sled. His eyes, however, tried to obey Newton's First Law of Motion. To see what happened, turn to page 259 of the *National Geographic* magazine for August 1955. You will find the most frightening pair of "shiners" you have ever seen. Col. Stapp suffered a temporary loss of vision. The experiments with the Sonic Wind were stopped. The risk to vision was considered to be too great to permit further testing.

HEADLONG DASH TO INJURY

A lead article in *Medical World News* on skiing was introduced with the caption "HEADLONG DASH TO INJURY." The subtitle read, "For 12,000 skiers the trail this season will end in the doctor's office."

One dramatic photo of a falling skier had this caption: "Boot-top fractures of the leg bones occur when the ski jams against an obstruction. As the body continues its forward motion, force is exerted against stopped ankle, snapping bones."

POLE VAULTING

Pole vaulting is a magnificent demostration of Newton's First Law of Motion. A young man holding a pole runs forward at maximum speed. As soon as he thrusts the pole into the ground, the pole becomes an "external force" that changes the horizontal, straight-line motion of the runner into a vertical motion that may carry him to a height of 18 feet.

"COASTING" ON A BOEING 747

If you've ever made an air trip between distant cities, such as Chicago and San Francisco, you may have noticed something strange. While your Boeing 747 jet is still many miles from your destination, the pilot cuts down on the power of the engines. You become aware of a decrease in the noise of the jets. In the near-silence you feel as though you are "coasting" through the sky. And so, indeed, you may. The inertia of the jet keeps the Boeing 747 moving forward.

BROAD JUMP

When track season rolls around in the spring, perhaps you try to win the broad jump. You run as fast as possible, then leap. Once you leap, you depend on Newton's First Law of Motion to carry you to victory.

WHIPLASH

Newton's First Law of Motion can cause great pain in a whiplash injury. The car of the whiplash victim, whether at rest or in motion, is struck from the rear by a second vehicle, usually moving at an appreciably greater speed.

The impact of the collision acts instantaneously upon the seat of the car, since it is part of the chassis. The seat, in turn, pushes rapidly forward against the torso, or upper part of the body.

The weighty head, however, tends to stay in its previous position. The result is that the torso is forced by the impact to pass *under* the head. The effect is that the heavy head pushes down on the neck and spine, compressing them.

"A BODY AT REST TENDS TO REMAIN AT REST"

Perhaps you have demonstrated the first part of Newton's First Law of Motion on a school morning in mid-January when your mother called you to get out of bed. You proved only too thoroughly the fact that "a body at rest tends to remain at rest."

Activity 1

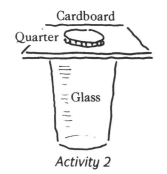

Activity 2

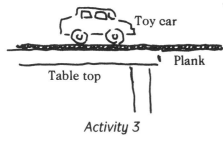

Activity 3

ACTIVITIES

1. BLOCK IN JAR   *Home*

Fill a wide-mouth gallon jar about ¾ full of water. The school cafeteria or a restaurant may be able to supply you with a gallon jar. Place a small wood block in the water.

Now take hold of the gallon jar with both hands. Lift the jar off the table. Turn the jar through half a turn. What happens? Why?

2. QUARTER AND GLASS   *Home*

Place a small square of stiff cardboard over the open end of a drinking glass. Place a quarter in the center of the cardboard. Now give the card a sudden snap on the edge with your finger. The card will scoot away, and the quarter will drop into the glass. The quarter tends to stay at rest. It does not suddenly move forward with the cardboard.

3. CAR ON PLANK   *Supervised Classroom*

Place a small plank or heavy piece of cardboard on one side of a table, with about one foot of the plank extending out over the end of the table.

On top of the plank place a heavy toy car. Now grasp the free end of the plank and pull rapidly. Newton's First Law will keep the car on the table. It wants to remain at rest.

4. EXPERIMENT WITH THIS BOOK   *Home*

Instead of using a plank and a car, as in the previous experiment, try placing a piece of strong wrapping paper on top of the table. Leave about four inches of the paper sticking out over the edge of the table. On top of the paper place this book. Now take hold of the paper with both hands. Give a rapid pull on the paper. The paper will come with you, but the book will be left sitting where it was. This simple demonstration illustrates the fact that "a body at rest tends to remain at rest."

5. *HOW TO GET GOING*   **Supervised Classroom**

Hook a spring scale to a heavy block of wood or a toy automobile. Pull rapidly on the scale. Notice the indicator the moment you jerk the block into motion. What happens when you continue to pull? Why?

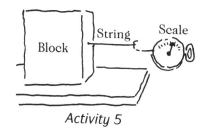

Activity 5

6. *ROLLING MARBLES*   **Home**

Place a couple of marbles in the "back" end of an open cigar box. Push the box rapidly to the left, as indicated by the arrow pointing to the letter A. Stop the box suddenly. Note that the marbles will continue to move forward in the direction of A.

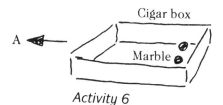

Activity 6

7. *WHIRLING WATER*   **Home**

In this experiment we again use the wide-mouth gallon jar we used in our first experiment. After you fill the jar about ¾ full of water, do the following.

Insert a wooden ruler vertically into the jar and stir the water. When the water is racing around the walls of the jar at top speed, remove the ruler. Drop a small wooden block into the jar. What happens? Why?

Activity 7

8. *CABBAGE PATCH DOLL*   **Home**

Tie an empty shoe box (or any other similar box) to a skateboard. Seat a Cabbage Patch doll, or any similar object, in the back of the box. Give the skateboard a swift push so it rolls swiftly across the sidewalk to collide with a brick or rock. Explain what happens.

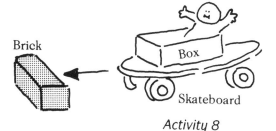

Activity 8

9. *YO-YO*   **Home**

Put a yo-yo in motion and explain how it demonstrates Newton's First Law of Motion.

10. *GYROSCOPE*   **Supervised Classroom**

One of the most interesting demonstrations I do for my students is this. I mount a big bike wheel (along with its heavy balloon tire) on an axle. On the ends of this axle I mount handles.

Activity 9

Bike wheel

Activity 10

I pick up the bike wheel with my left hand and hold it in a vertical position. I grasp the tire with my right hand and give the wheel the fastest spin I can. I now place one handle of the rapidly spinning wheel into the right hand of a student. I ask the student to turn the spinning wheel from a vertical to a horizontal plane.

Students find this most difficult to do. The spinning wheel tends to stay in motion in one plane—in this case, a vertical plane. It resists any attempt to make it change.

11. SPINNING STOOL   Supervised Classroom

The next demonstration is even more interesting. I ask a student to sit on a swivel lab stool that is about 2½ feet high. I ask the student to sit far enough back on the swivel stool so his feet do not touch the floor. I ask him to extend both hands and grasp the handles of the bike wheel mentioned in the previous experiment. I ask him to keep the wheel in a vertical position.

Now I grasp the tire with both hands. With all the strength at my command, I give the wheel a spinning force. I instruct the student to turn the spinning bike wheel from a vertical to a horizontal position. As soon as he does so, the student finds that he is spinning around on the swivel stool.

Now I ask the student to turn the wheel 180° so the bike wheel is spinning in the opposite direction. As soon as he does, the swivel stool also changes the direction of its spin.

Students delight in conducting this experiment for themselves long after the class period is over.

12. PING-PONG BALL   Home

Is it true that an object moving in a circle is trying to travel in a straight line?

You can find out by whirling a safe "slingshot" that won't cause damage. Get a strong thread or string about 2 feet long. Use a darning needle to run the string through a ping-pong ball. After you've pulled the string through and tied a knot to hold it in place, pick it up and whirl it.

You soon become aware that the ping-pong ball is pulling on the string. This is because the whirling ping-pong ball keeps moving outward from the center of rotation. This outward pull is known as centrifugal force. ("Centrifugal" comes from a Latin term that means "to flee from the center.")

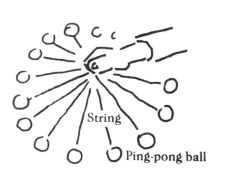

String

Ping-pong ball

Activity 12

Now let the string go. The ping-pong ball becomes a body in motion in a straight line.

13. MARBLE IN GLASS BOWL

Home

Put a marble in a big glass bowl. Pick up the bowl with both hands. Give it a rotary motion. What happens? Why?

Activity 13

14. RECORD PLAYER

Home

An old 78 rpm record player with adjustable speed control is an excellent piece of equipment to demonstrate how centrifugal force depends on weight, radius, and speed of the objects placed on the turntable.

   a. Place various small weights on the rim of the spinning turntable. What happens?

   b. Place a weight at various distances from the center of the spinning turntable. What do you notice?

   c. Vary the speed of the turntable. What happens to the weights placed on it?

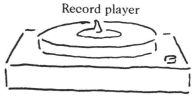

Activity 14

15. REDUCE THE RADIUS

Home

What happens when you reduce the length of the radius of the circle in which a body is turning?

To find out, get a piece of strong thread, or string, about 10 inches long. Tie one end of the string around the index finger of your right hand. Tie the other end of the string to a paper clip or small key. Whirl the paper clip in a circle. Stop moving your hand suddenly. Note the change in the circling time as the string winds around your finger. Note that the smaller the radius, the faster the paper clip picks up speed.

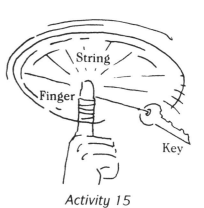

Activity 15

16. INCREASE YOUR SPIN

Home

Here is an interesting experiment for you to do if you have a revolving piano stool. Sit on the stool with your arms extended as far out as possible. In each hand hold a heavy book. Let a friend start spinning you slowly. Now pull the books in toward your chest. Note what happens.

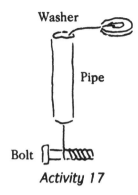

Activity 17

17. PIPE AND BOLT   *Supervised Classroom*

Run a string through a small pipe about 6 inches long. Tie a washer or big cork to the top end of the string. Tie a small bolt or nail to the other end.

Hold the pipe in an upright, vertical position. When there is no motion, the heavier bolt will draw the washer to the top rim of the pipe. Now give the pipe a stirring motion. What happens when you increase the speed of rotation?

18. PAINT WITH CENTRIFUGAL FORCE   *Supervised Classroom*

For a science fair, some of my students conducted this delightful and artistic demonstration of centrifugal force. They secured:

—an old 78 rpm record player with speed control
—three empty plastic squeeze bottles (they once held honey)
—three small cans of paint (red, blue, and green)

Each can of paint was poured into one of the plastic squeeze bottles.

The students collected a number of smooth, white pieces of cardboard of the type that are inserted in shirts when they are returned from the laundry. These cardboards were cut into circles big enough to cover the turntable of the record player.

Now the experiment was ready.

The students placed the turntable inside a cardboard box about 5 inches deep. This was to protect bystanders from unwanted results of centrifugal force. A piece of cardboard was pushed down over the spindle and positioned snugly against the turntable. The turntable was set in motion. Now a student picked up the plastic bottle with the red paint. Pointing the nozzle at the center of the card, he squeezed a few drops of red paint on the spinning cardboard. He then did the same with the blue and green paints.

The results are so fantastic, there is no way to describe them. You will have to do this demonstration yourself to enjoy the artistic results. Repeat the experiment several times, and change the speed of the turntable each time.

19. WATCH YOUR DOG   *Home*

The next time your dog comes out of a lake or pond, watch how he puts Newton's First Law of Motion to work to dry himself.

HIGHLIGHTS OF THIS CHAPTER

- The "Highway Killer" lurking on our expressways is Newton's First Law of Motion. It kills more than 48,000 Americans each year.

- Newton's First Law of Motion informs us that "Every body persists in a state of rest, or in uniform motion in a straight line, unless acted upon by an external force."

- The tendency of a body at rest to remain at rest, and a body in motion to remain in motion in a straight line, is called inertia. When we say that matter is inert, we mean that it does not have the power to move itself or, if it is put into motion, to stop itself.

Multiple-Choice Questions

1. When you receive a whiplash it is because:
    a. your head is moving rapidly in a forward direction.
    b. your head makes you top-heavy.
    c. your head tends to stay in its previous position.
    d. your body is not inert.

2. Judged by the number of Americans it has killed, the most dangerous weapon in the United States today is:
    a. the atom bomb.
    b. the hydrogen bomb.
    c. a handgun called the "Saturday Night Special."
    d. the automobile.

3. As a baseball travels the 60½ feet from the pitcher's mound to home plate, it drops:
    a. one to two feet.
    b. two to three feet.
    c. three to four feet.
    d. less than one foot.

4. If you don't leap out of bed when your alarm clock goes off at 6:30 A.M., this is most likely due to:
    a. lack of will power.
    b. lazy muscles.
    c. inertia.
    d. the fact that your mind is not yet in focus.

5. If a driver turn sharply to the left and the right door is not securely closed, it may swing open. This is because:
    a. it wants to keep going in a straight line.
    b. an object traveling around a curve tends to keep moving in a circle.
    c. the counterclockwise motion of the car imparts a clockwise motion to the door.
    d. there is not enough centrifugal force.

True or False Questions

1. Whiplash results from an unplanned demonstration of Newton's First Law of Motion.

2. A pitcher's mound is made three to four feet higher than the bottom of the strike zone at home plate because the speeding baseball is compelled by an external force to change its straight-line motion.

3. When a spinning ice skater draws her limbs in toward the center of her body, she will spin more slowly.

4. If you spin a lasso, centrifugal force throws the rope outward.

5. A basketball is said to be inert because it does not have the power to move itself or, if it is put into motion, to stop itself.

Chapter 2

HOW TO KEEP FROM BEING KILLED

It Depends on Time

It was circus day at Baraboo, Wisconsin, on Wednesday, July 11, 1979. I looked up in utter fascination as a trapeze artist swung back and forth high over my head. With each swing the man on the flying trapeze swung swiftly in ever-widening arcs.

With a final burst of speed, he released his hold on the trapeze and sailed out into thin air. His fingers were extended, ready to grasp the hands of his partner on a second trapeze.

Alas, his fingers failed by mere inches to contact the hands stretched out to grasp him. He fell earthward.

Despite his fall, the trapeze artist was not injured. He bounced up from the safety net to make a second and successful try.

As you are fully aware, without a safety net the man on the flying trapeze will make but one mistake—his first and last. As medical people would say, the results would be "terminal."

If he has a net, he can bounce back for another try. How come?

The answer is given in Newton's Second Law of Motion: **"THE FORCE REQUIRED TO ACCELERATE AN OBJECT IS PROPORTIONAL TO THE MASS OF THE OBJECT AND THE ACCELERATION GIVEN IT."**

Acceleration is the rate of change of velocity.

If an object is gaining speed, it has positive acceleration.

If an object is losing speed, it has negative acceleration, or deceleration.

"Pickup" is another word for acceleration. Car owners often speak about pickup, which means how quickly the car can increase speed.

We can express Newton's Second Law of Motion in the following formula:

$$\text{FORCE} = \frac{\text{MASS} \times \text{VELOCITY}}{\text{TIME}}$$

Mass is the quantity of material in a body. The attraction between the mass of the trapeze artist and the mass of planet Earth is called his weight.

Suppose that our trapeze artist were to hit solid ground. His body might be stopped in $1/10$ of a second. If he lands in a net, the time may be extended over 2 seconds. Since the time would be 20 times greater, the force needed to stop him would be only $1/20$ of what it would be with a solid landing.

EAGER-BEAVER ENGINEERS

Do you know that eager-beaver engineers cost the United States railroads over $100 million a year? An eager-beaver engineer who starts a freight train may forget that the merchandise in the boxcars tends to remain at rest. Result—the back of the boxcar slams into the freight, causing damage to a total of 3 billion tons of merchandise per year.

In an effort to minimize this loss, the Union Pacific railroad built a special boxcar with Plexiglas sides so railroaders could look in and see what happens when the car is coupled too fast. The Union Pacific was confident that its "Package Pullman" demonstration would do more good than all the previous decades' warnings and instructions.

IN THE BAG

Newton's Second Law is used to overcome the effects of Newton's First Law! Spurred on by the climbing cost of damage, the railroads investigated more secure ways to pack boxcars.

Results—in the bag!

An empty rubber bag manufactured by Goodyear is inserted between the boxes of merchandise and then inflated. The Super-Cushion Bags have reduced damage as much as 50%. Now, if a boxcar starts or stops too suddenly, the air-cushion will absorb the shock by increasing the stopping time.

SHOULDER STRAP AND SAFETY BELT

Do you know that shoulder straps and safety belts are dynamic examples of Newton's Second Law of Motion? Without them, when a car comes to a sudden stop, the bodies of passengers continue in a forward motion and are in danger of hitting the windshield or the metal framework. Since the stopping time is very short, the force is powerful enough to injure or kill.

The straps restrain passengers from plunging forward. They exert their stopping force over a greater interval and thus prevent injury.

AIR BAGS

According to some scientists air bags are effective safety devices for head-on automobile crashes. When a frontal collision occurs, electric signals ignite a canister of sodium azide in the steering column. The chemical instantly converts to nitrogen gas, inflating an air bag to cushion the driver. A second air bag is installed in the dashboard on the passenger side. Both bags are made of a porous material that deflates rapidly to prevent dangerous rebound off the bags.

HOW NEWTON'S SECOND LAW AFFECTS DETROIT

Push a gallon of milk across the breakfast table. Then push a quart of milk across the table. Since the quart of milk has less mass, it is easier to move.

This is what Newton's Second Law is all about. It informs us that the more mass or weight an object has, the greater is the force required to move it.

How does all this apply to the manufacturing of automobiles? Very simply! The less the mass or weight of a car, the less fuel it takes to make it go.

No wonder that Detroit is turning to aluminum. In 1948, the average automobile contained only 12 pounds of aluminum. By 1958, the amount quadrupled. More recently the total use of aluminum reached 114 pounds per car.

Using aluminum instead of steel makes it possible to trim 477 pounds off a typical 3,500 pound car. This weight savings can save 1,150 gallons over the 100,000-mile life of an automobile. That could save the nation about 12 billion gallons of gasoline each year.

Another interesting way to save on weight is to use a front-wheel drive. This eliminates the floor hump caused by the transmission and provides more interior room. The front-wheel drive permits the use of a transverse engine, which is laid in sideways. This allows for a shorter hood and, in turn, lighter weight and reduced fuel use.

To reduce the weight of cars still more, Chrysler replaced metals in many parts of their cars with plastics. This reduced the weight of some models by 1,000 pounds. Chrysler's "poly-car" was named for the weight-saving parts derived from poly-meric, a reinforced plastic.

Owens-Corning Fiberglas Corp. and PPG Industries, Inc. say that their light-weight plastics are replacing more and more automobile parts. They also claim that these new plastic parts are stronger than the ones they are replacing.

WHY 55 MILES PER HOUR?

If you wonder why you save gasoline by driving at 55 mph rather than at a higher speed, consider this formula again:

$$\text{FORCE} = \frac{\text{MASS} \times \text{VELOCITY}}{\text{TIME}}$$

The formula informs us that the greater the velocity, the greater is the force required to keep an object in motion. Scientists inform us that a car driven at 50 mph uses about 20% less gas than one driven at 70 mph.

KNOCKING BIRD

If you hit a tree with your fist, the tree hits you back with the same force. Action and reaction are equal. Why, then, doesn't a woodpecker knock itself out? The tree hits back with the same force. Why isn't the countryside littered with dazed and dying woodpeckers?

Researchers from the Brentwood Veterans Administration Hospital in California and the Neuropsychiatric Institute at UCLA decided to find out why. The research team used high-speed filming techniques to measure the impact velocity and deceleration of an acorn woodpecker's head as it hammered into a tree.

Analysis of film shot at speeds up to 2,000 frames per second revealed that the woodpecker's beak slammed into the trunk at speeds of 20 to 23 feet a second, about 15 miles per hour. One complete peck took $1/1000$ of a second or less, creating an impact deceleration on the order of 1,000 g. One g is the acceleration needed to overcome the earth's gravity. An astronaut in a Saturn 5 rocket experiences only 3.5 g during lift-off.

The researchers discovered that woodpeckers blink for a few milliseconds as their beak is about to hit the tree. This may protect the eye from chips or simply keep it in its socket during repeated sharp decelerations.

Several physical factors protect the woodpecker brain during all this pounding. The brain is very light, weighing less than an ounce, and it is tightly packed into a brain case of tough, spongy bone. Sets of opposed muscles may act as shock absorbers.

NEWTON'S SECOND LAW DOOMS THE WORLD'S HIGHEST FLYING COMMERCIAL AIRLINER

The needle-thin, aluminum-skinned Concorde aircraft leaps up from London's Heathrow runway at 240 mph, 35 mph faster than a Boeing 747. A half-hour into its flight it reaches its cruising altitude of 60,000 feet, over 11 miles above the earth.

Passengers seated by the windows can now catch glimpses of the curvature of the earth. The Concorde's speed is now Mach 2 or nearly 1,400 mph.

Three hours and 35 minutes after leaving London the Concorde touches down in New York. It arrives in the United States one hour earlier than it left London. It traveled faster than the time zones it was flying through.

On a round trip from London to New York a traveler can save a total of seven to eight hours of flying time—but at what a cost! The round trip fare is $4,484.

Why so expensive? Take a look at Newton's Second Law of Motion:

$$\text{FORCE} = \frac{\text{MASS} \times \text{VELOCITY}}{\text{TIME}}$$

You will notice that the greater the velocity of an object, the greater is the force required to keep it in motion. The Concorde uses four times as much fuel as a Boeing 747 on the same route. This fact has sealed her fate. Only 16 Concordes were built. Today seven are in service with British Airways, and four with Air France. Three of the aircraft are being stripped for parts. There are no expectations that the Concorde will ever go back into production.

The president of British Airways, Lord King, said, "Until airplane makers can solve the payload factor it is unlikely that any new supersonic passenger planes will be built."

FLYING BICYCLE PEDALED ACROSS ENGLISH CHANNEL

The world welcomed a new hero to aviation history on June 12, 1979, when Bryan Allen successfully pedaled his tiny airplane, the *Gossamer Albatross*, across the English Channel.

He shared honors with Dr. Paul MacCready, designer of the aircraft that was powered by human muscle. For 2 hours and 49 minutes, Allen pedaled the flying bicycle 23 miles to make it the first human-powered aircraft to cross the Channel.

The design of the flying-bicycle-airplane was based on Newton's Second Law of Motion. Look at the formula:

$$\text{FORCE} = \frac{\text{MASS} \times \text{VELOCITY}}{\text{TIME}}$$

If you make the mass very small, and fly at a slow speed, you can cut down on the force needed.

Designer Paul MacCready built the birdlike plane of lightweight plastic. He used carbon graphite tubing (lighter than aluminum) and a synthetic string called Kelbar 29 (as strong as piano wire). The fragile aircraft had a wingspan of 94 feet. The total weight was approximately 70 pounds.

WORLD'S LARGEST STEAM LOCOMOTIVE

The Union Pacific Big Boy locomotives illustrate the fact that it takes a tremendous force to move a great mass. In order to pull long freight trains up and over the mountains of the west, the largest and heaviest steam locomotives were built in the early 1940s. A Big Boy locomotive is 132.9 feet long. It weighs 1.2 million pounds.

The Union Pacific Big Boy locomotives numbered 24. They worked in the rugged mountain country between Cheyenne, Wyoming, and Ogden, Utah. The driving wheels had a diameter of 68 inches. A Big Boy locomotive had a pulling force of 135,375 pounds.

FITCH INERTIAL BARRIER

John Fitch is a former top racing-car driver. His desire to turn "hard" accidents into "soft" accidents began when he witnessed a terrible application of Newton's First Law of Motion. It was during the annual automobile endurance race at Le Mans, France, on June 11, 1955. A Mercedes Benz driven by his teammate, Pierre LeVegh, failed to make a turn and shot into the crowd. LeVegh and 83 spectators were killed!

Following this disaster, John Fitch devoted most of his time to making driving safer. His greatest contribution to highway safety is considered to be the development of the Fitch Inertial Barrier.

This barrier consists of a cluster of large plastic containers filled with sand. Each pillbox-shaped container (about three feet high and three feet in diameter) is designed to shatter easily. Thus, when a car strikes one of them, the plastic container flies apart and sand showers around the car. A car crashing into a series of these containers will slow down and come to a stop in a "sea" of sand.

Tests conducted by the Connecticut Highway Department proved most successful. Cars were driven into the barriers at 50 mph. About 20 feet from the initial impact point, each car came to a stop in a deluge of sand.

In all tests, damage to the cars was light. Hoods were buckled and front grills and radiators were dented, but each car was able to be backed up and driven away under its own power.

NEWTON'S LAWS AND OUR SPACE AGE

A Saturn 5 rocket sitting on its launching pad is a good example of Newton's First Law of Motion. A body at rest tends to remain at rest.

To get the rocket off its pad we need to apply Newton's Second Law of Motion. A given force acting for a certain time is required to move a given mass at a certain rate of speed.

The force needed to blast a rocket into space is tremendous. When the 36-story Saturn rocket leaped for the moon on December 21, 1968, the 6.5 million-pound vehicle rose out of the flames, thrust upward by a power equal to that of 180 million horses (or 450 diesel locomotives, or 85 Hoover Dams). Cheers followed as the rocket, burning up more than 14 tons of fuel a second, streaked skyward.

The scheduled blastoff came at 7:51 A.M. Eastern Standard Time. Just 2½ minutes later, the 7.5 million-pound thrust of the Saturn 5 first stage ran out of fuel.

In boosting the mighty rocket through the atmosphere, 48 tank cars of fuel (kerosene and liquid hydrogen) were burned up. At a height of 57 miles, the huge empty first stage dropped away.

JUMP OFF A CLIFF!

Is it possible for a person to jump off the top of a tall cliff for thrills, and then come back to do it all over again?

At the annual Westby, Wisconsin, Snowflake Ski Meet a few years ago, an 18-year-old boy named Jeff Benney shot out 353 feet to set a North American hill record.

No doubt you have watched Olympic skiers zoom down snow-covered slides, then sail out into the wide, blue yonder, high over the treetops below. The "secret" to their safe landing is that the stopping time is very great. It is spread out over a great interval.

NURSERY SCHOOLS

If you ever visit a nursery school, you may notice that the school has thick carpets on the floor. The thick nap of the rug slows down the little bodies over a greater time interval, thus lessening the impact of a fall.

ACTIVITIES

1. *HOW TO STOP A BASEBALL*   **Home**

You can give yourself a finger-tingling demonstration of Newton's Second Law of Motion the next time you catch a baseball
with bare hands.

As you may be aware, you can stop the baseball in one of three
ways:

1. You can stop the ball by holding your hands stationary.
2. You can move your hands forward to meet the baseball.
3. You can move your hands backward at the moment of
    impact to "give" with the ball.

In all three methods:

The **MASS** of the baseball remains the **SAME**.
The **VELOCITY** of the baseball remains the **SAME**.

As you can prove, **THE LONGER THE TIME** required to stop
the baseball, the **LESS FORCE** is needed to stop it.

2. *THWACK A CATCHER'S GLOVE*   **Home**

Here's another way to demonstrate Newton's Second Law of
Motion. Put a catcher's mitt on your left hand. Pick up a sawed-
off broomstick with your right hand. Smack the glove a resound-
ing blow. The thick glove "gives" with the stick. It reduces the
impact on your hand by increasing the stopping time, as well as
by spreading the force over a greater area. You would never dare
hit your bare hand a similar blow without the protection of the
glove.

3. *BASKETBALL VERSUS MARBLE*   **Home**

To show how the force required to accelerate an object varies
with the mass, place a marble and a basketball on the table. Give
each an equal flick with your finger. The marble, having the
smaller mass, will move rapidly. The smaller the mass, the
easier it is to accelerate an object.

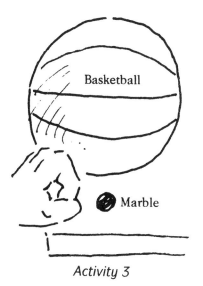

Activity 3

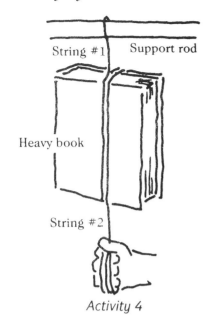

String #1   Support rod

Heavy book

String #2

Activity 4

4. *WHERE WILL THE STRING BREAK?*   **Home**

Get a long string. Tie one end of the string securely around a heavy book. Tie the free end of the string to a strong support. Now tie a second string around the book. Let the free end of this string fall toward the floor.

Now take the free end of the string #2. Wrap it securely around your hand. Pull down as rapidly as you can. Which string will break, #1 or #2? Why?

Replace the broken string. This time when you pick up the free end of string #2 pull very, very slowly, gently increasing your pull.

Which string breaks? Why?

5. *BRICK ON SIDEWALK*   **Home**

Place a brick on a sidewalk. Push it wih sufficient force to accelerate the brick fast enough to travel 1 foot in 1 second. Then push with enough force to make the brick travel 2 feet in 1 second. Finally, push with enough force to make the brick travel 3 feet in 1 second. What do you discover?

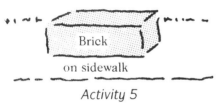

Brick

on sidewalk

Activity 5

6. *THREE BRICKS*   **Home**

Place a brick on a sidewalk. Push against it. The force you exert on the brick causes it to change from being at rest to being in motion. The brick is accelerated.

Now place a second identical brick on top of the first one and push again. If you wish to get the same acceleration you did previously, you will have to push twice as hard.

Add a third brick. Now you will have to push with still greater force to get the same acceleration you did the first time.

What have you proven?

Activity 6

HIGHLIGHTS OF THIS CHAPTER

Newton's Second Law of Motion informs us that the force required to accelerate an object is proportional to the mass of the object and the acceleration given it. Force equals Mass times Acceleration.

Multiple-Choice Questions

1. Fitch Inertial Barriers are popular because:
    a. they are easy to install.
    b. the sand can easily be replaced.
    c. the plastic containers are cheaper than steel.
    d. they distribute a crash over a long time interval.

2. A Concorde uses four times as much fuel as a Boeing 747 on the same route because:
    a. the Concorde is a much bigger airplane.
    b. it travels so fast.
    c. its fuselage is not as well streamlined as a Boeing 747.
    d. it has more mass.

3. More aluminum is being used in building automobiles because:
    a. it is cheaper.
    b. it lasts longer.
    c. it is lighter.
    d. it is easier to fabricate.

4. One of the advantages of air bags is:
    a. they are full of cotton balls.
    b. a lever causes a can of sodium azide to ignite on collision.
    c. they deflate rapidly, thus preventing a dangerous rebound.
    d. none of the above.

5. Which of the following is false?
    a. Newton's Second Law is the basis for all computations dealing with forces needed to propel vehicles.
    b. the force needed to put a vehicle into motion depends on its mass only.
    c. a given force acting for a certain time is required to move a given mass at a certain speed.
    d. the amount of force produced is equal to the mass multiplied by the acceleration.

True or False Questions

1. During World War II, the maximum speed allowed on highways was 35 mph. This was a dramatic application of the fact that the force (and fuel) needed to keep a vehicle in motion depends on its speed.

2. A teenager steps into a pickup and steps on the accelerator. It makes no difference on fuel consumption whether the car reaches maximum speed of 55 mph over a long period of time, or whether it leaps forward like a jackrabbit.

3. One reason that it is so painful to stub your toe against a rock is that the impact time is so short.

4. You have to make a trip of 120 miles. If you drive at 60 mph you will be on the road only half as long as you would be if you drove 30 mph. This will save on gas consumption.

5. Big jets require long runways due to Newton's Second Law of Motion.

Chapter 3

HOW TO TRAVEL IN SPACE
You Need Reaction

It was February 7, 1984. Navy Captain Bruce McCandless II, an astronaut aboard *Challenger's* 41-B mission, became the first person to walk untethered in space. He became the first human satellite by performing a feat no astronaut had ever attempted. He stepped into space without being fastened to a line.

McCandless maneuvered up to 320 feet away from *Challenger.* He was elated not only because he had reached the summit of his 18 years as an astronaut, but also because of the successful performance of the $10 million backpack that he had helped to create. The 335-pound backpack is called a Manned Maneuvering Unit (MMU). An astronaut can put on the MMU and remove it unassisted at a special flight support station in the space shuttle.

The MMU is powered by 24 nitrogen gas thrusters which are activated by hand controllers. These controllers, located at the end of the MMU's extendable arms, give an astronaut the luxury of moving in any direction. As the gas escapes from a thruster in one direction, the reaction moves the MMU in the opposite direction.

The MMU operates according to Newton's Third Law of Motion which says: **"TO EVERY ACTION THERE IS AN EQUAL AND OPPOSITE REACTION."**

Action and reaction are complementary. You can't have one without the other. But remember, these two forces of action and reaction act on different bodies.

Consider a jet engine, for example. Hot gases rushing out the tail pipe cause a reaction that thrusts the jet through the sky. In a jet or rocket, the **MASS** of the gas escaping out the exhaust multiplied by its **VELOCITY** equals the **MASS** of the jet multiplied by its **VELOCITY** in the opposite direction or, in formula form:

$$mV = Mv$$
$$\text{little mass} \times \text{BIG VELOCITY} = \text{BIG MASS} \times \text{small velocity}$$
$$\text{exhaust gas} \times \text{BIG VELOCITY} = \text{JET} \times \text{small velocity}$$

It may seem strange, but the mass or weight of the gas streaming out the tail pipe multiplied by its speed is equal to the mass of the jet multiplied by its speed forward.

The product of mv (mass times velocity) is called momentum. According to Newton's Third Law:

MOMENTUM FORWARD = MOMENTUM BACKWARD

A jet-propelled airplane streaking across the sky and a Fourth of July skyrocket both work because of Newton's Third Law of Motion. There is, however, a big difference.

A jet is an "air-breathing" machine. Molecules of air enter the front of the engine tube and pass into a compressor or supercharger that compresses them. The compressed air is then fed into a combustion chamber under high pressure. Liquid fuel is sprayed into the compressed air in the combustion chamber. The hot, burning gases rush out the tail pipe. This provides the thrust that propels the jet forward. Some of the hot gases are used to turn a turbine that drives the air compressor which, in turn, squeezes more air into the front of the engine.

ROCKETS

Unlike jets, rockets carry their own supply of oxidizer. Some burn kerosene and liquid oxygen. They have no moving parts except for pumps for the fuel and oxidizer. The fuel burns in a combustion chamber, and the exhaust gases are expelled from the exhaust jet to propel the rocket.

Solid-fuel rockets are similar, except that they do not require a separate oxidizer. The solid fuel is packed in the combustion chamber and is designed to burn rapidly at a steady rate.

RIFLES AND SHOTGUNS

Rifles and shotguns furnish superb examples of Newton's Third Law of Motion. The expanding gases that result from the explosion of the shell in the barrel do two different things to two different bodies. The force of the gas propels the bullet out of the barrel (action), and at the same time pushes backward on the rifle (reaction).

Each time you fire a rifle, the hot expanding gas resulting from the explosion of the shell does two things—it "shoots" the bullet forward and "kicks" the rifle backward.

DEADLY REACTION

If the momentum of the rifle backward is the same as the momentum of the bullet forward, why doesn't the momentum of the rifle kill you as the bullet could? The reason is that the broad butt of the gun distributes the force over a large area. Since pressure equals force divided by area, this means that the pressure on any one spot is very small. If the butt was as small as the barrel, however, the force would all be delivered to a small area. The pressure would soar, and so would you!

Duck hunters use Newton's Second Law of Motion to prevent shotguns from injuring their shoulders. They fasten a thick rubber pad or cushion to the butt of the shotgun. The cushion absorbs some of the kick by extending the stopping time over a greater interval and larger area.

WHAT IS THE RECOIL?

You have a shotgun that weighs six pounds. The shell contains $1/16$ pound of shot. If the forward velocity of the shot is 672 feet per second, what is the recoil velocity of the shotgun, if it is free to move?

$$
\begin{aligned}
mV &= Mv \\
\text{little mass} \times \text{BIG VELOCITY} &= \text{BIG MASS} \times \text{small velocity} \\
1/16 \text{ lb.} \times 672 \text{ ft. per sec.} &= 6 \text{ lbs.} \times v \\
672/16 &= 6v \\
42 &= 6v \\
42/6 = v &= 7 \text{ ft. per sec.}
\end{aligned}
$$

WHAT IS YOUR MOMENTUM?

You are the quarterback. You weigh 140 pounds. You are running forward with a speed of 12 feet per second. What is your momentum?

$$
\begin{aligned}
\text{Momentum} &= \text{Mass} \times \text{Velocity} \\
&= 140 \text{ lbs.} \times 12 \text{ ft. per sec.} \\
&= 1{,}680 \text{ ft. lbs. per sec.}
\end{aligned}
$$

HOW TO SLOW DOWN IN SPACE

If we wish to slow down in space, we can't rely upon friction as we do when stopping an automobile.

We must direct a rocket in the direction of our motion. This retro-rocket is a relatively small rocket unit, usually using a solid propellant installed on a rocket-propelled vehicle. It is fired in a direction opposite to the main motion to decelerate, or cut down, on the speed of the main unit.

PUTTING RETRO-ROCKETS TO WORK

It was 9:47 A.M. Eastern time, Tuesday, February 20, 1962, when John Glenn blasted off from Cape Canaveral, Florida, atop a giant Atlas rocket. He made three orbits around the earth at an average speed of 17,400 mph. Each orbit around the earth took 88½ minutes. When he was making his third and final orbit, Glenn fired three retro-rockets to slow him down. The braking rockets went into action about 600 miles west of San Diego. Three minutes later the tracking station at Guaymas, Mexico, established radio contact with Glenn and confirmed that his capsule was in a landing trajectory. At 1:43 P.M. the capsule landed safely in the Atlantic, completing a flight of 4 hours and 56 minutes. Newton's Third Law of Motion not only put Glenn into space, it also brought him back!

REACTION ON LANDING!

When you come in for a landing at the airport, do you ever get the feeling that as soon as the wheels touch down on the runway, some giant hands seem to push back on the plane?

Certain types of planes use Newton's Third Law to help stop their forward motion. If you are seated behind the wings of these planes, you may see what happens. As soon as the plane touches down, two blocker doors close around the turbofan exhaust. They look like giant hands that are cupped behind the tailpipes. These "clam-shell-type" thrust-reversers divert 40% of the engine's thrust in the opposite direction. This creates a counterforce that brings the plane to a stop in half the distance needed without thrust-reversers.

THROW RUG

If you have a throw rug in your living room, you may have given unplanned demonstrations of Newton's Third Law of Motion. As you step forward, the rug leaps backward and does just what its name implies—it throws you!

ROTARY LAWN SPRINKLER

The next time you see a rotary lawn sprinkler at work, you will be watching a demonstration of Newton's Third Law of Motion. As the stream of water shoots out one way, the reaction pushes the arms of the sprinkler in the opposite direction.

TENNIS ELBOW

If you play tennis frequently, you have experienced an unwelcome demonstration of Newton's Third Law of Motion. When you slam the tennis ball forward at maximum speed, the reaction travels down the handle of the racket and up your arm to your elbow. When this happens again and again, the result may be a painful ailment known as tennis elbow.

TENNIS TOE

A cousin of tennis elbow, tennis toe, is caused by Newton's First Law of Motion. This condition, almost unheard of years ago, is largely the result of improved tennis shoes. In sudden stops on hard-surfaced courts in shoes with good traction, the foot is forced to the front of the shoe, traumatizing the toenail. The tender tennis toe, usually the big one, is characterized by severe throbbing pain beneath the nail, a slight swelling of the toe, and a purpling under the nail (a sign of hemorrhaging).

The best way to prevent tennis toe, doctors say, is to buy shoes that are large enough so that even on short stops the big toe will not be crushed against the end of the shoe.

"OILBERGS"

Some of the most alarming and overpowering examples of momentum are given by oil tankers. Momentum, you may recall, is equal to Mass times Velocity. Think now of oil tankers almost a quarter of a mile long and weighing as much as 4,800 blue whales.

Fully-loaded supertankers weigh over 100,000 deadweight tons (dwt). A deadweight ton is 2,240 pounds. VLCC (very large crude carriers) are crude-oil-carrying supertankers that weigh between 200,000 and 400,000 dwt. ULCC (ultra-large crude carriers) weigh over 400,000 dwt.

There are over 600 supertankers in the world. More than 400 of them are VLCCs. A few of them are ULCCs. The VLCCs and ULCCs are sometimes called "oilbergs." Like icebergs, about 80% of the "oilberg" is underwater. Between 50 and 90 feet of a supertanker lie below the water. Supertankers, obviously, are not designed to travel in shallow water. In fact, their depth below the water keeps them out of most ports.

Supertankers are difficult to control. Suppose a 250,000-dwt "oilberg" is traveling at 16 knots. (Sixteen knots means 16 nautical miles per hour. One nautical mile equals 6,076 feet, or about 1.15 miles.) That tanker would need about 3 nautical miles—and about 20 minutes—to come to a stop.

What's more, a supertanker may be very difficult—sometimes almost impossible—to control when it is going very slowly (about 3-4 knots). High winds and strong currents can make the problem much worse. When a supertanker is going slowly, other ships must keep out of its way. It is also hard for a supertanker to turn. Imagine trying to get a ship the size of three or four football fields to turn!

ACTIVITIES

1. *FLY YOUR OWN PRIVATE JET*   **Home**

You can fly your own private jet for only pennies!

Simply purchase a toy balloon. Blow it up, then release it. The air rushing out the neck of the balloon (action) propels the balloon in the opposite direction (reaction).

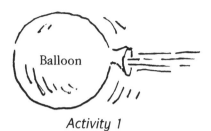

Activity 1

2. *EMPTY SHOE BOX*   **Home**

The only reason you can stand on the floor of your room is that the floor reacts with an equal and opposite force. It pushes up against your feet with as much force as you push down.

To demonstrate what happens when a floor can't push up with an equal and opposite force, stand on top of an empty cardboard box, like a shoe box.

3. *WALK-AROUND RECORD PLAYER*   **Home**

If you have an old 78 rpm record player, put in on the table. Let your fingers attempt to "walk around" near the rim of the turntable. Note the action and reaction.

Record player

Activity 3

4. *SPRING SCALES*   *Supervised Classroom*

Hold spring scale #1 in your hand. Ask a friend to hold scale #2. Link hooks on both scales together. Tell your friend just to hold and not to pull on scale #2. If you pull with a force of 20 ounces on scale #1, scale #2 will also read 20 ounces. Action equals reaction. Your friend is actually pulling.

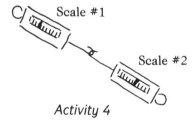

Scale #1

Scale #2

Activity 4

5. *JET SODA BOTTLE*   *Supervised Classroom*

Get an empty soda bottle and two small pipes or round pencils which will serve as "wheels." Place them on an uncarpeted floor.

To put "fuel" into the bottle, turn it upright, and insert five tablespoons of vinegar and five tablespoons of water. Add a teaspoon of baking soda (sodium bicarbonate) and cork securely. Turn the bottle to a horizontal position, as shown. Note

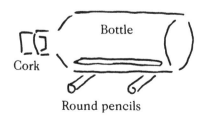

Bottle

Cork

Round pencils

Activity 5

Activity 6

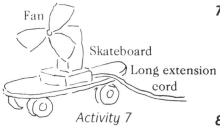

Activity 7

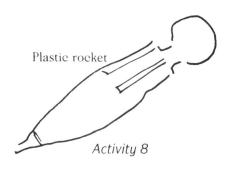

Activity 8

Activity 9

what happens when the carbon dioxide builds up enough pressure. Explain what happens.

(Trying to pour a teaspoon of baking soda into the bottle is messy. A more efficient way is to first spread open a little square of tissue paper on the table. Pour the baking soda on the paper, then roll it up into a neat tube. Twist the ends, and insert into the bottle without trouble.)

6. PIANO STOOL AND PILLOW   Home

Here is an experiment you can try at home. Sit on a revolving piano stool. Hold a pillow in your outstretched hand. Now, keeping your arm extended as far from your body as possible, attempt to throw the pillow forward! What happens?

7. REACTION ENGINE   Supervised Classroom

Place an electric fan on a skateboard. Use a long extension cord. Turn on the power. The fan may have enough power to stir up a breeze and give you a "jet-propelled skateboard."

8. WATER ROCKET   Supervised Classroom

Here is an interesting experiment you can do outdoors. You will need a plastic toy rocket that comes with a hand pump. The entire unit is about 10 inches long.

First, pump the rocket full of compressed air only. Release it. Note how high it goes.

Now add water to the level shown on the plastic chamber. Pump air into it as before. Release the rocket. What happens now? Why?

9. COCONUT CANOE

This is not an experiment, but simply a problem for you to solve. You are in a canoe loaded with coconuts in the middle of a lagoon. You have lost your paddle. You don't dare use your hands for paddles because of the crocodiles in the lagoon. How could you get to shore?

Activity 10

10. SLICK PROBLEM

Here is another problem for you. This time you are standing on a perfectly smooth pond of ice. There is absolutely no friction between your shoes and the ice. How could you get off?

11. HARD PROBLEM

Would you rather be hit by one pound of steel, or by one ounce of lead?

Before you answer, consider the facts. You are holding a hammer in your right hand so its steel head is 1 inch above your outstretched left hand. If you release the hammer, the steel head will land gently in your left hand.

The ounce of lead is a bullet that will be fired from a rifle with a velocity of over 1,000 feet per second.

You must know more about an object than its mass. You must also know its velocity. You must know its momentum.

12. BIKE OR FREIGHT TRAIN?

Now that you know how to tackle this type of problem, consider another one. Would you rather be hit by a bike or a freight train?

HIGHLIGHTS OF THIS CHAPTER

● Newton's Third Law of Motion says "**TO EVERY ACTION THERE IS AN EQUAL AND OPPOSITE REACTION.**"

● Hot gases rushing out the tailpipe of a jet cause a reaction that thrusts the jet through the sky.

● Mass times Velocity is called Momentum.

Multiple-Choice Questions

1. The reason you are not injured when you fire a rifle is that:
    a. Newton's First Law of Motion keeps the rifle from moving.
    b. the impact of the rifle is distributed over a large area.
    c. the momentum of the rifle is not the same as the momentum of the bullet.
    d. Newton's Second Law of Motion reduces the time interval.

2. A jet differs from a rocket in that:
    a. it "breathes" air.
    b. it is not a reaction type engine.
    c. it travels at a greater speed.
    d. it carries its own oxygen.

3. You are in a dining car on a train that is speeding down the tracks at 60 mph. You drop your knife. The knife will fall:
    a. behind the spot from which you dropped it.
    b. directly under the spot from which you dropped it.
    c. to one side of the spot from which you dropped it.
    d. ahead of the spot from which you dropped it.

4. If you stumble and hit your head against a wall, the wall hits you back. This is due to:
    a. momentum.
    b. Newton's First Law of Motion.
    c. Newton's Second Law of Motion.
    d. Newton's Third Law of Motion.

5. A boxer does not simply place his fist on the face of his opponent and push. The first thing he does is to get his fist moving as rapidly as possible. The purpose of this is to:
    a. surprise his opponent with a jarring blow.
    b. overcome Newton's First Law of Motion.
    c. increase the momentum of the blow.
    d. overcome Newton's Second Law of Motion.

True or False Questions

1. When you walk forward in a rowboat, the boat tends to move in the opposite direction. This is due to Newton's Second Law of Motion.

2. When you stand on the floor, the floor is pushing up against your shoes with a force equal to your weight.

3. You weigh 140 lbs. and are running at the rate of 6 ft. per sec. Your momentum is 840 ft. lbs. per sec.

4. The devastating momentum of "oilbergs" is due to their great velocity.

5. A 5,000-lb. truck moving at the rate of 22 ft. per sec. has the same momentum as a 2,500-lb. automobile moving at the rate of 44 ft. per sec.

Chapter 4

THE "INVISIBLE GLUE" THAT HOLDS US AT HOME IN SPACE

How to Lose Weight by Escaping the "Glue"

Can you grow two inches, then shrink?

Yes, if you are in a space lab!

According to NASA, the National Aeronautics and Space Administration, strange things happened during the Skylab missions.

The first thing the astronauts noticed was that their space suits were too tight. This seemed very strange. Each suit had been custom-tailored. Each suit had been thoroughly checked before the launch.

Imagine the surprise of the astronauts when they measured themselves and found that they had become taller by as much as two inches!

NASA calls this strange happening "in-flight growth." In the absence of the pull of gravity on the spinal column, it becomes loose and stretches. Since gravity is no longer squeezing the soft disks between the spinal bones, the body expands.

To allow for this "in-flight growth" the suits now issued to space-shuttle astronauts are made to grow with their wearers. Both the legs and sleeves of the suits have laced-in inserts to let out the suit a little when needed.

BALANCE ACT

We speak of the astronauts in their space shuttles as being in zero gravity. Actually, gravity is still there, pulling on them and on everything in the space shuttle. The acceleration of the space shuttle as it circles the earth cancels out or balances the acceleration of gravity.

HOW DO YOU "FALL"?

In order to understand how all this happens, we will begin our study of gravity by making a few simple observations.

If you lose your balance at the top of the cellar steps, or on top of a stepladder, in what direction do you "fall"?

"I fall down," you say.

You take it for granted, no doubt, that the only place to look for anything that "falls" is "down." After all, who ever heard of anything falling "up"?

From experience we know that raindrops fall "down" from the sky. Apples "fall" off trees. Rocks "fall" down mountain slopes.

No matter where you live, you have the feeling that you are walking on "top" of the earth. The sky is "up" over your head. If you stumble, you "fall" in the direction shown by #1.

If you are walking "on top" of the world, then is your friend on the opposite side of the earth walking around "upside down"? If he stumbles, does he "fall up"?

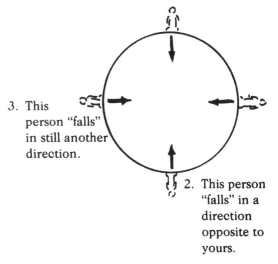

1. You "fall" in the direction of the arrow.

3. This person "falls" in still another direction.

2. This person "falls" in a direction opposite to yours.

How about person #3? If she stumbles, her "fall" will be in still another direction, as shown by the arrow.

The truth is that things do not "fall." They are "pulled" to the center of the earth. Why is this so?

One gentleman who thought about this question was the famous British scientist, Sir Isaac Newton (1642–1727). According to legend, Sir Isaac was resting in the shade of an old apple tree when an apple came loose and hit him on the head. The impact of the apple drove home an important idea.

The facts are not quite the same as the legend. In the year 1665, a great plague spread through many cities in England. Newton was then a young man studying in the city of Cambridge. To escape from the plague, Newton returned to his birthplace on the family farm at Woolsthorpe. On the quiet farm, Newton had ample time to think. During an 18-month period, Newton formulated the law of gravitation, invented calculus, and devised theories of light and color.

Newton did not publicly announce his law of gravity until 20 years later. During that time, he put a lot of thought into developing his ideas. In 1687 Newton published his famous book, the *Principia*, in which he gave us the Law of Universal Gravitation: **"ANY TWO BODIES IN THE UNIVERSE ATTRACT EACH OTHER WITH A FORCE THAT IS DIRECTLY PROPORTIONAL TO THE PRODUCT OF THEIR MASSES, AND INVERSELY PROPORTIONAL TO THE SQUARE OF THE DISTANCE BETWEEN THEIR CENTERS OF GRAVITY."**

WHAT IS YOUR WEIGHT?

The quantity of material in a body is called mass. A whale has more mass than a canary. The attraction between your mass and the mass of the planet is called your weight. Your weight is a measure of the force with which the earth attracts you.

The center of gravity is that point at which all the gravitational attraction or weight of an object may be considered to be concentrated.

The gravitational pull of the earth makes the center of gravity of a body get as close as possible to the center of the earth. The direction we call "down" is the direction that leads to the center of the earth. Objects do not "fall" down. They are "pulled" toward the center of the earth by gravity.

WHAT IS IT?

Gravity is most unusual. No substance we know of can shield us from gravity, make it weaker, or change the direction of its attraction. We cannot increase it or bend it.

By contrast, see what you can do with a beam of light. You can use a prism to bend a beam of light. A mirror will reflect it. A black cloth will absorb it.

You can send electricity through copper wires. Rubber and glass may be used as insulators to keep electricity where you want it.

Scientists point out that no one really knows for sure just what gravity is. In the latter part of his life, Einstein tried to show that gravity, electricity, and magnetism were all parts of one universal law, but he did not complete his work.

HOW TO FIND YOUR WEIGHT

The first part of Newton's Law of Universal Gravitation informs us that **"ANY TWO BODIES IN THE UNIVERSE ATTRACT EACH OTHER WITH A FORCE THAT IS DIRECTLY PROPORTIONAL TO THE PRODUCT OF THEIR MASSES."** This is expressed in the following formula:

$$F \quad = \quad Mm$$

F = the force of gravity. The pull of gravity on you is called your weight.

M = the mass of the planet you are standing on. For us on Earth the force of gravity is 1, or 1 g.

m = the number of units of mass in a body.

If your body has 120 units of mass, then:

$$F \quad = \quad Mm$$
$$F \quad = \quad (1) \ (120)$$
Your weight = 120 pounds on Earth.

Suppose that you were standing on the moon. Its mass is only $\frac{1}{6}$ that of this planet. Although your mass would be the same on the moon, your weight would be only $\frac{1}{6}$ of what it is on Earth:

$$F \quad = \quad Mm$$
$$F \quad = \quad \frac{1}{6} \ (120)$$
Your weight = 20 pounds on the moon.

MIGHTY JUPITER

The biggest planet, Jupiter, has a mass 317.9 times that of Earth. Can you imagine what you would weigh if you could stand on this planet?

HOW MUCH DO YOU WEIGH ON PLUTO?

You already know that since the mass of the moon is only $\frac{1}{6}$ that of the earth, your weight there would be only $\frac{1}{6}$ of what it is here.

Using the following information, estimate your weight on the following planets:

Mercury	has a mass	0.055	times that of Earth.
Venus	has a mass	0.08	times that of Earth.
Mars	has a mass	0.1	times that of Earth.
Saturn	has a mass	95	times that of Earth.
Uranus	has a mass	15	times that of Earth.
Neptune	has a mass	17	times that of Earth.
Pluto	has a mass	0.002	times that of Earth.

The second part of Newton's Law of Universal Gravitation informs us that "**ANY**

TWO BODIES IN THE UNIVERSE ATTRACT EACH OTHER INVERSELY PROPORTIONAL TO THE SQUARE OF THE DISTANCE BETWEEN THEIR CENTERS OF GRAVITY." This can be expressed in the following formula:

$$F = \frac{1}{d^2}$$

F   =   the pull of gravity on you; your weight

d   =   the distance from the center of gravity

HOW TO LOSE WEIGHT

If we limit ourselves to this planet, the diagram on the next page will show how you can lose weight simply by lessening the pull of the "invisible glue" on your body. To do this, simply move away from the center of the earth.

The pull of gravity varies inversely with the square of the distance. This means that if you were twice as far away from the center of the earth, you would weigh ¼ as much as you do now. If you were twice as close to the center of the earth, you would weigh 4 times as much.

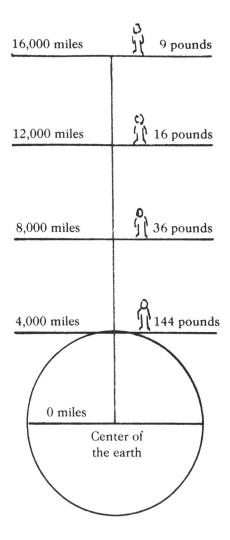

16,000 miles   9 pounds

12,000 miles   16 pounds

8,000 miles   36 pounds

4,000 miles   144 pounds

0 miles

Center of
the earth

The force of gravity, or weight, decreases as one goes away from the center of the earth.

SATURN 5 ROCKET

The Saturn 5 rocket gave a superb demonstration of Newton's Law of Universal Gravitation. In order to achieve the escape velocity of 25,000 mph (or 6.95 miles per second) needed to break free from the gravitational pull of the earth, three rockets were stacked on top of each other and fired in succession. The velocity increased with each firing because each section before firing was traveling with the velocity of the preceding stage. Since gravity decreases inversely with the square of the distance, each pound of thrust applied to the rocket 50 miles above the earth gave it more speed than it would when it was closer.

Lack of air drag at high altitudes is also a distinct advantage. Since gravitational pull also decreases with less mass, the rocket reduced its mass at each new firing by dispensing with empty fuel tanks. Energy thus saved from lifting useless mass was used to give further thrust.

DEAD SEA

The most I ever weighed was on Friday, August 13, 1965, when I stepped on a scale in a tourist pavilion located on the shore of the Dead Sea. The Dead Sea is the lowest spot on earth. It is 1,286 feet below sea level. On that August afternoon, I was the closest I have ever been to the center of the earth!

WHAT HAPPENS WHEN YOU ARE WEIGHTLESS?

Before our astronauts blasted off into space from the launching pad at the Kennedy Space Center, scientists wanted to find out how zero gravity would affect the human body.

The man who volunteered for the experiment was Captain Duane E. Graveline, a 27-year-old Air Force medic. He spent an entire week, clad in a diver's rubber suit, afloat on his back in 400 gallons of tepid water at the Air Force School of Aviation Medicine in San Antonio, Texas.

Technically, he was in a state of near weightlessness—the buoyancy or upward force of the water on his body made all muscular and body movement effortless. His muscles and bones were in a state of zero gravity.

After a week of zero gravity, and doing nothing, Captain Graveline attempted to leave his coffin-size tub of water. Things began to happen fast. His heart pounded wildly. His blood pressure dropped. His handsome face turned blue. He couldn't stand straight or speak in sentences that made any sense.

Graveline went through intensive medical tests. The results were surprising. "The body was literally disposing of unneeded muscle and bone," explained Graveline. "My muscles were like dough and my bones were becoming softer."

Fortunately, Captain Graveline was back to normal in four days.

His experiment showed that if forces are not applied to bone tissue, the bloodstream takes away the minerals that make them hard. If muscles are not exercised, they become limp and flabby. Even the walls of blood vessels become dangerously weakened if not exposed to forces.

One of the most important forces that keeps our bones, muscles, and blood vessels strong is gravity. Astronauts in orbit can prevent the weakening effects of zero gravity by exercises.

SKINNIER FEET AND STUFFED HEADS

The astronauts in Skylab noticed that they did more than grow taller. The body's fluids tended to travel away from the lower part of the body to the upper part. As a result, the astronauts had skinnier feet and narrower waists. Their chests and shoulders were slightly larger. Because of this, the standard-issue uniform for shuttle occupants has a jacket with elasticized pleats built in to expand with the body.

According to Astronaut Gerald Carr, who was commander of the third and longest Skylab mission of 84 days, the body fluids go to your head and clog the passages of your nose and ears. "You carry with you a constant state of nasal and head congestion in a weightless environment. It feels pretty much like you have a cold all the time. The senses of taste and smell are numbed."

As soon as the once weightless person returns to earth's gravity, this fluid drift is changed, and with a vengeance. The sudden rush of fluid to the lower part of the body takes needed blood away from the brain. Anyone not prepared for this violent change would black out.

For that reason, astronauts routinely wear what are called antigravity pants when they dress for reentry. Very simply, the pants are a pair of inflatable leggings that are pumped up to apply pressure to the lower body and thus cut down on the fluid shock.

The danger of blackout is very real, as Dr. Joseph Kerwin of the first Skylab crew found out. He had only partially inflated his suit before reentry and almost fainted. "Surprised the tar out of me," he later admitted.

EATING OUT

If you are like most people, you like to eat out. Eating out in space, however, is another story. It is impossible to pour water in zero gravity. The liquid simply breaks up into silvery spheres that drift around in the spacecraft. Liquids are drunk through a straw with a clamp attached to keep the straw pinched shut when not in use.

Salt and pepper shakers are useless. Gravity won't pull the salt and pepper from the containers. Even if a crystal of salt comes out of the shaker, it does not fall on the food. It drifts away in midair.

SLEEP IN A BAG!

Due to zero gravity, astronauts in a space shuttle can rest anywhere. Mattresses and pillows are unnecessary. At bedtime the astronaut steps into a bag anchored vertically or horizontally to a firm surface, zips the bag up from toe to chest, connects a waist strap around the bag, and then tucks both arms under the strap to keep them from flailing around during sleep.

WHEN DID SKIING TAKE OFF?

What was the "revolution" or "invention" that turned skiing into a popular winter sport?

The story began over half a century ago, on a hill behind Clinton Gilbert's house and barn two miles outside the town of Woodstock, Vermont. A handful of ingenious Yankees rigged an 1,800-foot loop of stout rope to a Model "T" Ford truck engine and started a skiing revolution.

A historical marker erected on the site of the first ski tow in the United States informs us: "In January, 1934, on this pasture hill of Clinton Gilbert's farm an endless-rope tow, powered by a Model 'T' Ford engine, hauled skiers uphill for the first time. This ingenious contraption launched a new era in winter sports."

For the first time in this country, skiers could enjoy their downhill runs without having to face painstakingly slow climbs back to the top.

GRAVITY PROVIDES "MORE VIOLENT MEANS OF AMUSEMENT"

Robert Cartmell is regarded by many as the nation's foremost roller-coaster historian and expert. He describes roller coasters as "one of the country's more violent means of amusement." Among the 10 best roller coasters in the United States, Robert Cartmell lists the Cyclone at Coney Island, Brooklyn, N.Y. The oldest and most famous coaster on the list, the Cyclone has terrified more than 10 million passengers. Its violent curves are the best anywhere and have been used to attempt cures for stuttering, hiccups, and even blindness. In the last analysis, gravity is providing you with the thrills.

WORLD'S MOST FAMOUS VICTIM OF GRAVITY

The Leaning Tower of Pisa, Italy, is a victim of gravity. It was begun in 1174 as a campanile, or bell tower, for the Pisa Cathedral. It was not even finished when wet soil at its base caused it to list. Attempts to straighten it failed. To adjust the center of gravity, the architects gave the upper stories a countertilt.

The tower continues to increase its leaning at the rate of .027 of an inch a year. A drastic cure was attempted in 1934: 301 holes were dug around the base of the tower and filled with 900 tons of cement. This steadied the tower for about 10 years. Then, during World War II, three bombs exploded in the vicinity, and the tower received a shock that caused it to renew the leaning. One Italian scientist calculates that the tower will topple and crash in the year 2151 unless a "starched undershirt" of concrete is installed on one side of its foundation.

When I was in Italy, I climbed the spiral stone stairway that leads up inside the Leaning Tower. When I stood on top of the tower, I felt as though I was astride a tramp steamer awash in a hurricane. The floor swung out from under my feet at a sickening angle. With great caution I walked to the side of the tower that leans 16 feet away from its base. When I dared to look down to the ground, I had the awkward sensation of suddenly becoming a heavy object about to take part in a demonstration of the laws of falling objects.

NIAGARA FALLS

Powerful as running water is, it is no match for water that leaps off a cliff. The swift waters of Niagara Falls, for example, plunge 165 feet to hit the pool below with a tremendous force. Tons of plunging, high-speed water cut into the soft shale beneath the cliff. The swirling current carries away the shale, thus under-cutting the cliffs above. Eventually left without support, the top rock tumbles off into the falls.

The eroding action of water moves Horseshoe Falls upstream at the rate of about three feet per year. In three and a half centuries, Niagara Falls has receded about 1,200 feet.

THE CHARLES ATLAS OF SPACE

According to NASA, Astronaut Joseph Allen was the first human in history to hold a 1,200-pound satellite overhead for one trip around the world. He did this on November 12, 1984, while he was cruising 225 miles above the surface of the earth.

With the help of fellow skywalker Dale Gardner, Joseph Allen made the first recovery of a disabled telecommunications satellite, the Palapa B2. When the astronauts tried to wrestle the Palapa B2 into the cargo bay of the space shuttle *Discovery*, they ran into trouble. Allen was forced to hold the Palapa B2 above his head for 90 minutes because a mechanism that the shuttle's robot arm was to have grasped could not be attached to the satellite.

Upon Allen's return to earth, he told a reporter that it doesn't take a Charles Atlas to hold a 1,200 pound satellite overhead in space. Even someone overweight and out of shape can do it. Weightlessness allows a person to move a "very, very massive object," said Allen, who had to manhandle the 9-foot by 7-foot satellite.

"You could do it," Allen told a middle-aged reporter. "We're certainly not weightlifters. We're mass lifters."

ACTIVITIES

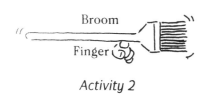

Activity 1

1. A RULER'S CENTER OF GRAVITY   Home

Extend the index finger of your left hand. Pick up a ruler with your right hand and place it on top of your left finger. Move the ruler slowly across your finger until it balances. When it does, the middle of the ruler will be centered over your finger. The center of gravity is that point at which all the weight of an object is considered to be concentrated. An object such as a ruler or yardstick will have its center of gravity in the middle.

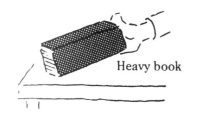

Activity 2

2. WHERE IS THE CENTER OF GRAVITY?   Home

Extend the index finger of your left hand. Place the handle of a broom on it. Slide the handle back and forth until you find a place where the broom balances.

Only in the case of a uniform body, such as a ruler or a ball, will you expect to find the center of gravity in the middle of the object. In the case of an object such as the broom, the center of gravity is not in the center of the handle. It is toward the end where most of the mass is found.

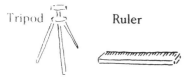

Activity 3

3. STABLE EQUILIBRIUM   Home

Lay a big, heavy book such as a dictionary flat on a table. Lift one end of the book about 2 inches off the table. When you release the book, it will return to its former position.

An object is said to be in stable equilibrium when a slight tipping raises its center of gravity. When the object is released, it tends to return to the position it had before being tilted.

"Stable" comes from a Latin word meaning "to stand."

"Equilibrium" comes from two Latin words meaning "equal balance."

The following are examples of stable equilibrium:

A drinking glass standing upright.

A funnel resting on its rim.

A camera tripod with its legs outstretched.

A ruler flat on the table.

4. UNSTABLE EQUILIBRIUM   Home

Get a tall book and place it on the table so that it is standing on one edge. Push against the top of the book. A slight tipping lowers its center of gravity. It is said to be in unstable equilibrium.

The following are examples of unstable equilibrium:

A drinking glass on its edge.

A funnel resting on its spout, or at an angle.

A tripod with its legs folded under it.

A ruler standing upright on its narrow end.

Tall book

Drinking glass

Funnel

Tripod   Ruler

Activity 4

5. NEUTRAL EQUILIBRIUM   Home

Place a baseball, billiard ball, or handball on the table. Give it a slight push. The center of gravity of the ball does not lower or rise. It stays the same distance from the top of the table.

Other examples of neutral equilibrium are:

A glass on its side.

A funnel on its side.

Rolling these objects in this position does not raise or lower their centers of gravity.

Ball

Glass

Funnel

Activity 5

6. PRISONER OF A CHAIR   Home

Sit up straight in a straight-back chair. Fold your arms over your chest. Keep both feet in front of you, knees together. Now, without leaning your body forward, or pushing against the back of the chair, attempt to stand up. What happens? Why?

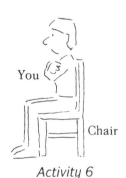
You   Chair

Activity 6

7. ROLL UPHILL   Home

Tape a bolt or any heavy piece of metal inside the rim of an empty tin container, such as one used for coffee.

Now place the metal container on its side on a mild incline with the heavy weight toward the top of the incline as shown. The can will roll uphill to lower its center of gravity.

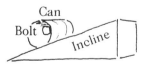
Can
Bolt   Incline

Heavy metal

Activity 7

8. *ROCKABYE* Home

For variety, place the container from Activity 7 on the top of a table, on its edge, with the weight near the top. Take your hand away from the container. What happens?

9. *HAMMER AND RULER* Home

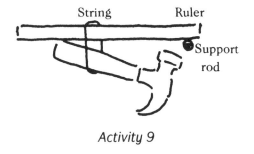

Activity 9

Tie a string in a small circle and slip it over the end of a stout wooden ruler. Now slip the handle of a hammer through the string so the end of the hammer makes contact with the flat underside of the ruler. Now rest the other end of the ruler on your index finger or, better yet, on a steel rod held in place by a support stand. Move the ruler back and forth on your finger, or the rod, until it balances. Now, with your free hand, gently tip the free end of the ruler. What happens?

10. *LEANING TOWER* Supervised Classroom

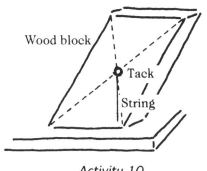

Activity 10

Diagonally saw an end off a rectangular block (a 6-inch piece of 2×4 will do) so it will lean like the Leaning Tower of Pisa. A *plumb line* may be used to find the center of gravity of the block. You can make a plumb line by fastening a large sinker to a piece of fishing line. To find the center of gravity, tack the fishing line near an upper corner of the block. Lift the block by grasping it between your fingers right at the tack, allowing the sinker to hang straight down. Make a pencil mark straight along the line of the fishing line. Repeat this procedure after tacking the line to the opposite corner of the block. If you have been careful to mark the lines accurately, the center of gravity will be where they cross. Now tack the plumb line to the center of gravity. Place the "tower" on the edge of the table and let the sinker hang straight down. As long as the plumb line falls within the base, the tower is stable and won't fall. If the line is outside the base, the tower topples. Test this theory by adding blocks of different heights and with larger "leans."

11. *TIPPING FLASK* Supervised Classroom

Pour sand into the bottom of a round-bottom flask. Stand the flask upright. Tip the flask gently. Notice how it recovers its former position, thanks to its low center of gravity.

12. BELT HOLDER   *Supervised Classroom*

Get a piece of plywood about ¼ inch thick and carve a wooden duplicate of the drawing sketched here.

Now rest a man's belt edgewise in the notched end. The buckle is to be at the bottom, as shown in the second sketch. Hold the thin edge of the device on the tip of your index finger. What happens?

Activity 12

13. HAMMER HOME A LESSON   *Home*

Here is an experiment you can not only see, but feel! Rest the head of a hammer in your outstretched hand, with the handle sticking up in the air. The head of the hammer will be "nestling" in the palm of your hand. It is content to stay in this position of rest, since its center of gravity is as close as it can get to the center of the earth at the moment.

Hammer

Now turn the hammer around so the end of the handle is pushing against your palm. With the head of the hammer in the air, note how hard it is to keep the hammer in this position. What type of equilibrium does this represent?

Activity 13

14. CAN YOU BEND OVER?   *Home*

Stand with your back against the wall, heels against the mopboard. Have someone place a book on the floor in front of your toes. Now, reach down with both arms together and try to pick up the book without bending your knees! What happens?

You

Activity 14

15. HOW STABLE ARE YOU?   *Home*

Close both eyes, and stand on one foot. See how long you can keep one foot lifted and maintain your position without swaying, opening your eyes, or clutching for support.

As a variation, keep both eyes closed and stand with feet as close together as possible—heels together and toes together. See how long you can maintain this position without swaying.

You

Activity 15

REPORT FROM VAIL, COLORADO

As we conclude this chapter on Newton's Law of Universal Gravitation, you may wish to keep in mind the words of a man who left the ski slopes of Vail, Colorado, on crutches. "I did not know that the law of gravity was so strictly enforced!"

HIGHLIGHTS OF THIS CHAPTER

- According to Newton's Law of Universal Gravitation, "ANY TWO BODIES IN THE UNIVERSE ATTRACT EACH OTHER WITH A FORCE THAT IS DIRECTLY PROPORTIONAL TO THE PRODUCT OF THEIR MASSES, AND INVERSELY PROPORTIONAL TO THE SQUARE OF THE DISTANCE BETWEEN THEIR CENTERS OF GRAVITY."

- The quantity of material in a body is called mass.

- The attraction between your mass and the mass of the planet you are standing on is called your weight. Your weight is a measure of the force with which the earth attracts you.

- The center of gravity is that point at which all the gravitational attraction or weight of an object may be considered to be concentrated.

- The gravitational pull of the earth makes the center of gravity of a body get as close as possible to the center of the earth. The direction we call "down" is the direction that leads to the center of the earth.

- An object is said to be in stable equilibrium when a slight tipping tends to raise the center of gravity.

- An object is in unstable equilibrium when a slight tipping lowers its center of gravity.

- An object is in neutral equilibrium when a slight tipping does not raise or lower its center of gravity.

Multiple-Choice Questions

1. A billiard ball rolling across a table is an example of:
   a. neutral equilibrium.
   b. stable equilibrium.
   c. unstable equilibrium.
   d. none of these.

2. If you were 5 times as far away from the center of the earth as you are now:
   a. you would weigh $1/5$ as much.
   b. you would weigh $1/10$ as much.
   c. you would weigh $1/20$ as much.
   d. your mass would stay the same.

3. Which of the following is false?
   a. The direction we call "down" is the direction that leads to the center of the earth.
   b. The gravitational pull of the earth makes the center of gravity of a body get as close as possible to the center of the earth.
   c. Einstein explained what gravity is.
   d. There is no shield against gravity.

4. If you were 6 times closer to the center of the earth than you are now, your weight would be:
   a. 6 times greater.
   b. 36 times greater.
   c. $1/6$ as much.
   d. the same.

5. Mexico City is approximately 1.5 miles above sea level. If a track meet were to be held there, which of the following would be true?
   a. Your weight would increase.
   b. A javelin would travel farther than it would at sea level.
   c. A discus would be influenced by the sidewise pull of neighboring mountains.
   d. A high jumper could not leap as high.

True or False Questions

1. A ballerina standing on her toes is an example of unstable equilibrium.

2. Newton claimed only to have explained the behavior of gravity, not its nature.

3. We can lose weight without losing a pound of fat.

4. On Jupiter your mass would be 317.9 times what it is now.

5. No one spends money to be entertained by gravity.

Chapter 5

HOW FAST CAN YOU FALL?

Why Is 5 Miles per Second a "Magic Number"?

If you wish to see a picture of the only man to fall 19 miles, go to your library and look up the *National Geographic* magazine for December, 1960. On page 855 you will see a picture showing Captain Joseph Kittinger at the very moment he leaped from the door of a basket suspended from an onion-shaped balloon over 18½ miles above the New Mexico desert.

Kittinger's job was to test equipment for high-altitude fliers faced with an emergency return to earth.

Concerning his record-breaking jump, Kittinger said that no wind whistled or tugged at him in the initial drop. Though his stabilization chute opened at 96,000 feet, he accelerated for 6,000 feet more before hitting a peak of 614 miles an hour. During his 4½ minutes of free fall, he fell 16 miles before his main chute opened at 18,000 feet.

Although Newton gave us his Law of Universal Gravitation, he did not tell us how fast gravity accelerates a body. The scientist who gave us that information was Galileo Galilei (1564–1642).

DISTRACTION BEGINS SCIENTIFIC CAREER!

Galileo began one of the most amazing scientific careers in history while he was saying his prayers in church!

Twenty-two-year-old Galileo had entered the Cathedral in Pisa, Italy, to say his prayers. As Galileo looked toward the altar, he was distracted. He watched as the sacristan lighted the sanctuary lamp that hung from a long chain fastened to the high ceiling. As the sacristan left, he accidentally pushed against the lamp, which began to swing. Galileo became fascinated by the back-and-forth motion of the lamp. He timed it with the beating of his pulse. He placed the fingers of his right hand on his left wrist, as he had been taught to do in one of his medical classes.

As Galileo watched the swinging lamp, a strange thing happened! The lamp began to swing through smaller and smaller arcs. (An arc is a curved line.) The distance covered on each swing was less, yet—and this was the interesting thing— the lamp took as much time to swing through a small arc as through a large one. Overcome with curiosity, Galileo continued with experiments in his home.

INSPIRATION AND EXPERIMENT

Scientists arrive at new visions of truth in different ways. Newton did not arrive at his Laws of Motion and Law of Universal Gravitation by conducting experiments in a lab. These truths leaped directly into his mind while he was on a quiet farm in England.

In this respect, Newton was like Dr. Charles Townes, the outstanding twentieth-century scientist who was awarded the Nobel Prize for his work that led to the ruby red laser. Dr. Townes admitted that the ideas that led to a laser leaped into his mind while he was sitting on a park bench in Washington, D.C. admiring azaleas in a flower bed.

Galileo used what is known today as "the scientific method." He arrived at his conclusions by making many experiments and then studying the facts he gathered from them.

In this chapter we will "walk along" with Galileo, "peer over his shoulder," and duplicate experiments similar to those he worked centuries ago. By working the following experiments, we can gain an appreciation of the scientific method and learn how it works.

ACTIVITIES

1. FIND THE PERIOD   **Home**

Get a piece of string about 3 feet long. Tie one end of the string to some fixed support, such as a shower rod, so it will be free to swing.

On the free end of the string tie a weight, which is called the bob. The weight or bob may be anything handy—a key, a nail, a ring, or even an apple with a strong stem. The string with the bob tied on the end is called a pendulum.

In the figure on the right, B is the bob at rest. Pull the bob to A. Let the bob go. It will swing from A to C. This distance from A to C is called an arc.

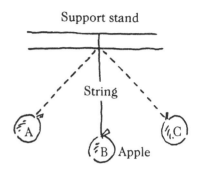

Activity 1

The time needed for the bob to swing from A to C and back again is called the period of the pendulum.

It is easier to find out how long it takes the bob to make one complete swing from A to C and back again to A, if you have help from a friend. The friend will have the job of watching the second hand of a clock or watch.

Pull the bob a small distance to one side in the direction of A. Tell your friend, who is looking at the second hand of a clock, to say "Go" when the second hand is on 1.

When your friend says "Go," let go of the bob. Let the bob swing from A to C and back again to A. When the bob returns to A, say "Stop." At this moment your friend is to note where the second hand is on the clock. Write down the time it took to make one swing.

Let the bob swing through an arc of 4 inches. Then let it swing through an arc of 6 inches, 10 inches, etc.

To make it easier to time the pendulum, you may allow the bob to make about 10 swings on each trial. Check with the second hand of a clock or watch.

What do the results indicate?

2. HEAVY VERSUS LIGHT   **Home**

Now get another string of exactly the same length. Tie a heavier weight to it. Be sure this pendulum is the same length as that

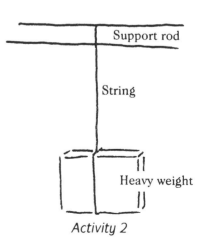

Activity 2

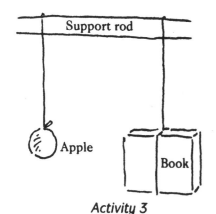

Activity 3

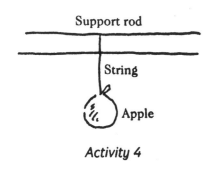

Activity 4

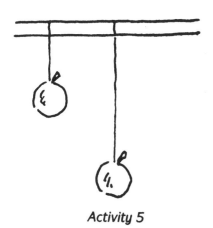

Activity 5

used in the previous experiment. Repeat the experiment you made with the lighter bob. What do you find?

3.   BOTH TOGETHER   Home

Another way to prove that the weight of the bob has nothing to do with its speed is to tie two strings alongside each other. Both strings must be the same length, but one will have a light bob, and one a heavy bob. Take both bobs in your hands at the same time and pull them in the same direction to one side. Let both bobs go at the same time. Note what happens. The bobs keep time, swinging back and forth together, even though one is lighter than the other.

4.   CHANGING LENGTHS   Home

Now let's see whether or not the length of the pendulum has anything to do with its period, or the time required for it to make a complete swing.

Begin with a string 36 inches long and any size bob you wish. Let the pendulum swing about 10 or 20 times. Time it with a watch. Take the average time for the round trip for the period of the pendulum.

Now repeat the experiment, this time using a string 9 inches long. What do you find?

5.   LONG AND SHORT TOGETHER   Home

Another way to prove that the time needed for a pendulum to make a swing depends on its length is to tie short and long strings beside each other on a support rod as shown in the figure. Use any weights you wish for bobs. Take both bobs in your hands at the same time and pull them in the same direction to one side. Let both bobs go at the same time. Note what happens. The bobs do not keep time. The shorter pendulum swings faster.

6.   INCLINED PLANE   Home

Perhaps you will be as amazed as Galileo was to find that the time needed for the pendulum to make a swing back and forth does not depend upon the size of the arc through which it swings. It does not depend on the size or weight of the bob. It depends only on the length of the pendulum.

To further prove that the speed of a falling body does not depend on its weight, Galileo continued with still another experiment which you, too, can do.

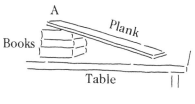

You will need a smooth board or plank about 4 inches wide and about 3 feet long. Place one end of the plank on the top of a stack of books, or anything else handy, and let the other end rest on the top of the table. This is called an inclined plane.

Activity 6

Now get two round objects of different weights. A big and a small marble will do. Take both marbles and hold them at the top of the inclined plane at position A. Be sure that both marbles are lined up so they are the same distance from the table. Let both marbles go at the same time. What do you notice?

SCIENTIFIC METHOD

If you did the experiments with the pendulum and the marbles, you found out how one scientist went about his work, and you used what is called the scientific method—the method, or way, to solve problems. Let us go back and trace the steps in this scientific method:

1. First, there was a problem. Galileo wondered, "What does the time needed for a pendulum to make one complete swing depend upon?"

2. He made a number of guesses. Perhaps the time would depend on the arc, or the distance through which the bob swings. Perhaps the weight of the bob would change the time. Perhaps the length of the pendulum would change the time.

3. The next step was to collect data, or facts. This he did by letting the bob swing through both small and big arcs. He used different weights for bobs. He used pendulums of different lengths.

4. The answers, or conclusions, he drew from the data were: the time needed for a pendulum to make one complete swing does not depend on the arc. It does not depend on the weight of the bob. It depends only on the length. In other words the speed of a falling body (in this case the bob) does not depend on its weight.

5. To be sure that his conclusions were correct, Galileo repeated his experiments many times, and checked for any mistakes, or errors.

6. As an added proof of the fact that the speed of a falling body does not depend on its weight, Galileo placed heavy and light balls at the top of an inclined plane. He let them go and found that they reached the bottom at the same time. (Please keep in mind that we have ignored the effect of air resistance, which would cause a big snowflake or a sheet of paper to fall at a different rate than a rock.)

7. WHAT DETERMINES THE FINAL SPEED?   Home

Use the same plank you used in the previous experiment. Place a toy car (or marble, or tennis ball, or anything else that will roll) 2 inches from the end of the plank that is resting on the table. Release the car. Notice its final speed when it reaches the table. Note how far it rolls across the table. Put a small piece of paper there to mark the spot.

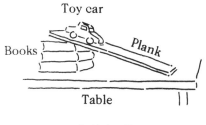

Toy car

Books

Plank

Table

Activity 7

Now place the car 4 inches up on the plank and repeat the experiment. Again, observe the final speed of the car when it hits the table. Mark the distance the car rolls across the table before it comes to a stop.

Repeat the experiment, releasing the car from various heights on the plank. The demonstrations illustrate that the final speed depends upon the time the object accelerates. The stopping distance increases according to the speed of the vehicle.

By adding more books to the tall end of the plank, you can vary the amount of acceleration. What does this illustrate?

FIND YOUR SPEED

To find your speed, simply take the distance you have gone and divide it by the time it took to go that distance. If you walk 12 miles in 4 hours, your average speed is:

$$S_a = \frac{D}{T}$$

S_a = average speed
D = distance
T = time

$$S_a = \frac{12 \text{ miles}}{4 \text{ hours}} = 3 \text{ miles per hour}$$

Speed may also be expressed in feet per second and centimeters per second.

Speed tells you how your distance changes with time.

SPEED + DIRECTION = VELOCITY

The rate of motion or the speed of an object is given in units of length and time. A speed of 30 miles per hour may also be stated as a speed of 44 feet per second. A speed of 15 miles per hour may be stated as a speed of 22 feet per second.

An object in motion has more than just speed. It has speed in a certain direction. This combination of speed and direction is called velocity.

If you say that your car is moving 30 mph, you give only its speed.

If you say that your car is moving 30 mph due north, you give its velocity.

Velocity is the rate of motion in a particular direction.

8. *FIND THE VELOCITY*

Since velocity has direction, we may represent it with an arrow. The length of the arrow represents the amount or the magnitude of the velocity—the miles per hour or feet per second.

Arrows that show velocity are called vectors. They represent both speed and direction.

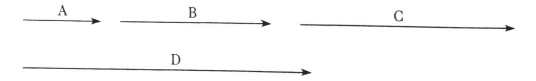

A represents a speed of 15 mph due east.
B represents a speed of 30 mph due east.
C represents a speed of 45 mph due east.
What does D represent?

ACCELERATION IS SPEEDING UP

An increase in speed is known as acceleration.

Acceleration tells you how your speed changes with time.

Suppose you enter your car and turn on the ignition switch. At this moment, the speed of your car is zero. Its acceleration is zero.

Now slip your car into gear. One second later the speedometer reads 3 mph. This does not mean that you have gone 3 miles. It simply indicates that at that moment the speed of the car is 3 mph. Since it took one whole second to make this change, we say that the acceleration is 3 miles per hour per second.

If you keep the same acceleration for the next 4 seconds, we can sum up the results as follows:

TIME	SPEED	ACCELERATION
0	0	0
1st second	3 mph	3 mph per sec.
2nd second	6 mph	3 mph per sec.
3rd second	9 mph	3 mph per sec.
4th second	12 mph	3 mph per sec.

Note that your speed changes from second to second, but the rate of change, or acceleration, stays the same: namely, 3 mph per sec.

Your final speed is given in this formula:

$$S_f = at$$

S_f = final speed
a = acceleration
t = time

If you accelerate for 10 seconds, your final speed would be:

$$S_f = at = 3 \times 10 = 30 \text{ miles per hour}$$

When Galileo worked his experiments with an inclined plane, he did not discover directly what the acceleration of gravity is. It was only through his great knowledge of mathematics that he was able to take the facts that he got from the inclined plane and work the material through to a conclusion.

Let us use the following chart to indicate what happens to the speed and acceleration of a freely falling body (neglecting air resistance):

TIME	SPEED	ACCELERATION
0	0	0
1st second	32 feet per second	32 feet per second per second
2nd second	64 feet per second	32 feet per second per second
3rd second	96 feet per second	32 feet per second per second
4th second	128 feet per second	32 feet per second per second

Note that the speed changes from second to second, but the rate of change, or acceleration, stays the same: namely, 32 fpsps.

This "per second per second" may sound odd, but it simply expresses speed in feet per second rather than miles per hour. Change in speed divided by time becomes "feet per second per second."

If a freely falling body accelerated for 10 seconds, its final speed would be:

$$S_f = at = 32 \times 10 = 320 \text{ feet per second}$$

The average speed of a freely falling body is half of the final speed:

$$S_a = \tfrac{1}{2} S_f$$

The average speed of the above-mentioned object would be:

$$S_a = \tfrac{1}{2} S_f = \tfrac{1}{2}(320) = 160 \text{ feet per second}$$

The distance covered by a freely falling body is given by this formula:

$$D = \tfrac{1}{2} at^2$$

D = distance
a = acceleration
t = time

How far does a body fall in 1 second?

$$D = \tfrac{1}{2} at^2 = \tfrac{1}{2}(32 \times 1^2) = 16 \text{ ft.}$$

DEADLY WEAPON

Now you can see why such a thing as a falling rock or dumbbell can become a "deadly weapon." At the end of each second it is moving 32 feet per second faster than it was at the start of that second.

Some years ago, a five-pound dumbbell fell eight stories from television star Arlene Francis' Park Avenue apartment. The dumbbell, used in exercising, had been placed on a window ledge in the Ritz Towers apartment. When the dumbbell rolled out, the acceleration of gravity turned it into a skull-cracker. It struck and killed a man from Detroit who had come to New York with his wife to celebrate his sixtieth birthday.

MAKE YOUR OWN CHART

The following chart shows only the first 4 seconds of a freely falling body. Using the information it offers, construct your own chart showing the first 8 seconds.

SPEED (final)		DISTANCE COVERED	TOTAL DISTANCE
1st sec. 32 fps	32 fps	16 ft. during 1st sec. only	16 ft.
2nd sec. 64 fps	32 fpsps	48 ft. during 2nd sec. only	64 ft.
3rd sec. 96 fps	32 fpsps	80 ft. during 3rd sec. only	144 ft.
4th sec. 128 fps	32 fpsps	112 ft. during 4th sec. only	256 ft.

Note that the acceleration, or change in speed, stays the same throughout.

To find the distance covered, remember the formula $D = \frac{1}{2} at^2$

BULLET VERSUS ROCK

Suppose you place a rifle in a horizontal position with the muzzle pointing out over the edge of a cliff 16 feet high. At the same time you pull the trigger, your pal drops a rock from the edge of the cliff.

Which will hit the ground first, the rock or the bullet?

Strange as it may seem, both bullet and rock hit the ground at the same time!

Why? Because both are pulled down by gravity at the same rate. Though both objects hit the ground at the same time, the bullet will be farther from the foot of the cliff. Reason—the forward, horizontal flight of the bullet is independent of the downward pull of gravity. The forward velocity of the bullet and its fall downward operate independently of each other.

During the first second of free fall, all objects (neglecting air resistance) will drop 16 feet. But while the rock has been merely falling in a vertical position, the bullet, in addition to falling "downward" like the rock, has also been moving forward.

If the forward velocity of the bullet is 1,000 feet per second, it will land 1,000 feet from the base of the cliff, and at the same time the rock lands.

The combination of the bullet's forward motion and downward motion is a curved path called a parabola.

CAN YOU WALK 5 MILES IN A STRAIGHT LINE?

If you tried to travel 5 miles in a horizontal direction, as shown by the line AB, you would find it impossible. For each 5 miles of horizontal distance, the earth curves or "falls" 16 feet. This means that instead of being at B, you would be at C. (Figure is *not* drawn to scale.)

HOW TO ORBIT

Now see how all this applies to Astronaut Bruce McCandless when he was in orbit. There is no air in space. A breeze is impossible. Since the astronaut was traveling in a near-vacuum, there was nothing to blow him backward or slow him down.

Left to himself, McCandless' forward speed of 18,000 miles per hour would have carried him 5 miles straight forward, from A to B, in one second.

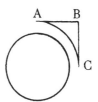

During the same time, however, gravity pulled McCandless and his space capsule 16 feet toward the center of the earth as shown by the line BC (*not* drawn to scale). The result of these two forces was that McCandless traveled in the path AC. Note that at C the astronaut and his capsule were no closer to the earth than they were at A.

Orbiting objects repeat this procedure every second. Gravity continually pulls the object toward the earth, yet it always remains the same distance away. It is always "falling," or being pulled down by gravity, but never landing.

Why is 5 miles per second the "Magic Speed" for astronauts and man-made satellites?

Because at this speed, while the satellite is going 5 miles in a forward direction, it is being "pulled down" 16 feet by gravity. This means that its path "matches" or runs parallel to the curvature of the earth. It is continually "falling" over the horizon.

No doubt you have figured out what would happen if the speed of the satellite is less than 5 miles per second. Instead of "falling over the horizon" and following the curvature of the earth, the satellite would fall toward our rooftops, since the pull of gravity would be greater than its forward speed.

However, if its forward speed is greater than the pull of gravity, the satellite would continue to move out into space, leaving earth far behind. The velocity that a satellite needs to remain in orbit around the earth is 5 miles per second, or approximately 18,000 miles per hour.

FARTHER AWAY = LESS GRAVITY

As we get farther and farther away from the center of the earth, the acceleration of gravity becomes less and less. At comparatively large distances from the earth, a satellite will not fall as far toward the earth as it passes over each mile of the earth's surface. So its orbital velocity, or speed forward, need not be as great.

An object as far away as the moon (240,000 miles in round numbers) needs an orbital velocity of about 2,000 miles per hour.

THE MOON IS "FALLING DOWN"

When you look up at the moon, it appears to be a "stationary" satellite of the earth. Actually, the moon is speeding along at about three times the speed of sound, as it is "falling down"!

Each second the moon moves forward through space about 3,350 feet and "falls," or is deflected from its straight-line path, by about 1/19 of an inch toward the earth. "Falling" 1/19 of an inch each second is just enough to keep the moon in orbit around the earth. If it didn't "fall" it would keep going in a straight line out into space, and we would have no harvest moon to pour its burnished gold across our October cornfields.

OUR PLANET IS "FALLING"

We Earth people actually live on a giant perpetual motion machine, the earth. We depend upon "falling" to keep us in place!

Each second your watch ticks, the earth "falls" toward the sun. If it were not for the gravitational pull of the sun, our planet would go sailing off into space. Fortunately, Earth's forward speed of 65,000 miles per hour is "balanced" by the inward pull of gravity exerted by the sun 93 million miles distant.

BULLETS FROM THE SKY!

If all falling objects continually increased their speed by 32 feet per second each second of fall, think what would happen if you were caught in a storm. Raindrops would drop on you like thousands of small hammers. Hailstones would become bullets. Your roof would be punched full of holes. You would look like Swiss cheese.

Fortunately, air offers resistance, or friction, which increases or grows larger with an increase in speed. When the force of air friction equals the pull of gravity, the falling object will no longer accelerate. It will descend with a constant velocity called the terminal velocity.

"LAZY" SNOWFLAKES

Big, fat, lazy snowflakes silently drifting down from a grey sky are good examples of objects whose air friction is great enough to keep them from accelerating. Instead of speeding up, they maintain a constant velocity.

9. DROP A HAMMER ON YOUR HAND   Home

Hold out your left hand, palm up. Pick up a hammer with your right hand. Hold it 1 inch above your outstretched palm. Release it. The impact won't bother you since the hammer accelerates for only a short time.

Now release the hammer from a height of 3 inches and note the results. At what height do you decide to call a stop to this experiment?

10. PAPER NAPKIN   Home

To show how the amount of surface exposed to the air increases friction and thereby cuts down on speed, try this experiment. Unfold a paper napkin or tissue paper and release it so the tissue floats to the floor like an erratic parachute. It will dilly-dally, so to speak, all the way to the floor.

Now wad the tissue paper into a small ball. The more compact ball will fall with greater speed. It has less resistance to offer to the air.

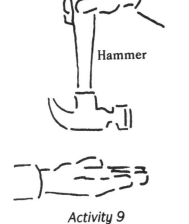

Hammer

Activity 9

Tissue paper

Activity 10

11. SPEEDY PENDULUM   **Home**

A pendulum illustrates how final velocity depends on the time of the acceleration.

Lift a bob to position B and release it. Note its speed when it arrives at position A.

Now lift the bob to position C and release it. Note how much greater its speed is when it reaches position A. The longer acceleration time gives it greater final velocity.

Vary this experiment by lifting the bob to various heights and noting its speed when it arrives at position A.

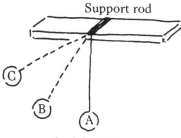

Activity 11

12. ACCELERATING PENDULUM   **Home**

A pendulum furnishes a delightful demonstration of "positive" and "negative" acceleration.

Raise the bob to position A, then release it. Gravity takes over the job of speeding up the bob as it falls from A to B. This gain in speed is called "positive" acceleration.

As the bob continues to swing from B to C, gravity "puts on the brakes" and slows the bob down at exactly the same rate it speeded it up. The slowing down is "negative" acceleration.

Gravity "speeds up" the bob from A to B, then "slows it down" from B to C. If it weren't for friction, position C would be exactly as high as position A.

What happens to the bob on the return trip from C to A?

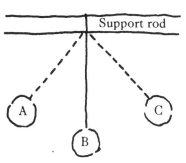

Activity 12

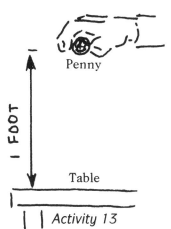

Penny

1 FOOT

Table

Activity 13

13. HOW LONG?   **Home**

From what you have learned so far in this chapter, can you figure out how long it will take an object to fall one foot?

14. INTERCEPTION   **Home**

If your garage has a side door that opens to your backyard, perhaps you may be allowed to put a small nail or hook in the middle of the top of the door frame. If you don't have a garage, you could use a shower rod.

Suspend a string about a yard long from this hook. Tie a heavy bob, such as a bolt or empty bottle, to the free end of the string.

Activity 14

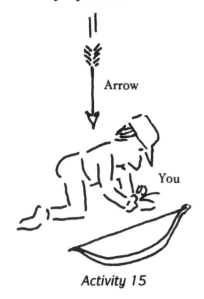

Arrow

You

Activity 15

Swing the pendulum and note that it swings to the same height on each end of its swing. While the pendulum is swinging, put a broomstick across its path, about halfway along the string's length. What happens when the string meets the broomstick? How high will the bob go?

15. *SHOOT AN ARROW*   *Home*

What do you think would happen on a perfectly calm day if you shot an arrow straight up into the sky, then bent over to tie your shoelace?

16. *ROUND TRIP BASEBALL*   *Home*

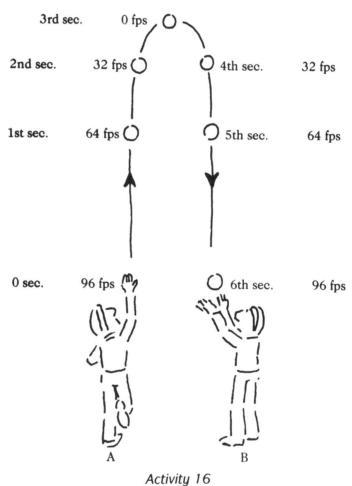

Activity 16

This diagram shows what happens when you throw a baseball straight up into the air. Suppose that the baseball leaves your hand (position A) with a speed of 96 fps. By the end of the 1st second the negative acceleration of gravity reduces that speed to 64 fps. At the end of the 2nd second, the speed will be 32 fps. By the end of the 3rd second, gravity will bring the baseball to a complete stop.

On the return trip, the positive acceleration of gravity will speed up the baseball at the same rate it slowed it down. Neglecting air resistance, the ball will hit your hands (position B) with the same speed it had when it left your hands.

17. GARAGE DOOR PENDULUMS   Home

A delightful way to watch changes in velocity is to go out to the garage door and tie a string only 2 inches long to a hook or small nail at the top of the door. For the bob you may use an apple with a good stem, a key, or any other convenient object. Note how rapidly the pendulum swings back and forth.

Now use the same bob with a string about 5 to 6 feet in length.

What do you notice when you put the pendulum into motion?

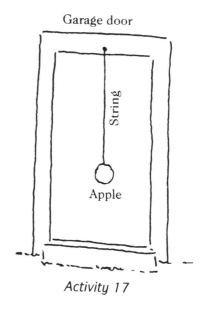

Activity 17

18. TIME THE BASEBALL   Home

With the knowledge you have acquired in this chapter you can now throw a baseball straight up into the air and tell:

How fast the baseball left your hand.
The impact when it lands in your hands on its return trip.
How high it went.
What the average speed was.

The only thing you need, besides a baseball, is a friend with a stopwatch. As soon as the ball leaves your hand, your friend is to start the watch. Stop the watch as soon as the ball hits your hands on the return trip. Now you can use the formulas you learned in this chapter.

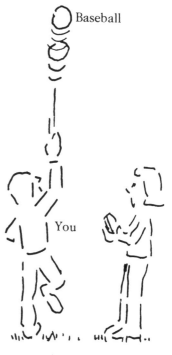

Activity 18

HIGHLIGHTS OF THIS CHAPTER

● The period of a pendulum is independent of the size of the arc and the weight of the bob. The period depends on the length of the pendulum.

● A change in speed is called acceleration.

● The acceleration due to gravity is 32 fpsps.

● The final speed of a freely falling body is expressed as $S_f = at$.

● The distance covered by a freely falling body is expressed as $D = \frac{1}{2} at^2$.

Multiple-Choice Questions

1. 32 feet per second is:
   a. the speed of a freely falling body during the first second.
   b. the speed of a freely falling body at the end of the first second.
   c. the speed of an object falling in space.
   d. the speed that a freely falling body maintains during its entire fall.

2. The greater the mass of the bob on a pendulum:
   a. the fewer the number of swings.
   b. the greater the time required for a complete swing.
   c. the less the time required for a complete swing.
   d. the greater mass won't effect the period.

3. When Astronaut David Scott was on the moon he dropped a feather and a hammer simultaneously. They both hit the surface of the moon at the same time. This was due to the fact that:
   a. the gravity pull on the moon is $\frac{1}{6}$ that of earth.
   b. the final velocity of objects falling on the moon is less than that of objects falling on the surface of the earth.
   c. there was no air resistance.
   d. the acceleration on the moon is 20% slower than on earth.

4. To make a pendulum swing faster, you need to:
    a. make the pendulum shorter.
    b. make the pendulum lighter.
    c. let the bob swing through a shorter arc.
    d. add more weight to the bob.

5. A rock falls from a cliff in the Grand Canyon and hits the Colorado River with a velocity of 128 feet per second. From what height did the rock fall?
    a. 96 ft.
    b. 144 ft.
    c. 256 ft.
    d. 320 ft.

True or False Questions

1. Velocity includes both speed and direction.

2. In the first ¼ second of free fall a body will fall a distance of 1 foot.

3. Galileo's experiments with the inclined plane proved that heavier objects fall faster than lighter ones.

4. Every second the moon is falling $1/19$ of an inch toward the earth.

5. If you throw a baseball straight up into the air, it will come back and hit your hand with the same speed with which it left your hand.

Chapter 6

WHAT IS THE PRESSURE ON YOUR HEAD?

It's the Same Pressure that Blows Airplanes Apart!

In the early days of jet travel, some airplanes blew themselves apart. One example is that of the British Overseas Airways jet plane that blew apart over the Mediterranean Sea in 1954.

Extensive investigations of planes of the same type revealed that there was one weak spot in the fuselage where the metal had not been able to withstand the constant stress due to pressure changes. Engineers called it "metal fatigue." Just as a pinprick causes a balloon to burst suddenly, so one tiny weak spot is enough to allow a pressurized plane to explode.

DEFECTIVE GLOVE IN SPACE

When Joseph Kittinger rode a balloon to a height of 18½ miles in the sky, he ran into trouble. At a height of 43,000 feet the pressure glove on his right hand failed to work properly.

If you wish to see what Kittinger's hand looked like when he landed by parachute in the New Mexico desert, look up the *National Geographic* magazine for December, 1960, and turn to page 873.

WHY "HALF-EMPTY" BALLOONS?

Have you ever noticed from pictures in magazines, newspapers, or TV that high-altitude balloons are released when they are only partially inflated? Do you know why?

Atmospheric pressure decreases with height. As the atmospheric pressure falls off, the pressure of the gas inside the balloon makes it expand more and more until the balloon is fully inflated. If the balloon were fully inflated at ground level, then as it rose to great heights where atmospheric pressure is low, the gas inside the balloon would expand so much it would break the balloon.

OUR BLANKET OF AIR

When you and I look "up" from the earth, we seem to be surrounded by a beautiful blue sky that appears to extend forever outward. Yet, in photos of the earth taken from the moon, the earth appears to be "lost" or "floating" in a void of utter black. What happened to our sky? How "tall" or "thick" is our sky?

Some folks think we live on top of the world. Actually, we live at the bottom of a great sea, a sea of air over 600 miles high and weighing more than 5 quadrillion (5 million billion) tons. This "blanket" of air is squeezing down on every square foot of your body with an overwhelming pressure of 2,016 pounds! The only reason you aren't flattened out is that air is also inside your body pushing out.

Scientists know that there is a thin sprinkling of air 100 miles above the earth because meteors burst into flame at this height due to friction with molecules of air. At some vague, undetermined spot the particles of air fade away like ghosts in the night. Beyond is the blackness of space. So thin is air in the upper regions of the atmosphere that, even though a few particles may be found 600 miles or so above sea level, half of the earth's atmosphere lies below 4 miles.

The deep blue of the sky extends upward only about 12 miles. Beyond this it fades into dark violets and deeper purples. Around 20 miles high, the blackness of space encompasses you, and you can see the stars at high noon.

HOW MUCH IS YOUR "AIR PROTECTION" WORTH?

How much is your "air protection" worth? How much would it cost to pay for the safety and security afforded by our "blanket of air"?

The astronauts who went to the moon know the answer. Each space suit, custom-fitted for moon wear, cost $100,000. *Life* magazine referred to the astronaut's suit as an "awesome smorgasbord of synthetics."

On the outside of the 21-layer body suit is a layer of Beta fiber, a fireproof Fiberglas fabric covered with Teflon, the material used in frying pans. Then come 15 alternating layers of aluminized plastic and Beta cloth. Next come two layers of nylon coated with neoprene (synthetic rubber), a nylon restraining layer, an airtight bladder of neoprene-coated nylon, and a nylon liner. Underneath this the astronaut wears underwear consisting of elasticized plastic and, next to the skin, a layer of delicate nylon chiffon.

Each of these layers must be individually cut to order and fitted and refitted by hand. The suit protects the astronaut from deadly extremes of temperature (from 250° above zero to 250° below zero), the threat of bombardment by tiny particles known as micro-meteoroids, and a complete lack of oxygen and atmospheric pressure. The suit's outer layers are built to take care of temperatures and micro-meteoroids. The middle layers, which are interlaced with a network of tubes, provide oxygen and protection against decompression.

ROCKY MOUNTAIN HIGH

Not only does air pressure decrease as you climb a mountain, but temperature does likewise. One hot July when I was visiting in Denver, the temperature in the downtown streets was 96°. As I drove west into the high mountains, the temperature began to drop. By the time I stopped at the top of Mount Evans 14,260 feet above sea level, the temperature was a chilly 32°.

THE AIR OUT-PULLED SIXTEEN HORSES

A German scientist, Otto von Guericke, gave a very vivid demonstration of air pressure in the seventeenth century. After he had invented a pump that could draw air from a closed container, he made two hollow copper hemispheres, or half spheres, 20 inches in diameter. These were fitted together very tightly. Von Guericke then removed most of the air from inside the sphere with his air pump. The pressure of the air outside the sphere was so great that 16 horses couldn't pull the two sections apart. When air was put back into the sphere, anyone could pull them apart.

AIR PRESSURE

Otto von Guericke demonstrated the fact that air exerts pressure. The man who figured out what that pressure is was named Evangelista Torricelli (1608–1647). He was a pupil of Galileo. Torricelli obtained a tube 1 inch in diameter and 36 inches long, closed at one end. This was filled with mercury. Then, holding his thumb over the open end, Torricelli immersed the tube in a bowl containing mercury. When he withdrew his thumb some of the mercury ran out of the tube, but 30 inches remained. He repeated the experiment with tubes of various sizes and shapes. The mercury always remained at about 30 inches. Although there was empty space above the mercury, the level was no higher or lower in longer tubes

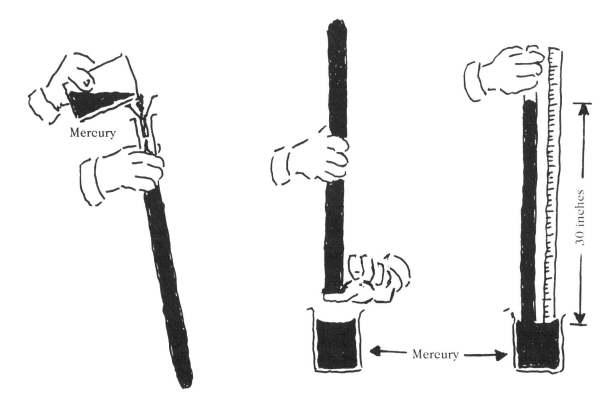

or tubes with more space at the top. Torricelli therefore concluded that it was the pressure of air on the mercury in the bowl that held mercury in a tube at 30 inches. Since a column of mercury 1 inch in diameter and 30 inches high weighs 14.7 pounds, air exerts a pressure of 14.7 pounds per square inch.

Torricelli's interest had first been aroused by the fact that a lift pump raises water no higher than 34 feet. The experiment was tried with mercury, which is 13.6 times as heavy as water. It was much easier to work with tubes that were 36 inches long rather than 35 feet. The pressure of 14.7 pounds per square inch holds up a column of water 34 feet high. This is called a pressure of 1 atmosphere or of 1 atm.

CLIMB THE MOUNTAIN!

Torricelli's work was done at sea level. Some years later Blaise Pascal (1623-1662) decided to find out what would happen to the column of mercury as one climbed a mountain.

At the foot of the mountain the tube was filled with mercury and turned upside down in a cup of mercury. The column of mercury was 30 inches high. Then the tube was carried to the top of the mountain, 3,000 feet high. At the top of the mountain the column of mercury was 3 inches less than it had been at the beginning of the climb. This proved that air pressure decreases with altitude.

THE FIRST BAROMETER

The tube of mercury that Torricelli used to demonstrate air pressure was really the first barometer. This is a Greek word meaning "weight measuring," for the barometer tells the weight of the air that surrounds it. Changes in air pressure are related to storms and air movements, so knowledge of air pressure is important in weather forecasting.

Since a liquid barometer is so tall and must stand upright, it is not used as extensively today as the aneroid barometer. Aneroid is a word from the Greek "a," not, and "neros," wet. This barometer contains no liquid. Inside the aneroid barometer is a small metal box or chamber from which most of the air has been removed. When the air pressure increases even slightly it presses on the box, for there is almost no air inside. When air pressure decreases, the sides of the box push out again. The movement of this metal chamber is very slight, but it is magnified by a system of levers connected to a pointer or needle.

The pointer moves across a scale on the dial. The pressure is indicated in inches or in millibars, a unit based on the metric system. If the aneroid barometer points to 30, it means that the air would push a column of mercury up 30 inches in Torricelli's tube.

Weather maps indicate air pressure in millibars. A reading of 30 inches would be equivalent to 1013.25 millibars.

WITCHCRAFT UNDER THE ROOF!

One of the first users of a barometer was accused of witchcraft!

Otto von Guericke made a water barometer. He ran a long, wide-diameter tube from a tank of water in his cellar up through a hole in the roof of his house. The glass tube was closed at the top. Inside the tube, floating on the column of water, was a wooden statue of a man.

On fair days the increased air pressure forced water up inside the tube. The statue rose high above the roof and could be seen by the neighbors. When a storm was brewing the water level sank because of the lowered air pressure. The statue dropped below the roof level to hide in the attic. Unfortunately, the neighbors didn't understand that changes in air pressure made the water rise and fall. They thought that Otto was brewing black magic.

FIRST PHOTO OF CURVATURE OF EARTH

The first photograph ever made that showed the actual curvature of the earth was taken from a balloon manned by two army officers. It rose to a height of 72,395 feet on November 11, 1935. At this height—almost 14 miles—only 4% of the earth's atmosphere was above the camera when the picture was taken, and there was practically no dust or other substances to scatter and reflect sunlight. As a result, the upper sky was very dark and showed up on the photograph as black.

BUILDINGS THAT BLOW THEMSELVES APART

The whirling motion of a tornado lowers the air pressure on the outside walls of buildings in the path of the tornado. The air trapped inside the buildings is no longer held in check by the equal pressure of outside air. Instantly this "inside air" smashes walls and pushes up roofs. In addition to property damage, tornadoes cause the death of approximately 250 people each year in the United States.

FORCE AND PRESSURE

Before performing experiments dealing with force and pressure, we should understand the meanings of these two words.

Force is a push or pull. The pull of gravity on you is called your weight. Pressure is equal to the force divided by the area:

$$P = \frac{F}{A}$$

P = Pressure
F = Force
A = Area

WHAT IS THE PRESSURE UNDER YOUR FOOT?

How much pressure do you exert on each square inch of your sole if you weigh 120 pounds and are standing on 40 square inches of shoe leather?

$$P = \frac{F}{A}$$
$$P = \frac{120 \text{ pounds}}{40 \text{ square inches}}$$
$$P = 3 \text{ pounds per square inch}$$

Can you reduce your weight by standing on only one foot on the bathroom scale? If you try it, you find that your weight remains the same, but since you are standing on one foot only, you reduce the area on which you stand by one-half. The pressure soars to twice what it was before. It is now 6 pounds per square inch.

If you take off your shoes and succeed in balancing yourself on one big toe over an area of one square inch, the pressure would zoom to 120 pounds per square inch.

A YOUNG WOMAN CAN MAKE A GREAT IMPRESSION

Do you know that a young woman can make a greater impression than an elephant?

A 120-pound woman wearing a steel-shaft type of heel with a surface area of 0.02 square inches can exert as much as 3,500 pounds of pressure per square inch. The pressure under an elephant's foot is only 50 to 100 pounds per square inch.

The Louvre and all other state-owned museums in France have banned stiletto heels to save their floors and carpets. Women touring the sites must wear flat shoes or rent plastic slippers.

SNO-BUGGY

A huge 23-ton vehicle called the LeTourneau Sno-Buggy is built to mush through snow in the far north. Its tires are 10 feet high. They leave 4-foot-wide tracks. Despite the weight of the Sno-Buggy, the tires carry only five pounds pressure.

WHAT HAPPENS WHEN YOU SKATE?

When you skate on ice, the pressure of your skate melts the ice and forms a thin film of water over which the skate moves. You are really skating on water. When you lift your foot, the water freezes immediately.

On very cold winter days the pressure from the skate cannot melt the ice. Skating is more difficult on such days.

SNOW LIKE SAND!

When you leaped on your sled to speed down a snow-covered hill, the pressure exerted by the blades tended to melt the snow. This made the snow slippery. You shot downhill with glee.

Scientists who explore the frigid regions around the South Pole report that sometimes the weather is so cold that runners on sleds cannot warm up the snow enough to let the sled glide or slip through the snow. The result—trying to pull a sled through such snow is like trying to pull the sled through sand.

A WHALE OF A TALE!

Every now and then giant whales wash up on beaches and die. One reason given for their death is pressure. When the whale is floating in the ocean, its tremendous weight is distributed over thousands and thousands of square inches of area. The water is like a mighty hand helping to hold up the whale's weight.

When a whale washes up on a beach, its entire weight is now centered only on the area of its body in direct contact with the shore. Since so much weight is concentrated over a much smaller area, the pressure soars. This terrible pressure ruptures the whale's internal organs.

WHEN YOUR EARS "POP"

When you travel up a mountain road in a car, notice how your ears "pop" as you ascend higher and higher. The air pressure is decreasing, but the air inside your body has the same pressure that it had when you left level ground. Since the air outside does not counterbalance the air inside, you experience the discomfort of popping ears.

The same effect is often felt when you ride a fast elevator to the top floor of a skyscraper.

WHY SO MANY WHEELS?

Keep your eyes open when you drive from one state to another. You may see huge signs informing truck drivers of the number of axles required for the load they carry.

Why do big trucks have to have so many wheels? More wheels spread the weight of the freight over as large an area as possible. This decreases the pressure and wear on the highway.

FROM SEA TO SHINING SEA

"From California to the New York island, from the redwood forest to the Gulf Stream waters," the formula $P = F/A$ is applied from coast to coast.

Do you know where this formula is applied from sea to shining sea?

The answer—in railroad tracks!

Imagine what would happen if the steel wheels of a freight train tried to run on a dirt road. After a rain, especially, they would sink into the ground.

The weight of a train is first distributed to the steel rails. The steel rails, in turn, distribute the weight over thousands and thousands of railroad ties. This is a superb example of how an increase in area decreases the pressure.

PEBBLE IN YOUR SHOE

One of the most exasperating demonstrations of the pressure formula takes place when you pick up a pebble in your shoe. The small area of the pebble increases the pressure on your foot—a sole-stirring experience!

BOYLE'S LAW

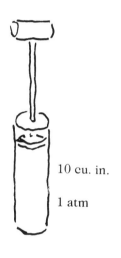

What happens when you apply pressure to a confined volume of air, such as pushing down the plunger of a basketball, football, or bike pump?

The answer is given by Boyle's Law: "**THE VOLUME OF A GAS IS INVERSELY PROPORTIONAL TO THE PRESSURE AT CONSTANT TEMPERATURE.**"

Suppose we have a hand pump with the plunger at the top of the cylinder. The volume of the air inside the cylinder is 10 cubic inches, the pressure is that of the atmosphere itself. This is called a pressure of one atmosphere, or 1 atm. It is 14.7 lbs. per sq. in.

10 cu. in.

1 atm

Now push down on the plunger until the volume inside the cylinder is reduced to 5 cubic inches, or half of what it was before. The pressure soars to twice what it was previously, or 2 atm.

We can express this proportion as follows:

$$\frac{2 \text{ atmospheres}}{1 \text{ atmosphere}} = \frac{10 \text{ cubic inches}}{5 \text{ cubic inches}}$$

The second pressure is to the first as the first volume is to the second. This is called an inverse proportion. If we use letters, we can write:

$$\frac{P_2}{P_2} = \frac{V_1}{V_2}$$

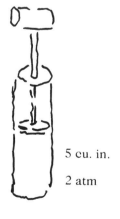

5 cu. in.

2 atm

P_1 = the first pressure V_1 = the first volume
P_2 = the second pressure V_2 = the second volume

Six cubic feet of air at an atmospheric pressure of 15 lbs. per sq. in. are forced into a balloon. This compressed air inside the balloon has a pressure of 18 lbs. per sq. in. What is the volume of the balloon?

$$\frac{P_2}{P_1} = \frac{V_1}{V_2}$$

$$\frac{18 \text{ lbs. per sq. in.}}{15 \text{ lbs. per sq. in.}} = \frac{6 \text{ cu. ft.}}{V_2}$$

$$18 \times V_2 = 6 \times 15$$

$$V_2 = \frac{90}{18} = 5 \text{ cu. ft.}$$

ACTIVITIES

1. UPSIDE-DOWN GLASS   Home

Sometimes we refer to an object as being "light as air." To find out whether or not this is a good comparison, try the following:

Get a small, square, light cardboard wide enough to cover the top of a drinking glass. Fill the glass to the brim with water. Press the cardboard on top of the glass. Make sure that the cardboard touches the glass all the way around the rim.

Now invert the glass. Remove your hand from the cardboard. Air pressure pushing up against the cardboard should hold the water in the glass. (Just in case something goes wrong, do this experiment over the sink.)

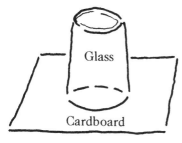

Activity 1

2. AIR PUSHES   Home

For this experiment, you may use a long-necked flask or an empty catsup, wine, or soda bottle. Fill the bottle with water. Then place a drinking glass upside down over the neck of the bottle so the bottom of the glass rests on the mouth of the bottle.

Use your right hand to hold the glass firmly against the mouth of the bottle. With your left hand, grasp the bottle. Turn the entire unit around so the bottle is upside down with its neck inside the drinking glass.

Now raise the bottle so its rim is about 1/16 inch above the bottom of the drinking glass. What happens?

Activity 2

3. SUCTION CUP   Home

Press a suction cup firmly against a smooth surface like a tabletop. Try to lift it up. Remember, the only thing holding the cup to the table is "light" air! Can't you exert a force equal to that of the air?

Slip a fingernail file or knife blade under one side of the suction cup. Air rushes in to make the atmospheric pressure the same on both sides of the cup. Now you can pick up the cup with ease—a dramatic proof of the "push" exerted by air.

Suction cup

Activity 3

Activity 4

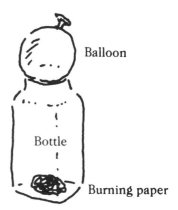

Balloon

Bottle

Burning paper

Activity 5

Burning paper

Activity 6

Bottle

Bowl

Activity 7

Candle

Bowl — Wax

Activity 8

4. TWO SUCTION CUPS   Home

Press two large suction cups firmly together. Then try to pull them apart. Here is dramatic proof that our "thin" air is "heavy" enough to hold the cups together.

5. BALLOON AND BOTTLE   Supervised Classroom

For this experiment you will need a bottle with a medium-size mouth. Some supermarkets sell orange juice in quart bottles that may be used for this experiment. Another bottle that may be used is a 32-ounce catsup bottle.

You will also need a toy balloon. Blow up the balloon to the size of a tennis ball and tie it securely.

Now strike a match and set fire to a scrap of paper. Drop the burning paper into the empty bottle. As soon as the flame burns out, immediately place the balloon on top of the bottle. Describe what happens.

6. BIGGER BALLOON   Supervised Classroom

For a variation of this demonstration, blow up the balloon to the size of a big grapefruit. What happens this time?

7. UPSIDE-DOWN BOTTLE   Supervised Classroom

Get a glass bowl about 5 inches wide and 4 inches deep. Pour in about 3 inches of water. Now take an empty bottle (a quart-size bottle is excellent). Set fire to a scrap of paper and drop it into the bottle. The very instant the fire goes out, turn the bottle upside down and submerge it (neck down) in the water until the rim of the bottle almost touches the bottom of the glass bowl. What happens? The results are so dramatic, you will have to see it to believe it.

8. CANDLE IN BOTTLE   Supervised Classroom

Get a candle about 3 inches long and insert it in a candleholder in the center of a bowl. If you do not have a candleholder, let hot wax fall on the center of the bowl and force the base of the candle into the melted wax.

Pour about 2 inches of water into the bowl. Light the candle. Now take your empty bottle, turn it upside down, and hold it over the candle. Hold the neck of the bottle close to the bottom of the bowl. What do you notice?

9. SQUEEZE AIR   **Home**

To find out what happens when you squeeze air, try the following. Fill a wide-mouth gallon jar about ⅔ full of water and place it on the table.

Now turn a drinking glass upside down. Push it, open end first, into the gallon jar until the rim of the glass is touching the bottom of the jar.

How far up in the glass does the water rise? Why?

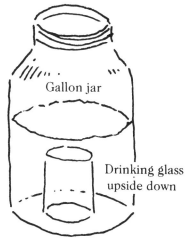

Activity 9

10. DRY SUBMERGED PAPER   **Home**

Crumple a sheet of typing or any similar paper and ram it in the bottom of a drinking glass. Now turn the glass upside down and submerge it in the gallon jar of water.

Remove the drinking glass. Take the crumpled paper from the glass. It stayed dry. This experiment represents the principle of the diving bell, or caisson. ("Caisson" comes from a Latin word meaning "box" or "case.") Because air resists being squeezed, it keeps the water out. This makes it possible for people to work under rivers and lakes to put down the foundations for bridges. Compressed air is forced into the diving bell until it equals the water pressure exerted by the river or lake.

Activity 10

11. CORK FLOATS UNDER WATER   **Home**

Can you make a cork "float beneath the surface"? This demonstration is so delightful and fascinating, you will have to try it as soon as possible.

Place a cork on the surface of the water in a gallon jar. Turn a drinking glass upside down over the cork. Push the glass down until it touches the bottom of the jar. The air compressed inside the glass allows only about a centimeter of water to rise inside the glass. The cork "floats on the bottom" of the gallon jar!

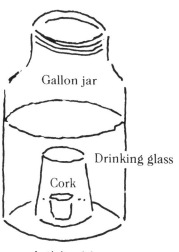

Activity 11

Rubber bulb

Basting tube

Glass of water

Activity 12

Soda pop bottle

Activity 13

12. BASTING TUBE   *Supervised Classroom*

What happens to air if you "squeeze" it? Boyle's law give the answer: The volume occupied by a body of gas is inversely proportional to its pressure, if its temperature remains constant.

To prove it, insert the open end of a basting tube in a glass of water. Now squeeze the rubber bulb. This decreases its volume, which increases the pressure of the air it contains. This increase in pressure forces some of the air out the open end of the tube.

Release the bulb. Its elasticity makes it spring back into shape. This increases its volume and decreases the pressure of the air inside the tube. Now the air pressure on the surface of the water pushes liquid up inside the tube.

To get the liquid out of the tube, you employ Boyle's law once more. You squeeze the rubber bulb, thereby decreasing its volume. This increases the air pressure, which forces the liquid back out of the tube.

Repeat this experiment several times so you will learn that a **DECREASE IN THE VOLUME OF THE GAS** (bulb squeezed) means an **INCREASE IN PRESSURE** (air goes out open end). An **INCREASE IN THE VOLUME OF THE GAS** (bulb springs back to original shape) means a **DECREASE IN PRESSURE** (outside air pushes water up tube).

13. POP   *Home*

Uncork a bottle of soda pop. Hold it up against the light. Explain what happens.

14. DO YOU REALLY INHALE?   *Home*

At this very moment you are giving a living demonstration of Boyle's law.

Your lungs are like a bellows. When you squeeze them into a smaller volume you increase the pressure of the gas within them, which forces out the air. When you "exhale," you decrease the volume of your lungs. This decrease in volume automatically builds up the air pressure and forces air out of your lungs.

We don't "inhale"! We don't "breathe in" fresh, cool air. In reality, all we do is increase the volume of our lungs. This means that there is lower air pressure inside the lungs. The atmosphere pushes fresh air into our lungs.

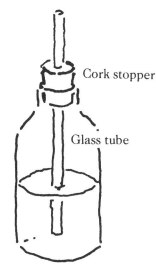

Activity 15

15. AN EYEFUL   Supervised Classroom

Get a bottle about 6 inches tall and with a mouth of convenient size to take a cork. Drill a hole through the cork just wide enough to admit a long glass tube or a strong plastic straw. (You could also use a rubber stopper from the lab with a hole already in it.) Make this tube long enough so you can shove it down to within about ½ inch of the bottom of the bottle.

Now that the apparatus is ready, remove the cork from the bottle and fill the bottle about half full of water. Replace the cork. Push it down firmly so it fits snugly. Now test your lung power by blowing as hard as you can into the tube. What happens?

What happens if you use less water in the bottle?

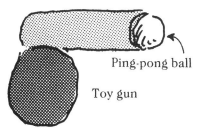

Activity 16

16. SHOOT   Home

An enterprising toy company puts Boyle's law to work with a rubber pistol that shoots a ping-pong ball.

The mouth or muzzle of the rubber pistol is just wide enough to hold a ping-pong ball snugly. When you squeeze the balloon-shaped handle of the rubber pistol, you decrease the volume of the gas. This increases the pressure and shoots the ping-pong ball from the muzzle.

Activity 17

17. A BALLOON IN JAIL   Home

Insert a small balloon, bottom down, into the neck of a pop bottle. Slip the mouth of the balloon over the lip of the bottle.

Now try to blow up the balloon. What happens?

18. POP GOES THE CORK!   Supervised Classroom

A popgun is an example of Boyle's law at work. Push down on the plunger rapidly. The sudden decrease of volume builds up great pressure and shoots the cork from the muzzle. The

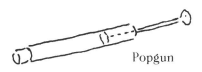

Activity 18

compressed air, suddenly released, expands to make the familiar "pop" we hear when the cork flies out of the gun.

19.   *BASKETBALL PUMP*   Home

A basketball pump affords a dramatic demonstration to prove that the smaller the volume into which you try to compress a gas, the higher the pressure.

Put your finger over the end of the exhaust port to prevent the air from escaping. Now see how far down you can push the plunger. The pressure builds up so fast, you are soon brought to a stop. You can push the plunger no further.

20.   *SMOKING IS BRAINLESS*   *Supervised Classroom*

When a person smokes, all he or she does is reduce the air pressure on the side of the cigarette in his mouth. Atmospheric pressure then pushes the smoke through the cigarette and into the mouth.

To prove that it takes no brains to smoke, I put one end of a cigarette in the opening of a small hose. I connect the other end of the hose to a vacuum pump. I turn on the vacuum pump, then light the cigarette. As the vacuum pump reduces the air pressure on the end of the cigarette in the hose, the atmosphere pushes the smoke through the machine and out the exhaust port.

I put a clean cloth over the exhaust port of the vacuum pump and "trap" some of the smoke as it pours forth into the room. The amount of the stain and deposit on the cloth from even one cigarette amazes the students.

21.   *SQUEEZE-ME TUBE*   *Supervised Classroom*

Get a plastic squeeze bottle, such as honey or mustard sometimes comes in. Place a lighted candle on the table. Aim the nozzle of the tube or bottle at the flame and squeeze.

The decrease of the volume of the bottle increases the pressure. Air is forced out the nozzle and blows out the candle.

Relight the candle. This time, squeeze down on the bottle before you bring the nozzle near the candle flame. What happens when you release the pressure on the bottle?

Basketball pump

Activity 19

Plastic squeeze bottle

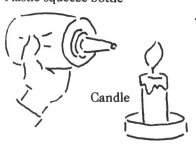

Candle

Activity 21

22. *LET IT SNOW*   **Supervised Classroom**

You most likely have seen the artifical "snow" that comes in aerosol cans and can be sprayed on windows and trees. I bring a container of this artifical "snow" to class. When I press down on the release valve on top of the can, a "cloud" of "snow" rushes forth to envelop nearby students.

I call attention to the fact that Boyle's law is put to use in many pressurized containers—from shaving cream to whipping cream, from deodorant to hair spray. When you push down on the valve on these aerosol containers, the gas confined inside the container is allowed to escape and expand, thus pushing the contents up and out the nozzle.

Snow

Activity 22

23. *POP YOU CAN'T DRINK*   **Home**

Here is an experiment you can try the next time you purchase a can of pop. Punch only one medium-size hole in the lid. Put your lips around this opening. See how much pop you can drink at one swallow. Even though you keep the can turned upside down above your mouth, you will soon find that no more pop comes out.

As you drink the pop, the volume of the gas inside the container increases. This increase of the volume of the gas lowers its pressure so much that the air on the outside will keep the liquid from flowing.

24. *HOLES THAT DON'T LEAK*   **Home**

Here is an experiment you will have to see to believe! Get an empty peanut butter jar. Use a thin nail or ice pick to punch a number of small holes in the lid.

Now fill the jar with water. Replace the lid. Turn the jar upside down. What happens?

Peanut butter jar

Holes in lid

Activity 24

25. *SODA STRAW?*   **Home**

Some people, when they put a straw into a soda, think they "draw" or "pull" the liquid into their mouths. Actually, all they do is remove the air from the straw. The atmospheric pressure on the liquid pushes the liquid up into their mouths.

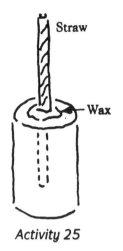

Activity 25

To prove it, make a small hole in the top of a can of soda and insert a straw. Pour melted wax from a burning candle around the place where the straw enters the lid to make an airtight seal.

Now place your mouth over the straw and see how much of the soda you can "draw" or "pull" into your mouth. As soon as the air pressure inside the can decreases, you will find that, no matter how hard you try, no more soda comes.

Now punch a second small hole in the lid. Suddenly it is easy to get the soda through the straw. Air entering through the second hole pushes the liquid up into your mouth.

26. *TRAVELING BAROMETER*   *Home*

Many homes today have inexpensive, small aneroid barometers. If you live in a city with skyscrapers, take your barometer with you and note its readings on the ground floor and then on the top floor of a skyscraper. If you live near the mountains, take the aneroid barometer with you the next time you travel up a mountain road in a car.

Notice that the barometer will fall about one inch during the first 1,000 feet of vertical climb. The drop per 1,000 feet becomes less and less as the height increases because the air becomes less dense.

Your barometer, in fact, can be used to measure altitude. A special barometer used to measure altitude is called an altimeter.

27. *WATCH COOKIES "GROW"*   *Supervised Classroom*

One of the most fascinating demonstrations I do for my students is to place three chocolate-covered marshmallow cookies inside a glass bell jar which is connected to a vacuum pump. As I pump the air out of the bell jar, the air trapped inside the cookies makes them expand. The chocolate covering cracks, then flies apart. The white marshmallow expands in all directions. The cookies become three to four times normal size.

Then I let air back into the bell jar. The inrushing air squeezes the cookies into little lumps of compact marshmallow only a fraction of their original size.

28. *AIRLESS BALLOON*   **Supervised Classroom**

I take a limp balloon and tie the neck tightly shut. I place the balloon inside the bell jar and turn on the vacuum pump. As the pump removes air from the bell jar, the air trapped inside the tied balloon makes the balloon expand until it completely fills the bell jar.

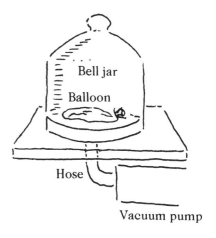

Activity 28

29. *THE FORCE ON YOUR HEAD*   **Home**

Consider your head to be shaped more or less like a box. To find the length of your head, lean your forehead against a wall. Place a ruler on top of your head so one end of it also touches the wall. Place the fingers of your free hand on the ruler at the place where the back of your head touches the ruler. You now have the length of your head in inches.

To find the width of your head, place one side of your skull against the wall and measure the distance to the other side.

Now that you have the length and width of your head, you can use this formula to get an approximation of the force pushing down on your head:

$$F = PA$$

F = Force
P = Pressure
A = Area

$$F = (14.7 \text{ lbs. per sq. in.}) \times (\text{length} \times \text{width})$$

As you will find out, the force pushing down on top of your head is staggering! Why, then, are you not crushed by this force? It is because the air is also inside your body pushing outward with the same pressure. The result is an apparent sense of freedom.

HIGHLIGHTS OF THIS CHAPTER

- Our blue sky seems to extend outward into space without limit, yet half of the earth's atmosphere lies below 4 miles. At a height of 12 miles, the blue sky fades into deeper purples.

- We are surrounded by an ocean of air that pushes down on us from all sides. At sea level this pressure is 14.7 pounds per square inch. This is enough to lift a column of water to a height of 34 feet. This is called a pressure of 1 atmosphere or 1 atm.

- A scientist who speaks of pressure refers to weight or force divided by area. The smaller the area over which weight is distributed, the greater the pressure. If you stand on one toe, the pressure on your toe is much greater than the pressure when your weight is distributed over the area of your two feet.

- Air pressure is measured by means of a barometer. A special type used to measure altitude is known as an altimeter.

Multiple-Choice Questions

1. You are leaning out the window of an apartment building. Directly below you on the sidewalk is a bottle of soda. A straw 35 feet long reaches from your lips into the bottle. You will be able to drink:
    a. all of the soda.
    b. none of it.
    c. about half of it.

2. If you submerge a drinking glass mouth downward into a gallon jar half filled with water, the water will rise up inside the glass approximately:
    a. ¼ of the way.
    b. ½ of the way.
    c. ¾ of the way.
    d. ¼ inch.

3. Snowshoes keep you from sinking into the snow because:
    a. they decrease your force.
    b. they increase your pressure.
    c. they increase the area over which you distribute your weight.
    d. they decrease your weight.

4. Our blue sky extends up over our heads to a height of:
   a. 4 miles.
   b. 12 to 20 miles.
   c. 50 miles.
   d. 600 miles.

5. Which of the following is false?
   a. Otto von Guericke proved that air exerts pressure.
   b. Evangelista Torricelli showed that air pressure is 14.7 lbs. per sq. in.
   c. Blaise Pascal showed that air pressure decreases with altitude.
   d. Robert Boyle proved that a decrease in the volume of a gas leads to a decrease in pressure.

True or False Questions

1. If you weigh 160 pounds and are standing on both feet covering an area of 40 square inches, your pressure is 8 pounds per square inch.

2. Whether you stand on one foot or two feet on the bathroom scale, your force remains the same.

3. You are shoveling a load of sand into the back of a pickup. This will not change the area of the tires in contact with the ground.

4. When Blaise Pascal carried his barometer up a 3,000-foot mountain, he discovered that the mercury in the barometer dropped approximately 1 inch for every 1,000 feet of altitude.

5. A barometer cannot be used as an altimeter.

Chapter 7

WILL THE DAY COME WHEN YOU CAN LIVE IN THE SEA?

How Can You Avoid a Diver's Number One Enemy?

According to some scientists, the day is coming when you may be able to live in the sea. How? By using an "artificial gill."

It will exchange oxygen and carbon dioxide directly with the surrounding water. This man-made gill is a film of silicone rubber that is only $1/1000$ inch thick. Completely free of holes, it retards the flow of water, but oxygen molecules in the water work their way through the film's molecular structure.

Various small animals, such as rabbits and hamsters, have been put in a cage covered with this thin membrane. The cage is submerged beneath the water. The animals' breathing gradually reduces the oxygen content and increases the carbon dioxide in the contained air. This leaves a lower percentage of oxygen in the cage than is dissolved in the water. This causes oxygen to pass from the water through the membrane into the cage.

Similarly, the increased amount of carbon dioxide in the cage will pass out through the membrane into the water. As long as fresh water is brought in contact with the membrane, the atmosphere in the cage will remain breathable.

ADVENTURES INTO THE VERTICAL

We live in an age of adventures into the vertical!

At the Kennedy Space Center in Florida, astronauts in shining suits climb aboard fire-snorting rockets to leap up into the sky and out into space.

Off the coast of California aquanauts in black suits don underwater breathing apparatus and drop into the waters of the Pacific.

You and I, it seems, are designed by nature primarily for travel in the horizontal. We need no special body equipment to journey by oxcart, banana boat, or car.

As soon as we attempt to travel in the vertical, however, we run into laws of physics that require understanding. In the previous chapter, we found out what happens if we soar into the atmosphere. In this chapter, we will find out what happens if we sink into the ocean. In both cases pressure is a major factor. As we soar into the sky we encounter decreasing pressure. As we sink into the water we encounter increasing pressure. The number one enemy of deep-sea divers is pressure.

WHAT IS THE PRESSURE?

What is the pressure on your body if you dive to a depth of 10 feet in a lake? What is the pressure on the sides of a submarine if it sinks to a depth of 1,000 feet in the ocean?

Before we can answer these questions, we need some background information. Get some old cardboard boxes. Cut out pieces measuring 1 foot long and 1 foot wide. Take as many of these pieces as you need to make a 1-foot-high stack and tape them together.

You now have a cubic foot. It is 1 foot long, 1 foot wide, and 1 foot high.

1 cu. ft.

If this were a cubic foot of water it would weigh 62.4 pounds. A cubic foot "sits on" or "occupies" 1 square foot of space. The pressure exerted by 1 cubic foot of water would be:

$$\text{PRESSURE} = \frac{\text{FORCE}}{\text{AREA}} = \frac{62.4 \text{ lbs.}}{1 \text{ sq. ft.}}$$

The pressure exerted by 1 cu. ft. of fresh water is 62.4 lbs. per sq. ft.

What would this pressure be in pounds per square inch?

Remember that 1 sq. ft. covers an area of 12 inches in length and 12 inches in width. This gives a total of 144 square inches.

$$\text{PRESSURE} = \frac{\text{FORCE}}{\text{AREA}} = \frac{62.4 \text{ lbs.}}{144 \text{ sq. in.}} = 0.43 \text{ lbs. per sq. in.}$$

A cubic foot of fresh water (62.4 lbs.) exerts a pressure of 62.4 lbs. per sq. ft., or .043 lbs. per sq. in.

Now you know what the pressure will be on you if you stretch out in your bathtub with water pushing down on you to a depth of 1 foot (0.43 lbs. per sq. in.).

If you dive 10 feet deep into a lake, the pressure will be 10 times that much (4.3 lbs. per sq. in.)

PUTTING WATER TO WORK

In the early days of this country, waterwheels were used for grinding grain and sawing wood. We still make wide use of one type of waterwheel called a turbine.

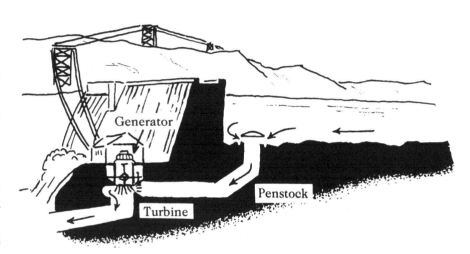

The word "turbine" comes from a Latin word meaning "to spin." The turbine has curved blades against which the water pushes. These blades spin horizontally like a merry-go-round. The blades are attached to a vertical shaft or axle. At the opposite end of this shaft, usually on a level above the turbine, is a giant generator that produces electricity.

Water rotates the turbine. The shaft from the turbine operates the generator. The generator supplies electrical energy. More than ¼ of all the electricity used in the United States and Canada is obtained from waterpower.

The vertical distance through which the water falls determines the amount of work performed by the water. The pull of gravity gives a weight of 62.4 pounds to every cubic foot of water. If a cubic foot of water falls 100 feet it can do 6,240 foot-pounds of work.

Niagara Falls is the greatest natural source of waterpower in North America. Here the thundering torrent of foaming water leaps from a cliff that is from 158 to 167 feet high.

There is also a Niagara that tourists do not see. Huge man-made tunnels gather water from the Niagara River just above the falls. This captured water is delivered to power plants about 8 miles downstream. The final fall of the water plunges straight down through big pipes that lead to the turbine wheels far below.

One of America's greatest engineering triumphs, Hoover Dam, is also one of the country's largest producers of hydroelectric power. Here the waters drop 500 feet, as compared with a drop of 150 feet at Niagara Falls.

THE DEEPEST PART OF THE OCEAN

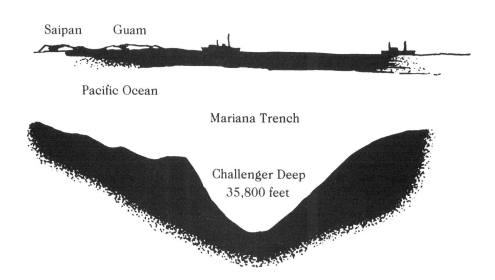

On January 23, 1960, scientists dropped down to the deepest place in the sea. They plunged 35,800 feet—almost 7 miles—into the Challenger Deep in the Pacific. The water pressure here is an overwhelming 7 tons per square inch. So tremendous is this pressure that even water, which is almost incompressible, is reduced in volume.

The underwater vehicle in which the scientists made the trip was called the *Trieste*. It looks something like a submarine with a huge steel sphere fastened to its underside. Scientists referred to the *Trieste* as an "underwater dirigible."

In order to float, a dirigible uses lighter-than-air gas. The *Trieste* uses lighter-than-water gasoline. The "submarine" part of the *Trieste* is in reality a huge gasoline can. Unlike a submarine, which is pressure proof, this gasoline tank is not pressure proof. To descend, a diver releases gasoline just as a balloonist releases gas. To rise, the diver drops 10 tons of BB-size iron balls. An opening in the bottom of the tank permits seawater to enter during a dive to equalize pressure so the tank won't be crushed.

The only part of the *Trieste* that is pressure proof is the cabin. This sphere has 5-inch steel walls to withstand the fantastic pressure of the depths. The special plastic windows are 6 inches thick.

FLOAT IN THE GREAT SALT LAKE

If ever you visit Salt Lake City, Utah, take time out, if possible, to float in the Great Salt Lake. This world-famous attraction averages 35 miles wide and is approximately 75 miles long. Its depth varies from 20 to 50 feet. The Great Salt Lake is second only to the Dead Sea as the saltiest body of water on earth. The water weighs 78 pounds per cubic foot.

YOU ARE NOT AS LUCKY AS A POP BOTTLE!

You may already know that the fizz of soda pop is due to the fact that gas (carbon dioxide) is forced into it under pressure. When you take the cap off the bottle of soda pop, this releases the pressure inside the bottle and allows the carbon dioxide to come out of solution in the form of tiny bubbles. The fizzing action may be so violent that it spews all over the place.

How does all this apply to you if you become a scuba diver?

Suppose you strap on your scuba outfit and dive to 34 feet. The water at that depth pushes in on you with a pressure of 14.7 pounds per square inch. Before you began your dive, the air itself was pushing in on you with a pressure of 14.7 pounds per square inch. This means that the water pressure plus the air pressure is equal to 2 atmospheres, or twice the pressure of the air at sea level. The air in your lungs is squeezed to half its original volume. How can you avoid the painful pressure of this squeeze?

There is a clever mechanism on your tank that supplies air for your body at the same pressure as that of the surrounding water. The air pressure inside your body equals the water pressure on the outside pushing in.

Your blood and body fluids act like soda pop. They absorb this gas under pressure. Since nitrogen makes up about 80% of the air, it exerts the largest partial pressure of all the gases in the air. More of it dissolves in your blood and tissues.

If you dive to 66 feet, nitrogen at three times atmospheric pressure is forced into solution in your body fluids in much the same way that carbon dioxide is forced into soda pop in a bottling plant.

What happens if you come to the surface too rapidly? The situation is similar to the carbonation of soda pop when the cap is removed and the bubbles rush out. You, however, are deprived of the benefit of a cap like a pop bottle.

When the human body contains dissolved nitrogen at a pressure more than twice the outside pressure, bubbles form in the bloodstream and tissues. Bubbles form faster than the lungs can eliminate the excess gas. If bubbles lodge in the joints, muscles, and bones, they produce the "bends," causing great pain. If they lodge in the brain and spinal cord, paralysis and death are the frequent results.

How can you avoid the bends? Ascend slowly to the surface, so the dissolved gas will have time to come out of solution and may be exhaled. The time required for this gas to be given off is known as the decompression time. The deeper you go and the longer you stay, the longer the decompression time.

TIMETABLE FOR AVOIDING THE BENDS

A deep-sea diver is brought to the surface in stages. There is a 10-minute rest for each 5 fathoms the diver is lifted. (A fathom is six feet.) In ordinary diving operations, a diver works at a depth of 35 fathoms (210 feet) for only one and one-half hours. It takes over an hour to bring the diver to the surface. This slow ascent is necessary to give the diver's body time to adjust to the decreasing pressure.

BREAKING RECORDS

In 1960 Hannes Keller, a mathematics instructor whose hobby was scuba diving, worked out a secret formula for a mixture of gases (oxygen, nitrogen, and helium) that would avoid the bends. During the summer of 1961, Keller descended to a depth of 728 feet in Lake Maggiore. Even more amazing, he surfaced from this depth in only one hour.

To appreciate what this means, recall that in 1956 a British Navy diver, George Wookey, had established the world's record with a dive of 600 feet. It took him *12 hours* to return to the surface. He had to linger every few feet while his body gradually adjusted to the decreasing water pressure.

In a subsequent dive near Catalina Island, off California, Hannes Keller and his companion, Peter Small, descended to 1,020 feet. Disaster struck and Small died of the bends. Keller survived.

NATURE'S MAGNIFICENT MISTAKE

The head of a full-grown giraffe is nearly 12 feet above its heart. The tremendous pressure needed to push blood up this immense neck makes the giraffe's heart the most powerful pump in nature. It weighs nearly ¼ as much as the animal's whole head.

When the giraffe suddenly lowers its head to drink there is a drop in altitude of nearly 18 feet. The blood has to be held back from the brain. Somehow the giraffe is able to keep its brain instantly supplied with just the right amount of blood.

Science does not yet know exactly why it is that when a giraffe lowers its head, there is little change in pressure. A jet pilot who could achieve this feat could pull out of powerful dives without blacking out.

SEARS HIGH PRESSURE

How much pressure does it take to force water to the top of the Sears Tower in Chicago? It is the tallest building in the world. Its 103rd floor is 1,353 feet in the air. Remember that if a water pipe has a cross-sectional area of 1 square inch then, for each foot of water, the pressure goes up by approximately half a pound.

The Sears Tower is said to be well prepared in case of fire. More than 40,000 automatic sprinklers cover every inch of the 4.5 million square feet of floor space. If city water pressure fails to keep the sprinklers going, they will be fed by three 20,000-gallon water tanks high in the building.

MERCURY VERSUS WATER

I place a sealed container holding one pint of mercury on my lecture table. Alongside it I place a similar sealed container holding a pint of water. I invite my students to come up to the lecture table after class and lift these containers a short distance, one at a time. I want my students to learn from personal experience that mercury is 13.6 times as heavy as water.

The relation of mass to volume is known as density. It may be expressed in this formula:

$$\text{DENSITY} = \frac{\text{MASS}}{\text{VOLUME}}$$

The density of fresh water $= \dfrac{62.4 \text{ lbs.}}{\text{per cubic foot}}$

Mercury   Water

$$\text{The density of salt water} \quad = \quad \frac{64.0 \text{ lbs.}}{\text{per cubic foot}}$$

In order to determine the pressure exerted by a liquid, we need to know its height and its density:

$$\text{PRESSURE} = \text{HEIGHT} \times \text{DENSITY}$$

WHAT IS THE PRESSURE ON A SUB?

What is the pressure on each square foot of a submarine that has submerged to a depth of 1,000 feet in salt water?

$$\text{PRESSURE} \quad = \quad \text{HEIGHT} \times \text{DENSITY}$$

$$= \quad 1,000 \text{ ft.} \times \frac{64.0 \text{ lbs.}}{\text{per cubic foot}}$$

$$= \quad 64,000 \text{ lbs. per sq. foot}$$

FREE GOLD?

Would you be happy if a friend of yours at Fort Knox said, "You are welcome to come down here and take home a 14-inch cube of gold. There is only one condition. You must carry the gold out of here in your arms."

A 14-inch cube of gold weighs one ton.

Even a cubic foot of mercury is too much for you to carry. A cubic foot of mercury weighs 850 pounds. By contrast, a cubic foot of aluminum is 170 pounds. A cubic foot of copper is 560 pounds.

CC

So far in this chapter we have been considering the unit of volume in the English system, which is the cubic foot. Now we consider the unit of volume in the metric system. It is the cubic centimeter (cc).

You can make your own cc. Many rulers have the English system of measurement on one side and the metric system on the other side. Get a small piece of cork or styrofoam. Place the metric ruler on the edge of one corner of the stryofoam. Mark off a square 1 centimeter (cm) long on each side. Use a sharp knife to cut out this cube.

By definition, the weight of a cubic centimeter (cc) of water equals 1 gram (gm). The density of water in the metric system is 1 gram per cubic centimeter. The density of water as expressed in the English system is 62.4 pounds per cubic foot.

Note that the density of water itself stays the same in all systems. We just use different units to express it. You will also notice that the unit of volume measurement is much larger in the English system than it is in the metric system.

Density is defined as the mass of a substance divided by its volume:

$$\text{DENSITY} = \frac{\text{MASS}}{\text{VOLUME}} = \text{(for water) } \frac{62.4 \text{ lbs.}}{\text{cu. ft.}} = \frac{1 \text{ gram}}{1 \text{ cubic centimeter}}$$

$$\text{DENSITY} = \frac{\text{MASS}}{\text{VOLUME}} = \text{(for mercury) } \frac{850 \text{ lbs.}}{\text{cu. ft.}} = \frac{13.6 \text{ grams}}{1 \text{ cubic centimeter}}$$

WHEN IS A MOUSE A FISH?

A white mouse was gently dropped head first into a glass jar filled to the brim with clear liquid. The lid was fastened to the top of the jar. Then the jar was turned on its side so as to afford a better view of the first mouse to "breathe liquid."

"Wait a minute," you say. "A mouse breathes air. How can it stay alive when submerged in liquid like a fish?"

The "secret" behind this experiment is that people who drown die primarily of suffocation. Ordinary water does not have enough oxygen dissolved in it to meet the needs of mice and men and other land creatures. In fact, ordinary water contains only 1/40th the amount of oxygen that is in the air at the earth's surface.

Dr. Johannes Kylstra of Duke University Medical Center dropped the white mouse into a special, man-made liquid called fluorocarbon. It was supercharged with 30 times more oxygen than ordinary water. In fact, the special liquid in the jar held three times as much oxygen as air itself.

For one long hour the mouse remained submerged in the special liquid, breathing it in and out. Since the fluid was so much heavier than air, the mouse had to gulp to move the heavy liquid in and out of the tiny passageways of his lungs.

After one hour of "breathing liquid," the mouse was "fished out" of the "aquarium" and allowed to breathe air once again. The mouse acted as though nothing out of the ordinary had happened. It adjusted with ease.

In the next experiment the mouse was put into a thick-walled cylinder filled with the special, oxygen-rich liquid. For 10 minutes it was subjected to a pressure equal to that of 2,500 feet below the surface of the ocean. Then the pressure was released over the span of a minute, and the mouse was taken out of the cylinder. It was unharmed and perfectly normal.

Dr. Kylstra was delighted with the success of these experiments. He hopes to keep improving on them until he has results that will benefit deep-sea divers. At present, there is trouble because the compressed air the divers breathe contains nitrogen and other gases that enter their bloodstreams. If a diver comes to the surface too rapidly, the quick change in pressure causes these gases to dissolve in the bloodstream and produce bubbles. Often the bubbles cause the "bends," doubling the diver up in agony. A diver who is not quickly put in a decompression chamber may die.

Dr. Kylstra hopes that divers in the future may be able to breathe liquids instead of air. In that way, they will avoid the bubbles that can cause death. Liquid-breathing divers may also be able to dive much deeper than is possible at present. They will require a good deal of extra equipment, but they will still have some advantages.

FINDING THE TITANIC

During the first week of September, 1985, the world was amazed to learn the details surrounding the finding of the *Titanic*, the 882-foot-long luxury liner that sank in about 2½ miles of water 560 miles off Newfoundland.

The *Titanic* was the most luxurious liner of its time. It was thought to be unsinkable, but on its maiden voyage it struck an iceberg. This buckled the 12-inch-thick plates on the hull enough to create a fatal leak. The mammoth steamer sank 4 hours later with the loss of 1,513 lives. About 700 escaped by lifeboats. The date was April 14, 1912.

"Preserved by the frigid North Atlantic waters of its gravesite, the *Titanic* is resting upright and virtually in mint condition 73 years after one of history's most celebrated disasters." So said scientists on Tuesday, September 3, 1985.

A day after a U.S.-French team discovered pieces of the luxury liner's boiler, the scientists reported that a submersible robot had photographed the entire hull and found it "like a museum piece." The unmanned craft, Argo, towed beneath a Navy research vessel, skimmed so close to the wreck that it nudged one of the *Titanic*'s smokestacks.

Dr. Robert Ballard, the chief scientist on the expedition that found the *Titanic*, said on Wednesday, September 4, that the Argo was sending up magnificent videotapes. "About 10 minutes ago we saw beautiful color pictures of cases and cases of wine bottles, totally undamaged plates, all sorts of other material that did not break up, whereas other parts of the ship were damaged."

Ballard went on to say that, "The upper part of the bow is in remarkably good condition considering it's the part that felt the iceberg and the part that collided with the bottom. The under part of the bow is badly damaged."

A NEW ERA IN UNDERSEA EXPLORATION

According to Dr. Ballard, the discovery and photography of the sunken luxury liner *Titanic* 2½ miles below the surface of the North Atlantic marks the start of a new era in undersea exploration.

No longer must oceanographers descend into the crushing depths aboard miniature submarines. Now they can tow platforms containing still and television cameras from surface ships. Riding aboard the platforms will be small robots which descend to the ocean floor to take 3-D pictures.

"It's the beginning of telepresence, of being able to project your spirit to the bottom, your eyes, your mind, and being able to leave your body behind," said Dr. Ballard.

Tiny manned submarines, which have been the mainstay of ocean exploration since the early 1970s, made some dramatic discoveries, but they are tediously slow in their ability to map the ocean bottom. Scientist must climb aboard, dive to great depths, remain on the bottom for only a short time due to limited oxygen and energy supplies, and then resurface. They have been able to map only a tiny part of the ocean bottom, which is larger than the surface of dry land.

The new sonar-video sled is called Argo. It is named after the Greek myth in which Jason and the Argonauts sailed aboard the *Argo* in search of the Golden Fleece. The Argo is attached to its mother ship, the *Knorr*, by a cable several miles long. Scientists guide the Argo by steering the sled from the deck of the *Knorr*.

"We were able to stay submerged for days on end," said Ballard, "something I've never been able to do in little submarines. With the Argo system you can sit in comfort and watch the bottom go by mile after mile after mile."

SUPERIOR DIVERS

What would you do if you lived in a beautiful country whose magnificent mountains provide breathtaking scenery but don't add much to the bread basket?

In area, Japan is smaller than California, yet it has a population of more than 116,000,000. Much of the Land of the Rising Sun consists of rugged mountains, so only a small percentage of the land can be farmed. Since the Japanese lack the ground area to grow enough crops, they turn to the bounty of the sea, and they call upon Ama girls.

Ama, or "diving girls," help feed a nation. Their work demands great stamina. The marine crop that beckons to the Ama girls is a variety of seaweed called "heaven grass."

Ama girls work from small boats—sometimes singly, sometimes in groups. Trained from early youth to familiarity with the sea, they can remain submerged for more than a minute in the marine gardens where the seaweed used for food and medicine abounds. Short breather intervals space the many hours of toil demanded of them.

Why are girls chosen for the hard and demanding task of diving for heaven grass? The answer is two-fold. First, women have greater lung capacity than men, so they can stay submerged longer. Also, women have a thin layer of fat directly beneath their skin that helps to insulate them from the frigid waters. Women can better withstand the bone-chilling waters.

Auto tire

TIRE PRESSURE

An automobile or bike tire is a good example of Pascal's Law. When you measure the air pressure of the tire, you actually put the air gauge in contact only with one small portion of the tire. Yet, because of Pascal's Law, you know that the pressure registered on the gauge at only one point of the tire is the same as the air pressure throughout the tire.

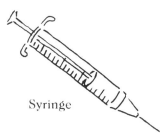

Syringe

PASCAL IN THE HOSPITAL

The next time you visit a hospital as a patient, stay alert for a demonstration of Pascal's Law. When a nurse fills a hypodermic syringe with liquid and pushes down on the plunger, notice that the pressure is transmitted undiminished in all directions.

HOOVER DAM

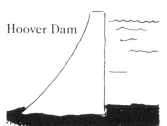

Hoover Dam

If ever you visit Hoover Dam, you may be surprised to learn that the crest or top of the dam is 45 feet thick. By contrast, the base is 600 feet thick. Why this difference?

The reason is in the formula,

$$\text{PRESSURE} = \text{HEIGHT} \times \text{DENSITY}$$

Since the dam is 730 feet high, the pressure at the bottom is:

$$P = hd = 730 \times 62.4 = 45,552 \text{ lbs. per sq. ft.}$$

FLOATING CONCRETE BRIDGE

If ever you find yourself in Seattle, Washington, be sure to visit the Lake Washington bridge. It is a massive concrete bridge 6,560 feet long and 60 feet wide. The lake is so deep that it was not practical to construct piers supported on the bottom of the lake. The Lake Washington bridge rests on closed, hollow cylinders called pontoons. This word comes from the Latin "pons" meaning "bridge."

Each pontoon is somewhat like a giant flatboat with tall sides and a roof, empty on the inside. These pontoons float for the same reason that a steel battleship floats. They push aside or displace an amount of water equal to their own weight.

U-505

One item you most certainly wish to see if you visit the Museum of Science and Industry in Chicago is the German submarine, the U-505. It is the only German submarine ever captured on the high seas.

An opening is cut through the side of this sub to make for easy entrance. This opening allows you to see the tanks between the outer and inner walls. When a submarine rides with its deck slicing through the waves close to the water level, the submarine is kept just slightly lighter than water. When the command is given to submerge or go below the surface, water is admitted into the the tanks, thus forcing the air out.

A submarine dives much like an airplane, by means of horizontal rudders, which can be tilted to put it in a power dive. To surface, compressed air is pumped into the tanks, driving the water out. As the submarine becomes less dense it rises to the surface.

Even if a submarine submerges to escape enemy action or observation, care is taken to keep it lighter than water. Otherwise an engine failure would let it sink to the bottom of the sea.

The Navy's first atomic submarine, the *Nautilus*, can submerge to depths of almost 1,000 feet. The submarines built previously could not go beyond a few hundred feet. A report of the historic trip made by the *Nautilus* under polar ice and the North Pole during the summer of 1958 states that the crewmen had little sensation of movement except when the sub jettisoned garbage. In order to do this, the *Nautilus* was brought nearer the surface to decrease pressure against the hull. The debris was carefully weighed and the ship's tanks were flooded slightly to compensate for the weight loss. Then the big submarine was taken back down to 400 feet.

WATER HAMMER

If you live in a city that has high water pressure, you may experience what is known as water hammer. When a faucet is closed rapidly it makes a noise as though someone has hit the pipe with a hammer.

Water in motion contains energy the same as any solid object in motion. When fast-moving water is brought to a sudden stop, this energy is expended by striking the sides of the pipe. The pipe moves and comes in contact with parts of the house or other objects to amplify the noise.

In normal building construction, the hot and cold water pipes that supply sinks, lavatories, and such plumbing fixtures are concealed within the walls of the room they serve. It is a common practice for a plumber to add a vertical extension about 2 feet long to each of these pipes. The extensions are known as air chambers because they are intended to remain filled with air. When a faucet is suddenly closed, the water in motion compresses the air in the chamber and this brings it to a gradual stop so the noise does not occur.

After several years of service, the air in the chamber may be absorbed by the water, which then fills the entire chamber. This condition can be corrected. First, turn off the water supply to the house and open all the faucets in the house, including the one at the lowest elevation. The pipes, including the air chambers, will drain. Close all faucets and turn on the water supply. The chambers will again be filled with air to serve their purpose.

ACTIVITIES

1. PIPE
Supervised Classroom

If you have a friend who is a plumber, perhaps you can get a pipe 1 foot long and with a cross-sectional area of approximately 1 square inch. Put your thumb over one end of the pipe. Turn it into a vertical position and fill it with water.

This is a convenient way for you to experience for yourself that a column of water 1 foot high and 1 square inch in cross-sectional area exerts a pressure of 0.43 pounds. If you wish to think of this in round numbers, simply keep in mind that a column of water 1 foot high, and with a cross-sectional area of 1 square inch, exerts a pressure of approximately ½ pound.

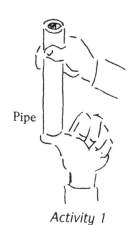

Pipe

Activity 1

2. DOUBLE IT
Supervised Classroom

For this demonstration you will need a second pipe of the same diameter but twice as long. Fill it with water in the same manner. Note that now you must exert more pressure to keep the water in the longer pipe. The pressure exerted by a liquid depends on its height.

Pipes

Activity 2

3. WHAT'S MY PRESSURE?

Suppose you have a pipe as tall as you are. What is the pressure required to push the water from foot level to head level?

4. SINK THAT BOAT!
Home

Take a little piece of aluminum foil and bend it into a cup shape so it will float when you place it in the water. Since it displaces its own weight in the water, it floats.

Now wad the aluminum "boat" into a compact little sphere. Drop it back in the water. It can no longer displace its own weight, so it sinks. All it displaces is its own volume.

Even though iron is 7.9 times heavier than water, steel ships float. The weight of the water they displace is equal to their own weight.

Activity 3

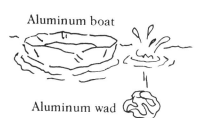

Aluminum boat

Aluminum wad

Activity 4

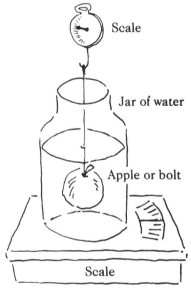

Activity 5

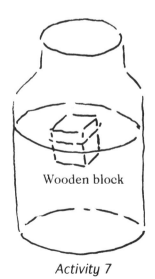

Activity 6

5. ROCKS THAT "GROW HEAVY"   Home

If you ever swim in a lake that has big boulders, try this while you are in the water. Pick up a large rock and carry it with you. You may notice that you can lift the rock without too much effort. When you lift the rock out of the water, though, it grows tremendously heavy.

Suppose the rock is 1 cubic foot in volume. This means that the water pushes up on it with a force of 62.4 pounds. This upward force of water, which acts against gravity, is call buoyancy.

Centuries ago, a Greek scientist by the name of Archimedes (287-212 B.C.) discovered the principle that is named in his honor, "**ANY OBJECT FLOATING OR SUBMERGED IN A FLUID IS BOUYED UP BY A FORCE EQUAL TO THE WEIGHT OF THE DISPLACED FLUID.**"

6. WILL IT WEIGH MORE?   Home

Place a widemouthed gallon jar ²/₃ full of water on the platform of a scale. If nothing else is handy, a bathroom scale will do.

If you have an apple with a good stem, tie a string to it. Hook the other end of the string to a spring scale. If you don't have an apple, use a small bolt or any handy object. Submerge the apple or object on the string, but do not let it touch the bottom or sides of the jar. Now look at the scale beneath the gallon jar. Look at the spring scale in your hand. What do you notice?

7. WATER PUSHES   Home

To demonstrate that a floating object displaces its own weight, get a widemouthed gallon jar and fill it ²/₃ full of water. Gently place a little pine block of wood in the water. Take the block out and use a ruler to find out how many centimeters the block sank. Multiply this number by the length and width of the block to find the volume of the block that was in the water. Keep in mind that every cubic centimeter of the block that was submerged pushed aside or displaced 1 gram of water.

Water doesn't like being shoved aside any more than you do. Each cubic centimeter of water that is "displaced" or "pushed aside" tries to get back. It pushes up against the intruder with a force of 1 gram. If 100 cubic centimeters of water are displaced,

Activity 7

the buoyant force counteracts the downward pull of gravity. The block floats.

Now weigh the block on a scale. If the block sank in the water so it displaced 100 cubic centimeters of water, the weight of the block will be 100 grams.

8. *JUDGING WEIGHT BY SINKING*   **Supervised Classroom**

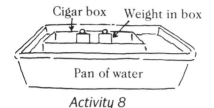

Activity 8

Cut the top off a shallow box and float the empty box in a pan of water. Draw a pencil mark along the waterline to show how deep the box was floating.

Now place a 100-gram weight in the box. Mark the new waterline. Repeat with another 100-gram weight, and then another. Each time mark the new waterline.

The results should convince you that you can calculate the weight of an object by knowing the amount of water it displaces.

9. *WHAT WILL THE EGG DO?*   **Home**

Activity 9

Fill a drinking glass about ⅔ full of water. Place an egg in it. What happens? Now pour a generous supply of salt into the water. What happens? Why?

10. *FLOATING*   **Home**

The next time you go swimming, look around the pool. What person floats with the greatest of ease? Why?

Activity 10

11. *VANISHING WEIGHT*   **Supervised Classroom**

Here is a demonstration to show that a body that sinks "loses" as much weight as the weight of the volume of liquid displaced.

I have an old billiard ball with a hook fastened to it. I get a 6-inch string and tie one end around the hook on the billiard ball. The other end I tie to a spring scale. I hold the scale up so the class can read the weight of the billiard ball, 230 grams.

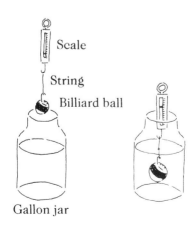

Activity 11

Now I submerge the billiard ball in a gallon jar ⅔ full of water. I make sure that the ball does not touch the sides or bottom of the jar. I have a student read the scale. It reads only 130 grams. The ball "lost" 100 grams of weight. It is being "pushed" or buoyed up by the 100 grams of water it displaces.

Activity 12

Activity 13

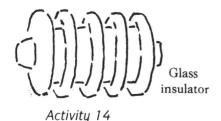

Glass insulator

Activity 14

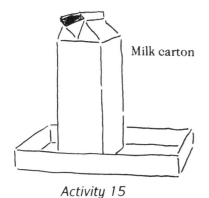

Milk carton

Activity 15

12. FINDING VOLUME   Supervised Classroom

Finding the volume of the billiard ball is easy. It "lost" 100 grams in weight, so it was being "pushed up" by 100 grams of water. One hundred grams of water occupy 100 cubic centimeters. Therefore, the volume of the ball is 100 cubic centimeters.

To prove this by a visible demonstration, I pour water into a graduated cylinder that is wide enough to accommodate the billiard ball. When I submerge the billiard ball the water level goes up 100 cubic centimeters. Since I'm using the same ball on the string and scale as in the previous demonstration, I ask students to keep their eyes on the scale and the cylinder as I submerge the ball. The scale "loses" as many grams as the number of cubic centimeters the water rises in the cylinder.

13. WEIGH YOUR HAND   Home

You can weigh your hand without detaching it! All you need is a gallon jar ²⁄₃ full of water. Place it on a bathroom scale and place your fist in the water. Do not touch the bottom or sides of the jar. Note how much the scale goes up.

The human body has approximately the same density as water. It displaces just about its own weight as well as its own volume.

14. IRREGULAR OBJECTS   Supervised Classroom

Imagine trying to find the volume of an irregular-shaped object such as a glass insulator. Its contours make the job a mathematical nightmare.

It is easy to find the volume of any irregular-shaped object by using water as our "mathematical friend." Tie a string to the glass insulator. Tie the other end of the string to a spring scale and note the weight indicated on the scale. Now submerge the insulator in a jar of water. Look at the scale now. Suppose it reads 20 grams lighter. This means that the insulator pushed aside 20 cubic centimeters of water. This is the volume of the insulator.

15. MILK CARTON PRESSURE   Home

To show how pressure varies with depth, fill a cardboard milk carton to the top with water and place it in a tray. Now take an ice pick or nail and jab a hole near the bottom, one in the middle, and one near the top. The flow of water out of each hole will indicate the amount of pressure behind it. What happens when you turn the carton on its side?

16. SUBMERGED STYROFOAM   Supervised Classroom

Here is a demonstration on buoyancy. You may wish to adjust the details to suit your own convenience.

I have a large graduated cylinder that holds 1,000 cubic centimeters of water. I fill it to the 500-cubic-centimeter mark and drop a styrofoam ball into the cylinder. The water level goes up approximately 10 cubic centimeters. Since any floating object displaces its own weight, we know that the ball weighs 10 grams.

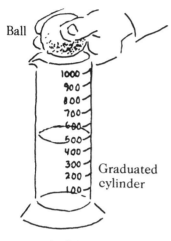

Now I ask a student to come up, take a wooden ruler, and push down on the ball until it is completely submerged. I ask the class whether they can figure out the additional force pushing up on the ball. Someone generally suggests that this additional force will be equal to the weight of the water displaced. If the water level climbed 200 cubic centimeters, this means that an additional force of 200 grams is pushing up on the ball. The total buoyancy is 210 grams. Since the ball is being pulled down by gravity with a force of 10 grams, this means that the force required to hold the ball under the water is 200 grams.

Activity 16

17. DANCING MOTHBALLS   Supervised Classroom

Here is a demonstration of Archimedes' Principle you will love. Put about a tablespoon full of baking soda in the bottom of a tall glass jar or graduated cylinder. Then fill it about ⅔ full of water. Now pour in about ½ cup of white vinegar. Finally, drop about six mothballs into the solution. What happens? Why?

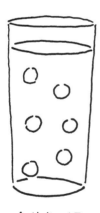

Activity 17

18. PISTOL FOR PASCAL   Home

As you know from experience, air can be compressed. Water ordinarily cannot. Any pressure applied to a confined liquid is passed on to all the liquid in the container. The French scientist Blaise Pascal (1623-1662) expressed the law that bears his name in the following way: "**THE PRESSURE EXERTED ON A CONFINED LIQUID IS TRANSMITTED UNDIMINISHED IN ALL DIRECTIONS.**"

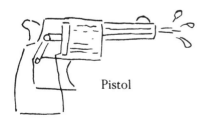

Activity 18

A plastic water pistol with transparent sides makes a wonderful demonstration of Pascal's law. Pull back on the trigger, which is really a plunger. It applies pressure to the confined liquid. The pressure is transmitted undiminished in all directions. It shoots a stream of water out the muzzle.

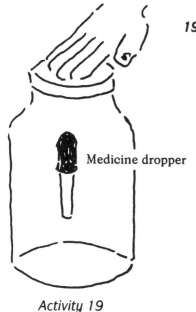

Medicine dropper

Activity 19

19.   MYSTERIOUS DIVER   *Supervised Classroom*

Fill a wide-mouth gallon jar with water. Get a medicine dropper and draw up enough water in it so it will barely float, bulb side up, when placed inside the jar. Put the lid back on the jar and press down hard. The medicine dropper will sink. Release your pressure on the lid and the dropper will float.

Pascal's law, Boyle's law, and Archimedes' principle explain the dropper's mysterious behavior. When you press the lid against the water, this pressure is transmitted to all parts of the liquid. This forces more water up inside the dropper and compresses the air in the bulb. The dropper becomes heavier than water and sinks. When you release the pressure on the lid, the pressure is removed from the water and the compressed air inside the dropper pushes out the excess water. The dropper is now lighter than water. It floats again.

20.   PASCAL AND YOU   *Supervised Classroom*

If you want to find out how much pressure your heart is developing, you don't have to go to a hospital and be wheeled into an operating room so the doctor can open up your chest and connect a pressure gauge to your heart. The procedure is much simpler. Wrap a cuff-type blood pressure gauge around your arm. Within seconds you will have the pressure. What makes all this possible? Pascal's law. A pressure applied (by your heart) to a confined liquid (your blood) is transmitted undiminished in all directions (through your arteries and veins).

Since the cuff is tightly bound around your arm, the blood pressure is transmitted to the air confined inside the cuff. This pressure, in turn, activates a gauge.

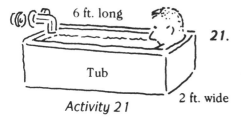

6 ft. long

Tub

Activity 21   2 ft. wide

21.   WHAT IS YOUR VOLUME?   *Home*

Can you find your volume and your weight when you take a bath? Yes, *if* you have a rectangular bathtub.

Suppose you have a tub 6 feet long and 2 feet wide. Fill this tub half full of water. Before you step in, notice how high the water level is. When you submerge, notice how much higher the water level rises.

Suppose the water rises by 2 inches. The volume of the water you displace is:

$$\text{VOLUME} = \text{Length} \times \text{Width} \times \text{Depth}$$

$$= 6 \text{ ft.} \times 2 \text{ ft.} \times \frac{2}{12} = \frac{24}{12} = 2 \text{ cu. ft.}$$

You are 2 cubic feet in volume. To find your weight, recall that the human body is almost the same density as water, namely, 62.4 pounds per cubic feet. Your weight is:

$$62.4 \times 2 = 124.8 \text{ lbs.}$$

22. WHAT IS THEIR WEIGHT?

A large flat-bottom boat is 3 feet wide and 12 feet long. When 6 young people step into the boat, it sinks 3 inches. What is the combined weight of the people in the boat?

23. WHAT IS ITS DENSITY?

A block of lead is 2 cm. on each side. It weighs 45.2 gm. What is its density?

HIGHLIGHTS OF THIS CHAPTER

● Our greatest "enemy" in the underwater world is pressure. With each foot a person descends into fresh water, the pressure increases approximately ½ pound per square inch, or 62.4 pounds per square foot (64.0 pounds in seawater).

● The density of water in the English system is 62.4 pounds per cubic foot. The density of water in the metric system is 1 gram per cubic centimeter.

● The Archimedes principle informs us that "ANY OBJECT FLOATING OR SUB-MERGED IN A FLUID IS BUOYED UP BY A FORCE EQUAL TO THE WEIGHT OF THE DISPLACED FLUID."

● Pascal's law informs us that "THE PRESSURE EXERTED ON A CONFINED LIQUID IS TRANSMITTED UNDIMINISHED IN ALL DIRECTIONS."

Multiple-Choice Questions

1. Every time you descend another foot into fresh water, the pressure:
   a. increases by one atmosphere.
   b. increases by approximately ½ pound per square inch.
   c. increases by 32 pounds per square foot.
   d. increases by one half an atmosphere.

2. When a bubble rises to the surface of a lake, it grows larger on the way up because:
   a. the pull of gravity is less.
   b. the pressure inside the bubble increases and pushes the bubble out.
   c. the water pressure decreases.
   d. the liquid becomes less dense.

3. If you dive to a depth of 30 feet in fresh water, the pressure on you is
   a. 12.90 lbs. per sq. in.
   b. 18.30 lbs. per sq. in.
   c. 23.15 lbs. per sq. in.
   d. 36.10 lbs. per sq. in.

4. A ship will not sink as long as:
   a. it can displace its own volume in the water.
   b. it can displace its own weight in the water.
   c. the pressure of the water is the same in all directions.
   d. its density is the same as that of water.

5. A block of wood weighs 2 pounds in air. In water, half of it floats above the surface and half below. A rock weighing 1 pound is placed on top of the block. The block will sink:
   a. $5/8$ of the way.
   b. $6/8$ of the way.
   c. $7/8$ of the way.
   d. all the way.

True or False Questions

1. A piece of metal is 10 centimeters long, 5 centimeters wide, and 2 centimeters thick. Since it weighs 1,050 grams, its density must be that of silver, 10.5 grams per cubic centimeter.

2. The pressure on the bottom of a dam depends on how far back the dam backs up the water.

3. The farther down you go in the ocean, the higher the water pressure.

4. A 14-inch cube of gold weighs a ton!

5. For a boat to float, it must displace its own volume in the water.

Chapter 8

NATURE'S "BELIEVE-IT-OR-NOT" ODDITIES

"Odd Fellows" Prove That Sometimes
One Plus One Does Not Equal Two!

What do you call something so strange it does not seem it can be true? The ancient Greeks came up with the word "paradox." "Para" means "contrary to" and "doxa" means "expectation." A paradox is a truth that seems contrary to common sense. It is an assertion that is seemingly contradictory. This chapter introduces some of nature's "believe-it-or-not" oddities.

The first paradox we will consider is called Bernoulli's principle. This 18th-century Swiss scientist discovered that "**THE PRESSURE EXERTED BY A FLUID DECREASES WHEN THE GAS OR LIQUID IS IN MOTION.**" In other words, if the speed of the liquid or gas is increased, the pressure within the fluid decreases. Bernoulli's principle applied to such different things as dimples on golf balls, the World Series, airplane wings, winning the Daytona 500 by "drafting," and fox burrows.

BERNOULLI AT THE WORLD SERIES

Although the fans who attend the World Series may not realize it, they often witness superb demonstrations of Bernoulli's principle.

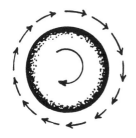

A baseball pitched at speeds of 70 to 90 miles an hour can curve a maximum of about 18 inches on the way to home plate. The rate of spin that makes a baseball curve most effectively is about 1,800 revolutions per minute, or about 30 revolutions per second.

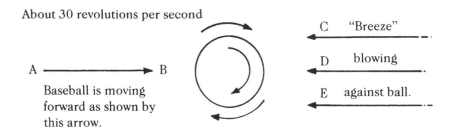

As indicated in this figure, the baseball is moving forward in the direction shown by the arrow AB. The ball is spinning in a clockwise direction. Even though the air is still, the motion of the baseball forward creates a "breeze" against it, as shown by the arrows C, D, and E.

As the baseball moves forward, friction between the spinning ball and the air tends to drag the air in the direction of the spin. This means that the spinning air on the top of the ball meets the "breeze" head on. This causes the air to "pile up" on the top of the ball.

On the bottom of the ball, the spinning air is moving in the same direction as the "breeze." This increases the speed of the air on the bottom. Because the pressure of air is less where it moves faster, the ball moves in the direction of the lesser pressure.

WHY DIMPLES ON GOLF BALLS?

To demonstrate the performance of golf balls with dimples versus those without dimples, A.G. Spalding & Brothers made a few smooth balls with the same specifications as their best dimple ball. They also made some balls with dimples on half the sphere and a smooth surface on the other half. A special machine tested all the balls. Each ball was hit in exactly the same way with exactly the same force.

The dimple balls flew straight out and landed in the center of the fairway, approximately 230 yards from the tee.

The first smooth ball took off on the same path as the dimpled ball, but only for 10 yards. Then, suddenly, it took an abrupt nose dive and hit the ground about 30 yards away. No smooth balls made a flight of over 35 yards. No two of them behaved exactly the same.

Some of the half-dimple-half-smooth balls were teed up with the dimple half on top and some with it on the bottom. Both batches made normal flights but went only about 100 yards. Then a few were tried with the dimple half on the right. These went about 100 yards, but in a violent right curve like a slice. Similarly, when the dimple half was placed on the left, the ball hooked to the left.

The smooth golf balls act like the baseball. As the ball spins, air is dragged around it in the direction of the spin. This increases the air pressure on the top where the air molecules "pile up." There is a decrease in the pressure on the bottom, where the air carried by the ball's spin moves in the same direction as the oncoming air. Because the pressure of the air is less where it moves faster, the ball moves in the direction of the lesser pressure—down.

The dimples on the golf balls act like "shovels" or "scoops" to carry air that would tend to pile up on one side and dump it into potential low-pressure areas on the opposite side. This prevents the forward flight of the ball from being cut short by Bernoulli's principle.

BIG $$$ IN THE FAST DRAFT

Did you ever have the frightening experience of riding in a car that came up close behind a big, fast-moving truck? Suddenly your car seemed to be "pulled" forward. For one terrifying moment you may have thought that you were going to "kiss" the bumper of the big truck ahead of you.

What you experienced was "slipstreaming" or "drafting." The big truck in front "drags" some of the air with it. This increase in the velocity of the air reduces its pressure.

Your car benefits from two things. You don't have to fight the air resistance in front of you because the truck does this for you. Not only does the truck cut the wind resistance in front of you, but the lower pressure or partial vacuum in the wake of the truck also lets the air behind you "push" you forward.

At the Daytona 500 Marvin Panch "drafted" himself to victory. "I'd hitch onto a fast car and stick behind him until either he or I had to make a pit stop. Then I'd pick up another one." Carefully conserving his own car so it could provide the few intense bursts of really high speed he needed, Panch drafted himself into the winner's circle with Bernoulli's principle and won $20,750 of first-prize money.

DON'T STAND CLOSE TO A FAST-MOVING TRAIN!

When President John Fitzgerald Kennedy's body was being transported by train to its final resting place, some of his admirers made the mistake of standing too close to the railroad tracks.

As the fast-moving train streamlined down the rails, two people were drawn under the wheels and killed. The high-speed train moved air along with it. Since this air was fast-moving, its pressure was reduced. The ordinary air behind the people, at simply atmospheric pressure, pushed them under the wheels.

BIG JETS MEAN DANGER!

A Cessna 310H with three aboard was on final approach to San Francisco International runway, 28L. Six hundred feet to the right, a jet airliner approaching a parallel runway came abreast of the small twin-engine plane. The big jet rapidly moved on and landed several thousand feet ahead. Seconds later, 75 feet above the runway, the Cessna rolled severely, crashed, and burst into flames.

Within a period of five years over 98 small planes went into violent spins and crashed during landing or takeoff. In each case a big jet was taking off or landing nearby. The deadly spin that caused the small planes to crash seemed to suggest that they had run into a violent whirlpool or vortex of air.

Could giant jets create whirlwinds powerful enough to twist small planes out of control? To find the answer, government engineers released colored smoke from a tower near an airport runway as a giant jet took to the sky. The chemical smoke piped from the tower made visible a deadly whirlpool of air twisting at 90 miles an hour in the wake of the jumbo jet!

When air meets the leading edge of an airplane wing, it splits into two streams. One stream flows across the top of the wing, the other across the bottom. Due to the shape of the wing, the upper air stream flows faster than the lower. This means that the air pressure on the upper surface of the wing is less than the air pressure on the lower surface. This difference of pressure produces an upward thrust called lift.

If we take a closer look at an airplane wing, we find another interesting fact. A plane's wings are thickest from top to bottom and broadest from front to back where the wings join the fuselage, the body of the plane. Toward the wing tips, the wings become steadily thinner and narrower. This means that the region of highest air pressure on a wing in motion is at the lower wing surface where it joins the fuselage. From there, pressure decreases outward to the wing tip. On the upper surface, pressure is highest at the wing tip and grows less toward the fuselage.

This pressure distribution causes whirlpools of air to form behind the wing tips. The air streaming over the upper wing surface veers toward the area of lower pressure at the fuselage. Air streaming under the lower wing surface veers toward the area of lower pressure at the wing tip. Veering streams meet at the wing's trailing edge. They corkscrew over each other in a twisting pattern that forms violent whirlpools. Jumbo-jet twisters remain dangerous for miles behind the plane.

The small tornadoes trailing behind a Boeing 737 are enough to damage even large planes. Fortunately, no large plane accidents have taken place. To ensure that they won't, the FAA issued regulations that a five-mile space must be kept at all times between jumbo jets and aircraft weighing less than 30,000 pounds.

BERNOULLI IN THE SHOWER

If you have a plastic shower curtain, note what happens to it when you turn on the shower full force.

ATOMIZER

When you squeeze the rubber bulb of an atomizer, air is squeezed out the nozzle with great velocity. This means that the air moving across the top of the tube that extends down into the liquid has less air pressure than the air inside the container. As a result, air pressure inside the container forces liquid to the top of the tube. There it is caught in the airstream and rushed along with it. The container must have an air hole in it to allow atmospheric pressure to enter and push on the liquid.

HOW TO "OUT-FOX" THE HEAT

The crafty fox uses Bernoulli's principle to build an underground home. Each fox burrow generally has two "doorways," and one of the "doorways" is usually higher than the other.

Friction slows the movement of air near the surface, but air just a bit above the surface of the ground moves faster. According to Bernoulli's principle, where the airspeed is greater, the pressure is less. This difference in airspeeds over the "doorways" creates a partial vacuum within the burrow that causes air to rush in through the lower doorway and continue out through the higher doorway. Air movement through the burrow continues as long as there is the slightest breeze outside.

This same "foxy" trick is also used by other animals, including ground squirrels.

DRY YOUR FACE WITH CAPILLARY TUBES

Do you ever stop to reflect that every time you use a towel you use capillary tubes to dry yourself? The spaces between the fibers of the towel act as capillary tubes. You get rid of the moisture on your face by smothering it in flexible capillary tubes, the towel.

CALIFORNIA REDWOODS

Scientists believe that capillary action helps to bring water to the tops of trees. According to this viewpoint, the tallest capillary tubes in the world are found in the giant California redwoods that leap up over 300 feet into the sky. The tallest of all the redwoods reaches a height of 367.9 feet.

MAGIC ON YOUR COAT

Did you ever admire the small drops of rain that sparkle on your sweater or coat on misty days? These spheres of shimmering magic are the result of surface tension. So, too, are the early morning dewdrops that condense on blades of grass. Rain falls in drops, but they are often pulled out of their original spherical shape by air friction as they fall.

WHY ARE HAILSTONES ROUND?

The answer is surface tension. Sometimes a drop of water in a huge thunder-cloud is caught in a tremendous updraft and carried upward to chill heights of 50,000 feet. Here the raindrop freezes.

As the frozen drop falls toward the earth, it picks up additional moisture. If the drop is blown back into the sky, the added coat of moisture freezes and produces another layer of ice. Such drops fall to earth as hailstones. If hailstones bump into each other as they fall, they lose their round shape.

If you slice open a hailstone, you may see a number of layers of ice that remind you of an onion. Each layer tells of a trip to the chill top of a cloud. By counting the layers you can tell how many times the hailstone began to plunge toward the earth only to be blown back up into the freezing sky. Hailstones have been known to grow as large as baseballs before they had sufficient weight to overcome the updrafts.

ACTIVITIES

1. *HOW AN AIRPLANE GETS ITS "LIFT"*   ***Home***

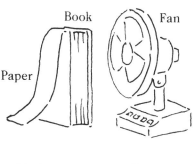

Stand a heavy book in a vertical position with a sheet of light paper between its pages. Allow the free end of the paper to drop down to the top of the table. Place an electric fan on the other side of the book and turn it on to behold a paradox.

You would imagine that the blast of air from the fan would "beat" or force the paper down closer to the book and the table. Instead, the moving air lowers the pressure on the top and the pressure of the still air beneath the paper pushes the sheet up into the airstream.

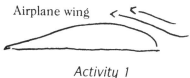

Activity 1

If you do not have an electric fan, place a piece of tissue paper or a paper napkin between the pages of a book so one end hangs down limply on the outside. If you blow across the top of the book, the tissue will rise.

Now let us apply what we have learned to the wing of an airplane. The wing of an airplane is constructed so the top side bulges up like a little hill. As air rushes over the wing, part of the airstream goes over the top of the wing and part below. The curved top surface of the wing forces the air moving over the top to go farther and therefore faster than the air moving under the wing. According to Bernoulli's principle, the air traveling over the top at greater velocity will exert less pressure than the air below the wing. The difference in air pressure on the top and bottom surfaces of the wings accounts for about 70% of the lift. The remaining 30% comes from the angle at which the wind pushes against the bottom of the wing.

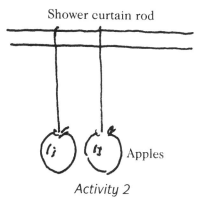

Activity 2

2. *WHAT HAPPENS TO THE APPLES?*   ***Home***

Suspend two apples by strings from a shower curtain rod. Keep the apples about one inch apart. Blow vigorously between the apples. What happens?

3. *BALLOON IN AIR*   ***Home***

Blow up a balloon and place it in the airstream from a fan directed vertically upward. Slowly move the fan, or pick it up and carry it. The balloon will move with it.

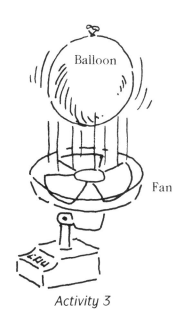

Activity 3

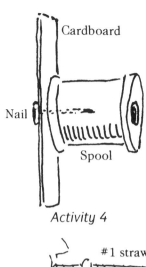

Activity 4

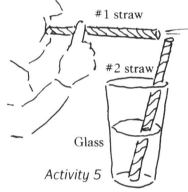

Activity 5

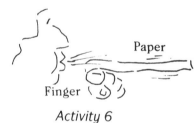

Activity 6

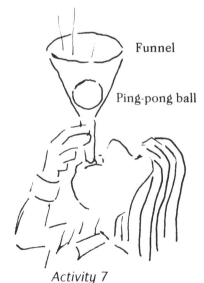

Activity 7

The balloon will stay in the airstream because the velocity of the moving column of air reduces the pressure in the stream itself. The ordinary air pressure of the surrounding air keeps the balloon a "prisoner" inside the "cylinder" of low air pressure.

4. *SPOOL AND CARDBOARD*   *Home*

Push a long, thin nail or a big pin through the middle of a piece of light cardboard about the size of a playing card. Put the nail inside a spool held in a horizontal position with the cardboard snugly against the spool. Blow slowly but steadily on the cardboard from the side with the spool.

If you refrain from blowing in sudden bursts you will not be able to blow the card off the spool. The nail simply keeps the cardboard from falling to the ground. The velocity of the air moving between the spool and the cardboard exerts less pressure than the still air on the other side of the cardboard.

5. *STRAWS IN THE WIND*   *Home*

Get two soda straws. Put straw #2 into a glass half full of water. Hold straw #1 so end "B" is above the open end of the straw in the water. Put end "A" of straw #1 in your mouth and blow. What happens? Why? (It will be best to pinch straw #1 at end "B" into a small opening.)

6. *BERNOULLI ON YOUR CHIN*   *Home*

Get a sheet of notebook paper or typing paper. Cut off a strip about 2 inches wide and 1 foot long. Wrap one end of the paper half-way around your forefinger and hold your finger firmly against your lower lip. Now blow. What happens? Why?

7. *PING-PONG BALL IN FUNNEL*   *Home*

Place a ping-pong ball in a funnel. Hold the funnel in an upright position over your lips and blow. Can you blow the ping-pong ball out of the funnel?

MORE ODD FELLOWS!

Bernoulli's principle is just one of the strange things we find in nature. We will now examine more amazing items, such as:

How to make water more wet.
A piece of steel that floats in water.
Water that climbs 360 feet.

Before we start our investigation of these amazing items, we will examine some of the ways in which matter acts.

8. TWO BECOME ONE   Home

You can roll two lumps of clay into one because the molecules cohere, or stick together. This property of molecules of the same substance to cling together is known as cohesion.

The cohesive power of soft wax, putty, and moist clay is small. In steel, the cohesive force is strong. Without cohesion there would be no bodies of matter, just individual molecules of different substances.

Activity 8

9. NICKEL VERSUS GINGERSNAP   Home

Hold a nickel between thumb and forefinger of your right hand and try to bend it. No luck. It has enough cohesive strength to resist you. Now try a gingersnap. It crumbles due to lack of cohesive strength. A soda cracker has even less cohesive strength.

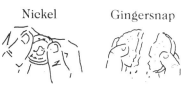

Activity 9

10. CHALK IT UP   Supervised Classroom

The particles of a piece of chalk "stick together" or "cling to each other" because of cohesion. The word cohesion comes from the Latin word that means "to stick together."

Now use the chalk to write on a blackboard. The fact that particles of chalk adhere to the blackboard is proof that adhesion is now the stronger force. The particles of chalk prefer to "cling to" the blackboard rather than to each other. Adhesion comes from the Latin word that means "to stick to."

Activity 10

Activity 11

Activity 12

Activity 13

Water

Activity 14

Cohesion is the force of attraction between molecules of the same substance.

Adhesion is the force of attraction between molecules of different substances.

11.   ADHESIVE WATER   Home

Did you every hear of "adhesive water"? To demonstrate what it is like, simply stick your finger in a glass of water, then draw it out. The water adheres or sticks to your finger. It is adhesive. It "wets" your skin.

12.   ON THE GO   Home

To demonstrate that molecules in a liquid are in constant motion, try this. Add a couple of drops of ink or coloring matter to a glass of water. Notice how rapidly the ink spreads out to all portions of the water. This type of motion is called "Brownian motion."

13.   FLOAT A RAZOR BLADE   Supervised Classroom

Gently place a razor blade on the surface of a glass of water. Despite the fact that steel is over seven times heavier than water, the steel does not sink.

In the glass of water, each molecule is surrounded by other molecules. Cohesive force holds them together. On the surface, however, the molecules are packed together more densely because they are acted upon only by the molecules in the water beneath the surface. There are no water molecules on the top side pulling in the opposite direction. This downward pull creates a surface tension that is strong enough to support the blade as long as the surface of the water is not broken.

Look closely at the liquid near the razor blade. The surface is depressed, but not broken. To sink the razor blade, simply push one end of the blade under the water. The blade will sink because the surface tension is broken.

14.   "HAYSTACK" OF WATER   Home

Fill a glass with water and place it on the table. Now gently add more water. The water will rise above the rim of the glass and bulge up like a haystack, a beautiful example of surface tension.

15. FASCINATING CORKS   Home

Here is an experiment so fascinating you will have to do it to believe it! Fill a glass half full of water. Place a cork in the center. What happens?

Now fill a glass with water until it bulges up like a haystack. Now place the cork on the surface of the water toward one side. What happens?

Activity 15

16. GOODBYE TOOTHPICKS   Home

Float two toothpicks close together and parallel to each other in a pan of water. Now place the edge of a bar of soap between them. You may also use a drop of oil between them. What happens?

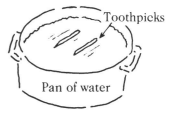

Activity 16

17. TORPEDO IT!   Home

Float a piece of steel wool in a dish of water. Now pour a few drops of liquid detergent into the water. What happens?

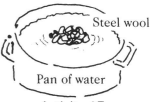

Activity 17

18. WATER STAYS PUT   Home

Fill a bottle with water and stretch a piece of cloth (a portion of an old sheet or pillowcase will do) over the mouth of the bottle. Secure it in place by tying a string around the neck.

Now turn the bottle upside down. Surface tension combines with atmospheric pressure to keep the water in the bottle.

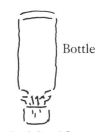

Activity 18

19. ONE STREAM FROM THREE   Home

Get an empty cardboard milk carton. Make three holes near the bottom about ½ centimeter apart. Now fill the container with water. Pinch the three streams of water together with your thumb and forefinger. Surface tension will combine them into one.

Activity 19

20. BUBBLE, BUBBLES   Home

Soap bubbles furnish some of the most fascinating demonstrations of surface tension. Get a bottle of "soap bubble liquid" and use the loop to fill the air with the shimmering magic of spheres of fleeting beauty.

Activity 20

Activity 21

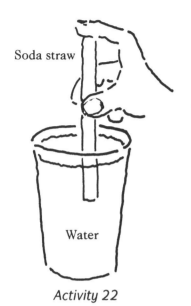

Activity 22

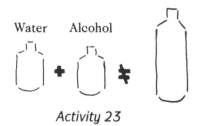

Activity 23

Activity 24

21.   *SILVER SPHERES*   Home

The tendency of liquids to form drops is an effect of surface tension. Put small drops of water on wax paper. What do you notice?

22.   *PIPETTE*   *Supervised Classroom*

A simple piece of apparatus that illustrates both air pressure and surface tension is a pipette. The word itself comes from the French and means a small pipe or tube. It is a narrow glass tube. If you don't have such a tube, simply use a straw.

Hold the straw about ¼ submerged in a glass of water. Close the upper end of the straw by placing your thumb over it. Pick up the straw. The liquid is kept up in the straw by air pressure. The water at the bottom of the straw is shaped like a half-circle because of surface tension.

23.   *ONE PLUS ONE DOES NOT EQUAL TWO!*   *Supervised Classroom*

Here is an interesting experiment to demonstrate that molecules are not all the same size.

Get 1 pint of rubbing alcohol and 1 pint of water. Pour them into a quart bottle, and behold! You won't fill the quart bottle.

This is what happens. Suppose you had a bushel basket full of baseballs. Now pour a pound of buckshot into the basket. The buckshot won't make any visible increase in the volume occupied by both baseballs and buckshot. The reason—the buckshot is so small, it drops into the space between the baseballs.

Something similar happens when the smaller alcohol molecules are poured in among the bigger water molecules. Like the buckshot, the smaller alcohol molecules tend to nestle in between the bigger water molecules.

24.   *BUBBLE BLOWER*   Home

Blow a big soap bubble with a bubble pipe. Remove your lips from the stem. The contracting soap bubble will force a small "breeze" out the stem. To make the effect of this "breeze" visible, hold the stem near a candle flame.

25. WHISKER COCKTAIL   Home

Immerse a camel-hair paintbrush in a glass of water. The hairs will stand out like whiskers.

Remove the brush from the water. Surface tension will draw the hairs into a neat "tail."

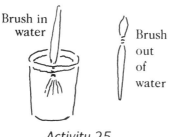

Activity 25

26. OLIVE OIL   Supervised Classroom

Pour 3 parts of water to 2 parts of rubbing alcohol into a glass. Use a straw as a pipette to insert a few drops of olive oil into the middle of this mixture. What happens?

Activity 26

27. CLIMBING WATER   Supervised Classroom

Look closely at a glass of water. You will discover that the surface is not a perfectly straight line. Where the water meets the glass, something strange happens. The water "climbs" up the sides for a short distance. Because water wets glass, the water curves upward along the glass making a concave surface.

If you look closely at a glass containing mercury, you will notice something different. Mercury does not wet the glass. It is pushed down and away from the glass, thus making a convex surface.

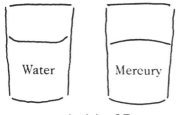

Activity 27

28. CAPILLARY TUBE   Supervised Classroom

Capillary action, or the tendency of liquids to rise in the tubes which they wet, is a fascinating property of water.

In the previous demonstration, the water in the drinking glass does not climb very far. The reason is this: the force of gravity pulling downward on the water is greater than the water's adhesive power to cling to the wall and the force of surface tension to pull the water up to the level on all sides.

If you put a small glass tube into water, however, the tendency of the water to adhere to the sides of the tube is more noticeable. As the concave surface tends to contract, the water climbs higher in the tube than it is in the dish.

The climbing continues until the surface tension of the water is exactly balanced by the weight of the column of water. The smaller the tube, the higher the water rises.

Activity 28

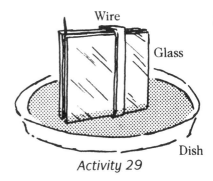

Wire

Glass

Dish

Activity 29

29. GLASS "WEDGE"   *Supervised Classroom*

Get 2 pieces of thick, heavy glass about 3 inches square. Ordinary window glass is all right but it is fragile. Snap a rubber band around the two plates of glass to hold them in place. Now, along one edge of the glass slip a long, thin wire. The plates will now form a "wedge."

Place the glass "wedge" in a shallow dish of colored water. What happens?

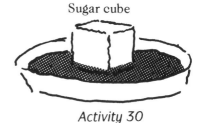

Sugar cube

Activity 30

30. SUGAR CUBE   *Home*

Hold one end of a wad of cotton, a piece of an old towel, or the edge of a sugar cube in colored water. Watch the capillary action.

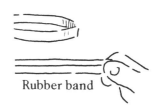

Rubber band

Activity 31

31. RUBBER BANDS   *Home*

Stretch a rubber band, then release it. Watch it snap back into its original shape. Pull on a string. Release it. It jumps back to its previous shape. These demonstrations illustrate elasticity, the property that enables a body to recover its original shape when the deforming force is removed.

A block of foam rubber furnishes another interesting example of elasticity. A "Jumping Jack" is a jolly example of elasticity.

32. PUTTY   *Home*

Get a lump of putty. You can mold it into any shape you wish. It "stays put." It is the nonelastic property of putty that makes it useful for putting into place around a window. It "stays put" and won't jump out.

Mousetrap

Activity 33

33. MOUSETRAP AND SOLDER   *Home*

Here is a demonstration for dramatic contrast. Set a mousetrap. Release it by dropping a cork on the trigger to which bait is attached. The spring snaps back into its original position with a bang.

Now get a long length of wire-form lead solder. You can twist it into a pretzel or pig's tail and it will stay put. It has no elasticity.

34. *HOW MUCH "BOUNCE"?*   **Home**

Balloon

Activity 34

Air is the most elastic material. It can be squeezed and compressed, but as soon as the original pressure is restored, it jumps back to its original volume.

To demonstrate this, blow air into a balloon. Tie the neck shut. Squeeze the balloon. Compress it. Press it down. As soon as you remove the deforming force, the balloon returns to its previous volume and shape.

Name some of the most important applications of the elasticity of air.

35. *WETTER WATER*   **Home**

Try washing your hands or laundry without soap or detergents!

The reason you use soap and detergents is to decrease the force of cohesion among the water molecules. The water molecules become more able to "cling to" or "wet" the surface of your hands and the threads of your clothes. Soap and detergents make water less "stand-offish" and therefore more wet.

HIGHLIGHTS OF THIS CHAPTER

- Bernoulli's principle informs us that **THE GREATER THE VELOCITY OF A FLUID (gas or water) THE LESS IS ITS INTERNAL PRESSURE.** Without cohesion, our world would fall apart.

- If water were not adhesive, we could not use it to wash our faces. Without capillary action, a towel would not remove water from our skin. A wick could never bring fuel to a hungry flame to give light and heat.

- Without the elasticity of air in our automobile tires, a ride down the highway would be a bone-tingling experience. How could we catch a mouse without the help of the elasticity of the spring in the mouse trap?

Multiple-Choice Questions

1. Cohesion:
   a. makes water wet glass.
   b. makes unlike substances stick together.
   c. makes mercury climb in thermometers.
   d. is greater in liquids than in solids.

2. The most elastic substance is:
   a. air.
   b. rubber.
   c. steel springs.
   d. water.

3. Bernoulli's principle informs us that:
   a. when the speed of a fluid is increased, its pressure is likewise increased.
   b. when the speed of a fluid is increased, the pressure within the fluid decreases.
   c. the pressure of the fluid increases with the square of its velocity.
   d. as the volume of a gas is decreased, its pressure goes up.

4. The reason that you use soap to wash your hands is that:
   a. soap increases the cohesive power of the water.
   b. soap increases the surface tension of the water.
   c. soap makes water more wet.
   d. soap decreases the adhesive power of the water.

5. Surface tension accounts for the fact that:
   a. molten drops of lead take a spherical shape.
   b. mercury climbs the glass walls of thermometers.
   c. the molecules of water are in constant motion.
   d. a steel spring under tension tries to regain its original shape.

True or False Questions

1. Oil has more surface tension than water.

2. Cohesion holds the particles of a piece of chalk together.

3. Adhesion enables the particles of chalk to cling to a blackboard.

4. The difference in air pressure on the top and bottom of an airplane wing accounts for about 30% of the lift.

5. A quart of water has a definite volume, but it has no definite shape. It fills any shape into which it is poured. This illustrates that cohesion in liquids is much stronger than it is in solids.

Chapter 9

FROM FIREBALLS AND FASTER WATER TO SKI FASHIONS

What Supplies Us with the Stops That Keep Us Going?

It was 9:47 A.M. Eastern time, Tuesday, February 20, 1962, when John Glenn blasted off from the Kennedy Space Center atop a giant Atlas rocket. He made 3 turns around the earth traveling at an average speed of 17,400 m.p.h.

As John Glenn neared the end of his third orbit, he fired the retro-rockets to slow down the spacecraft. Glenn was facing backward as the spacecraft began crashing through the atmosphere at very high speed.

Suddenly, brilliant flames of fire leaped past the window of his spacecraft, Friendship 7. Friction with the air had set fire to the space capsule. Glenn knew only too well that if the heat shield on the capsule failed to work, the whole thing would be devoured by flames. He and his ship would be burned to ashes. They would all float back down to earth as dust.

Despite the chunks of flaming metal flying past his window, John Glenn did not lose his cool. His only radio comment to space command headquarters was, "This is a real fireball."

HOT NOSE

It is one thing to fling an object into space and keep it there. It is another task to bring it back to earth. The near vacuum of space offers little friction as a missile plunges downward, but on re-entering the earth's thick blanket of air, it meets increasing friction. A missile with an ordinary nose cone meets destruction in the air about 14 miles above the earth.

Fortunately, scientists found ways to reduce this intense heat considerably. One way involves the use of a broad, blunt nose for the space vehicle. The snub nose acts as a potent insulator. The violent shock wave produced when the nose cone hits the atmosphere at high speed scatters a much higher percentage of this intensely hot gas than would one of the thin, streamlined noses formerly thought to be better.

Another solution is to cover the nose with ablating materials—a substance designed to be destroyed by heat. The ablating materials vaporize and blow away, leaving a cooler surface.

FIRST CONQUEROR OF THE HOT NOSE PROBLEM!

The first space-age conqueror of the hot-nose problem now rests in the Smithsonian's National Air Museum, Washington, D.C.

The black, heat-seared, rough, metal skin of the RVX 1-5 gives evidence of the tremendous heat energy encountered by the first re-entry nose cone to be recovered. The space flight of the RVX 1-5 was of intercontinental range—more than 6,325 miles.

The RVX 1-5 was projected into space on April 8, 1959, at the Kennedy Space Center. It traveled on a predetermined course to a point near Ascension Island in the South Atlantic at a speed of more than 15,000 m.p.h.

The RVX 1-5 demonstrates one solution to the hot-nose problem; namely, use a nose that is broad, stubby, and sturdy. So, if the mirror tells you that your nose is broad, stubby, and sturdy, be happy. You are aerodynamically equipped for space flight!

A SHOOTING STAR!

If you wish to see an object shooting through the air so fast that it catches on fire, just look up into the heavens tonight. If good luck is yours, you may see a shooting star.

A shooting star isn't a star at all. It is a hard lump of metal or stone that zooms in from outer space and crashes into our umbrella of air at speeds of around 40 miles per second.

Fortunately for us, friction between the fast-moving space object and our air sets it on fire. What you see is the white-hot burning trail of gas formed by friction. The intense heat of friction turns the space rock to ashes within a stretch of about 10 miles. Every 24 hours some 2 tons or more of these "heavenly ashes" fall upon us.

FRICTION SUPPLIES YOU WITH THE STOPS THAT KEEP YOU GOING!

The only way to stop a car is by getting rid of its kinetic energy of motion. One way is to run into a tough oak tree or a stone wall. A better way is to change the kinetic energy into heat by using friction.

When you slam on your brakes, the energy of forward motion is transferred or changed into heat in the brake drums, tires, and pavement. Friction helps you change forward motion into heat!

Heat is described as the motion of molecules. Friction helps us to change the motion of a car into the motion of molecules in the brake drum. What a tantalizing world we live in!

The next time you ride in a car, remember that your trip is based on friction. To get moving, you use friction to overcome inertia. To stop, you must use friction to overcome the momentum that tends to keep your going. Slowing down is just as important as speeding up.

HIGH PRESSURE OR LOW?

As you may know from riding your bike, there is less rolling friction between your bike's tires and the road if the tires are inflated to a high pressure.

STEEL ON STEEL

The next time you see a freight train rolling along the shining rails, remember that you are watching a demonstration of the fact that rolling friction can be reduced by using surfaces that are very hard and that do not deform easily.

FASTER WATER

Fighting a fire is fighting time. Every minute wasted may cost thousands of dollars in property destroyed. Every second saved may be a life.

And yet, fire fighters can't always move as fast as they would like. Their basic weapon is a 2½-inch fire hose. When full of water, it is about as hard and unyielding as a steel pipe. The only way to bend it around a corner is to shut the water off. To lug it up a flight of stairs is a test of any fire fighter's stamina.

All of this makes it easy to understand why a new product called Rapid Water Additive is revolutionizing fire fighting. Rapid Water Additive mixes easily with water, and makes it flow faster through a hose by reducing friction. Because the water flows faster, fire fighters can get just as much water as before using a smaller 1¾-inch hose that weighs half as much. The smaller hose makes a much better weapon. It bends around corners. It can be carried up a stairway fully charged. In short, it helps fire fighters get water to the fire faster. At the same time, it makes their job safer and less strenuous.

How did scientists discover Rapid Water Additive? The story begins with fish! For years people have noticed that many fish, including trout, have skins that secrete mucus continuously. Scientists have long surmised that mucus secretion helps fish swim faster with less effort.

The theory led to searches for an artificial substance with some of the characteristics of natural mucus. In the 1970s, researchers in several countries (including the Soviet Union and Great Britain) hit upon the family of long-chain, carbon-based molecules called polymers, which are also the basis of plastics. One of these, polyethylene oxide, can be dispersed in water to produce a liquid with a slightly slimy feel.

Scientists found that when even as little as 150 parts of polyethylene oxide per million parts of water is injected into a pipeline, the drag of the pipe wall on the fluid passing through it drops dramatically, so fluids can be pumped faster with less work. By the late 1970s, British sewerage systems were using polymer injection to increase the flow from crowded housing developments without using larger pipelines.

FASTEST MAN ON A BIKE

The world's speed record on a bicycle was set by a Frenchman, Jose Meiffret. He hit 124.3 mph on the Autobahn near Freiburg, Germany, on July 19, 1962.

The reason that Jose could set such a record is that he did not have to overcome air friction. He pedaled his bike directly behind a huge windshield that was fastened to a Mercedes-Benz sports car.

SKI SLOPE FASHIONS

Olympic skiers in a downhill race usually average between 60 and 65 mph. For brief periods they may get up to 80 mph. At these speeds wind resistance becomes a major factor. Reducing it can make a vital difference between otherwise evenly matched skiers.

When Jean-Claude Killy of France won his gold medal, he beat his nearest competitor by 3/1000 of a second. More recently, in the World Cup races at Grindewald, Switzerland, a snowflake-thin margin of less than half a second separated the top five finalists.

In the world of competitive skiing, fashion is less important than speed. Top-level skiers worry considerably about the clothes they wear. They are constantly seeking materials and designs that will cut wind resistance.

Racers thought that they had discovered the last word in speed with a supertight, superthin, and superslick "fishskin" plastic suit that apparently shaved valuable seconds off downhill times, but it also threatened to shave valuable skin off the skiers. The fishskin was so slick that skiers who fell in icy conditions found themselves skidding dangerously out of control on their shiny suits.

BARNACLE DRAG

After a year or more at sea, steel-hulled ships may become encrusted with barnacles. Growing in size and multiplying in numbers, barnacles can add a 200-ton drag to a ship, cut its speed in half, and double its fuel consumption. Every year American shipowners have to spend a whopping $100,000,000 to haul the ships out of the water for barnacle scraping, sand-blasting, and antifouling paint.

In recent years scientists have come up with a new idea. It's an antifouling solution in a thin rubber sheet. It is called Nofoul rubber. Applied to a ship's hull, the Nofoul rubber slowly releases a toxic substance that repels barnacles just like antifouling paint. The big difference is that with the paint, the ships must be beached, scraped, and painted every six months. The Nofoul rubber is good for five to six years.

FIGHTING AIR!

Do you know that the number of miles a driver gets per gallon of gasoline decreases as the speed of the car increases? Is this due to increased friction between the tires and the road? No, this varies hardly at all with the velocity. Why, then, the extra fuel consumption? The answer lies in the nature of fluid friction. The force of fluid friction increases with the square of the velocity.

When a car hits around 60 mph, it is using a lot of power just to fight the air! If you ride behind the silver, three-pointed star of a Mercedes-Benz at 80 mph, most of the gasoline is being used to fight air resistance. Gas mileage is best at speeds from 30 to 35 mph. At 40 mph, gas mileage is 10% less; at 60 mph, it is 31% less. At 80 mph, it is 52% less.

In order to save gasoline during World War II, autos and trucks were restricted to a top speed of 35 mph.

SOARING TEMPERATURES

An airliner traveling 300 mph will raise its exterior temperature 16°F. A plane traveling at twice the speed of sound can cause the temperature to rise 250°F.

The XB-70 aircraft has flown 2,000 mph—three times the speed of sound—at 70,000 feet. The outside skin temperature reached as high as 630°F.

When NASA pilot Joe Walker flew the rocket plane X15 at 3,930 mph, the temperatures on parts of the plane reached 1,100°F. Parts of the plane were still smoldering when it landed at Edwards AFB, California.

TRAVEL LOG

According to an item in *Everybody's Business*, this is how far the following conveyances will go on a gallon of fuel:

Moped (motorized bicycle), 120 miles
Harley-Davidson 1200 (motorcycle), 50 miles
Volkswagen Rabbit Diesel (automobile), 42 miles
Piper Cherokee (light plane), 15 miles (at 144 mph)
GMC Astro (tractor-semitrailer combination), 5.4 miles
GM (diesel locomotive), 632 yards (at 70 mph, pulling 40 to 50 fully loaded freight cars)
Boeing 747 (jumbo jet), 280 yards (carrying 385 people at 39,000 feet)
Ultra-large crude-oil carrier (supertanker), 31 feet (At 17 mph and fully loaded, this ship needs 41 gallons of fuel to travel its own length.)

GROUND GLASS IN KITCHEN MATCHES!

Do you know how match makers increase the coefficient of friction of the "strike anywhere" or "kitchen matches"? These matches contain potassium chlorate and phosphorus sesquisulfide as the main ingredients, with added quantities of iron oxide, zinc oxide, and glue. In addition, ground glass is added to increase the coefficient of friction. The heat produced by the ignition of a small amount of red phosphorus when the match is struck is sufficient to ignite the match head. The wood of the match is coated with paraffin to give a longer and more ready flame. It is impregnated with borax to prevent afterglow.

NOTE THE SKIDS

Next winter keep your eyes open and notice how long it takes a car to stop when on ice.

When a car is moving at the rate of 60 m.p.h.:

on a dry road, when the coefficient of friction is .8, the stopping distance is 151 ft.

on a wet road, when the coefficient of friction is .5, the stopping distance is 242 ft.

on an icy road, when the coefficient of friction is .1, the stopping distance is 1,210 ft.

ENERGY

Frictional forces act parallel to the surfaces between the objects. No two surfaces can move over one another without encountering the resistance of friction.

What is it that enables us to overcome friction? The "thing" that enables us to move matter is energy.

Potential energy is defined as the capacity or ability to do work. Work is defined as the product of force times the distance over which the force acts:

$$\text{WORK} = \text{FORCE} \times \text{DISTANCE}$$

How much work do you do if you hold a 100-pound sack of cement on top of your head for one hour? As long as the sack of cement is simply being held there, there is no force acting through a distance. A force multiplied by zero distance equals zero work. You do no work at all!

HAMMER WITH POTENTIAL ENERGY

If you lift a 2-pound hammer a distance of 2 feet, you put 4 foot-pounds of work into it. It has 4 foot-pounds of potential energy.

VARIOUS FORMS OF P.E.

There are various forms of potential energy, or P.E.

A horseshoe magnet has potential energy that is called magnetic. The magnet has the ability to lift up a nail.

The potential energy in a stick of dynamite is chemical. The dynamite has the ability to lift a building off its foundation.

The potential energy of a mousetrap that is set is mechanical. The spring has the ability to catch a mouse!

K.E.

Kinetic energy is called the energy of motion. The word "kinetic" comes from the Greek word that means "to move." The energy that a body has because of its motion is kinetic energy, or K.E.

If you get out of your chair and begin to walk, you are demonstrating kinetic energy. If you run, you show even more kinetic energy. The faster you run, the greater your kinetic energy.

The moment a stick of dynamite explodes, it becomes kinetic energy. As soon as the mousetrap is triggered, its potential energy becomes kinetic energy as the metal is triggered and it catches a mouse!

CAN YOU DO THE SAME AMOUNT OF WORK AS A HORSE?

A horse can haul a ton of sand in a wagon in one trip. You could haul a ton of sand also, but not in one trip. You would have to use a wheelbarrow and make many trips.

Both you and the horse would do the same amount of work, but not in the same length of time. Power is the rate of doing work. It is equal to the work done divided by time.

Suppose you weigh 100 pounds and climb an 11-foot ladder in 10 seconds. What is your power?

$$\text{POWER} = \frac{\text{WORK}}{\text{TIME}} = \frac{\text{FORCE} \times \text{DISTANCE}}{\text{TIME}}$$

$$= \frac{100 \text{ lbs.} \times 11 \text{ ft.}}{10 \text{ sec.}} = \frac{1{,}100 \text{ ft. lbs.}}{10 \text{ sec.}}$$

$$= 110 \text{ ft. lbs. per sec.}$$

H.P.

At the time when James Watt wanted to sell the steam engine he manufactured, most of the heavy work was done by horses. In order to give people an idea of how much work the engines performed, he decided to tell people how many horses an engine would replace.

This meant that he had to find out how many foot-pounds of work a horse could do in one second. The rate that Watt selected and called one horsepower (H.P.) was 550 foot-pounds per second (33,000 foot-pounds per minute).

One horsepower will lift a 55-pound weight 10 feet in one second. Watt must have had a strong horse. Most horses don't work that fast.

$$\text{HORSEPOWER} = \frac{\text{FOOT-POUNDS}}{\text{SECONDS} \times 550}$$

Suppose you weigh 110 pounds and you climb a 10-foot ladder in 4 seconds. What is your horsepower?

$$\text{H.P.} = \frac{110 \text{ lbs.} \times 10 \text{ ft.}}{4 \times 550} = \frac{1}{2}$$

HAVE YOU EVER SEEN ENERGY?

Although we define potential energy as the ability to do work, the truth is that we never see energy all by itself. We can't roll it up like a raincoat and tuck it under an arm. We can't extract the energy from a lump of coal like we remove an orange from its skin.

The fact is, we never see plain, naked energy as such. In this respect, energy is like a leprechaun—we talk about it a lot, but never see it.

Energy is an invisible, mysterious thing that seems to come "hidden" or "disguised." It "hides" in a box of Wheaties, in a stick of wood, or in a glass of tomato juice.

We don't see energy itself. All we see are chunks of matter that have energy—a gallon of gasoline or a slice of bread (potential energy), or we see matter in motion—a car speeding down Highway 101, a baseball flying over the fence (kinetic energy).

We don't pour naked potential energy into the tank of our Ford, but matter that contains energy. Also, we don't get simply "pure" kinetic energy of motion from this gasoline but, rather, matter (an automobile) that has kinetic energy.

We have mentioned that energy is not seen "naked" or "alone" but is manifest in **CONNECTION WITH MATTER.**

What a strange world! We can't hope to get matter into motion without potential energy "standing by" ready to "push" molecules into action (the potential energy in gasoline ready to propel your car down the road). Yet this potential energy necessary to get matter into motion is found "locked" or "waiting" in matter itself.

BOXING & K.E.

Boxing is a sport based on kinetic energy. If a boxer simply placed his glove against his opponent's cheek and pushed gently, the force exerted would be harmless. He must deliver rapid, pistonlike blows if he wishes to overcome his opponent. The more rapid the blow, the more paralyzing is the effect.

In his prime, Jack Dempsey could throw a punch that traveled 135 mph. Joe Louis' punch, at its fastest, traveled 127 mph.

HEART BEATS

Do you ever stop to consider the work that your heart does for you each day? The average heart weighs just a bit more than half a pound. It beats 72 times a minute, 4,320 times an hour, 103,680 times a day, and approximately 3 billion times in a 70-year lifetime. In less than a minute your heart pumps 5 to 6 quarts of blood through your body.

Compared to that of a bird, however, the human circulatory system is feeble. The heart of a blue-throated hummingbird, found in southern Arizona and Mexico, beats 1,260 times per minute. A canary's blood pressure is twice that of a human's. The smaller the bird, the more furiously the heart pumps.

WE LIVE IN TWO WORLDS

By now you are no doubt aware of the fact that we live in two worlds. One world we see. The other we do not.

The world we see is the one of cabbages and kings, gingersnaps, and Volkswagens. By night we see stars poised pale on the fringes of space. By day we may see the horizon, if there is no smog. The world we can see, hammer, measure, and weigh is the world of matter.

In addition, we are immersed or surrounded by an invisible world. Our lives depend on forces we never see. The invisible thing that enables us to move the hammer and pound a nail is what we call energy. The word itself comes from the Greek "en" meaning "in," and "ergon" meaning "work."

LIFT OR PULL

When you lift a chair, both the force and distance are vertical. You must overcome the force of gravity. If you push or pull the chair, the force and the distance are horizontal. You must overcome friction.

Friction comes from a Latin word meaning "to rub." It is the resistance to relative motion between two bodies in contact with each other. The amount of friction depends on the kinds of surfaces that are in contact. Whenever one object moves over another their surfaces interlock. The rougher the surfaces are, the greater the friction. Even what appears to be a smooth surface looks like a mountain landscape when seen through a high-powered microscope.

ACTIVITIES

Match

Glass

Activity 1

1. FRICTION MATCH   *Supervised Classroom*

A "friction match" is well named. You light it by dragging it across a rough surface.

The amount of friction depends on the kinds of surfaces in contact. To demonstrate this, try lighting a match on a plate of smooth glass or smooth ice. The smooth surface will offer so little friction, the match won't ignite.

By contrast, drag the match head across a piece of sandpaper.

You

Floor

Activity 2

2. FLOOR BURN   *Home*

If you play basketball you may have noticed the heat caused by friction when, after stumbling, you slid across the hardwood floor and acquired a "floor burn."

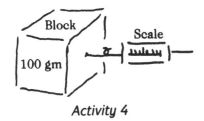

Ice

Activity 3

3. WINTER WONDERLAND   *Supervised Classroom*

Every winter I watch students give superb demonstrations that show how the amount of friction depends on the kinds of surfaces in contact. Many times the sidewalk that runs past my window is coated with ice. The ice is so smooth it offers little resistance to forward motion. Students enjoy sliding on the ice for great distances. No one tries to slide in like manner on a dry concrete sidewalk in bare feet.

4. COEFFICIENT OF FRICTION   *Supervised Classroom*

The coefficient of friction may be defined as the pull (the force needed to overcome friction) divided by the load (the force pressing the surfaces together):

$$\text{COEFFICIENT OF FRICTION} = \frac{\text{PULL}}{\text{LOAD}}$$

Fasten a hook to one end of a block of wood. Attach a spring scale to it. Hold the scale in your hand and pull the block across the surface of the table.

Suppose the block of wood weighs 100 grams and it takes 20 grams to pull it.

The coefficient of friction is:

$$\frac{\text{PULL}}{\text{LOAD}} = \frac{20}{100} = 1/5 = 20\%$$

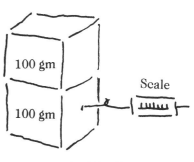

Activity 5

5. DOUBLE IT   Supervised Classroom

Put another 100-gram block on top of the first block. Pull the scale. What does it tell you about the coefficient of friction this time?

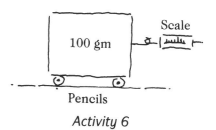

Activity 6

6. ROLL IT   Supervised Classroom

Put two round pencils under the 100-gram block of wood. Pull on the scale. Note how little pull is now required to move the load.

The most effective way to reduce friction is to change sliding friction to rolling friction. This is why we use wheels, roller bearings, and ball bearings.

Activity 7

7. HAND IN THE WIND   Home

If you are riding down a country lane where there is no traffic, try this. Roll down the window. Extend your hand only. Open wide your hand into a cup shape so your palm and fingers meet the oncoming wind full force. Now turn your hand sideways so it slices through the air like an airplane wing. What do you notice?

Activity 8

8. BIKE RIDE   Home

Ride a bike down a straight, level road. Move just fast enough to keep your bike upright. While moving at this slow speed, note how much energy is required to remain in motion. Now increase your speed to maximum. Explain what happens.

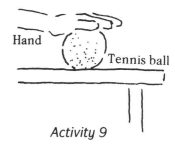

Activity 9

9. BEARINGS   Home

To demonstrate how ball bearings cut down on friction, try the following. Place a tennis ball on top of the table. Place your left hand, palm downward, on top of the tennis ball. Even though you push down with considerable force, the ball rolls easily.

Now, while still pressing down hard on the ball with your left hand, hold the ball between the fingers of your right hand so it cannot roll. Use your right hand to shove the ball across the table. It will take a lot more effort. Rolling friction is less than sliding friction.

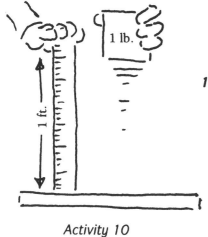

Activity 10

10. HOW TO MEASURE WORK   Home

Hold a foot ruler in a vertical position on the table. Lift a mass of 1 pound from the foot to the top of the ruler. The work done is:

$$\text{WORK} = \text{FORCE} \times \text{DISTANCE}$$
$$= 1 \text{ lb.} \times 1 \text{ ft.}$$
$$= 1 \text{ ft. lb.}$$

The 1-pound mass has also acquired 1 foot-pound of potential energy. If it is allowed to fall, it can do 1 foot-pound of work.

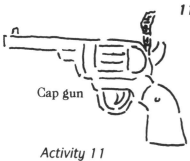

Cap gun

Activity 11

11. CAP GUN ENERGY   Home

A cap gun is a superb demonstration of potential energy. The caps have potential energy due to their chemical composition. When the hammer is in a cocked position, it has potential energy due to the mechanical configuration of the spring.

Pull the trigger. Immediately the potential energy of the hammer turns into kinetic energy of motion. When the hammer hits the cap, this kinetic energy of forward motion is converted into heat energy that sets off the cap. Immediately the potential energy of the cap is changed into heat and sound waves.

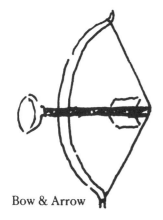

Bow & Arrow

Activity 12

12. BOW AND ARROW   Home

A toy bow and arrow tipped with a small suction cup make an excellent demonstration unit. Notch the arrow to the string and pull it back. The bow has as much potential energy as the work you put into pulling the string back. Suppose it takes an average force of 10 pounds to pull the string back 2 feet. The bow has 20 foot-pounds of potential energy.

When you release your hold on the arrow, the potential energy of the bow leaps into the kinetic energy of the speeding arrow which slams the suction cup against the wall.

13. GRAM-CENTIMETER   Home

To demonstrate how much a gram-centimeter of work is, lift 1 gram to a height of 1 centimeter above the table. The 1 gram-centimeter of potential energy will transform into kinetic energy as soon as you release the 1-gram piece.

14. P.E. TO K.E. TO P.E.   Home

Get a string about 2 feet long. Tie one end to the stem of an apple or any other convenient object. Tie the other end of the string to the rod of your shower curtain.

Lift the bob to position A. It is all potential energy. As the bob falls, it transforms potential energy into kinetic energy. At B, the halfway mark, the bob has lost half of its potential energy.

At C, the bob is all kinetic energy. As the bob starts to rise, it transforms kinetic energy back into potential energy. At D, its energy is part potential, part kinetic. At E, it is all potential energy again.

Why isn't this a perpetual motion machine?

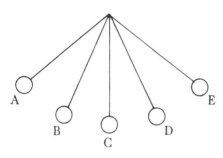

Activity 14

15. MIXING BOWL AND MARBLE   Home

Place a marble in a big mixing bowl near the rim, as shown by the letter A. As the marble falls, it converts potential energy into kinetic. At the bottom of the bowl it is all kinetic energy. As the marble rolls up the opposite side, it converts kinetic energy back into potential energy. Then it reverses direction. It keeps up this energy exchange until friction brings it to a stop. By this time the potential and kinetic energy the marble once had is transferred into the kinetic energy of the molecules of the glass which are thus heated.

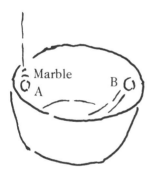

Activity 15

16. BASEBALL

Explain how you could use a baseball to demonstrate energy transfer.

Activity 16

17.   WHAT IS YOUR ENERGY?

You let yourself fall from a diving board that is 10 feet above the water. You weigh 120 pounds. What is your P.E. and your K.E. at each of the positions marked in the accompanying figure?

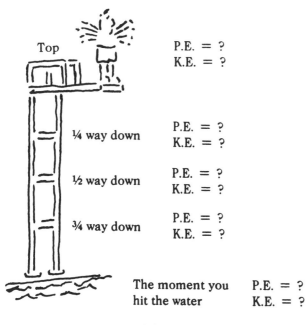

Top	P.E. = ?
	K.E. = ?
¼ way down	P.E. = ?
	K.E. = ?
½ way down	P.E. = ?
	K.E. = ?
¾ way down	P.E. = ?
	K.E. = ?
The moment you hit the water	P.E. = ?
	K.E. = ?

Activity 17

HIGHLIGHTS OF THIS CHAPTER

● The "thing" that enables us to move matter is energy.

● Potential energy is defined as the capacity or ability to do work.

● Work is defined as the product of force and the distance over which the force acts:

$$\text{WORK} \;=\; \text{FORCE} \times \text{DISTANCE}$$

Kinetic energy is the energy of motion.

$$\text{POWER} \;=\; \frac{\text{WORK}}{\text{TIME}} \;=\; \frac{\text{FOOT-POUNDS}}{\text{SECONDS}}$$

$$\text{HORSEPOWER} \;=\; \frac{\text{FOOT-POUNDS}}{\text{SECONDS} \times 550}$$

● Friction is the resistance to relative motion between two bodies in contact with each other.

● The amount of friction depends on the kinds of surfaces in contact.

● The coefficient of friction $\;=\; \dfrac{\text{PULL}}{\text{LOAD}}$

Multiple-Choice Questions

1. A falling raindrop:
   a. is losing K.E.
   b. is gaining P.E.
   c. has K.E. only.
   d. has both P.E. and K.E.

2. The coefficient of friction depends on:
   a. the amount of force needed to pull the object.
   b. the types of surfaces in contact.
   c. the weight you are trying to pull or push.
   d. the speed with which you pull.

3. The main difference between power and work is that:
   a. work requires less P.E.
   b. work depends on friction.
   c. power involves time.
   d. power gives greater P.E.

4. A 110-pound boy climbs a ladder to a roof 20 feet above the ground. While he is standing on the edge of the roof his:
   a. P.E. = 1,500 ft. lbs.
   b. K.E. = 0.
   c. K.E. = 2,200 ft. lbs.
   d. P.E. = 3,500 ft. lbs.

5. If the student in the previous problem climbed the ladder in 10 seconds, his horsepower would be approximately:
   a. 1/5 H.P.
   b. 1/4 H.P.
   c. 3/5 H.P.
   d. 2/5 H.P.

True or False Questions

1. Power is the rate of doing work.

2. Friction can cause a severe burn.

3. According to James Watt, a horse can work at the rate of 5,500 foot-pounds per minute.

4. You do the same amount of work whether you walk up the steps or run up.

5. Even though you hold a sack of cement on your head for 10 minutes you do no work.

Chapter 10

THE DANCE OF THE MOLECULES
How to Make Molecules Speed Up and Slow Down

Gigantic sculptures of Washington, Jefferson, Roosevelt, and Lincoln look out from the top of Mount Rushmore in South Dakota. Perhaps you think of these stone faces as "everlasting." By no means. Every year workmen risk their lives to protect America's majestic national monument from the forces of expansion and contraction.

On hot summer afternoons the stone faces may reach a temperature of over a hundred degrees. The stone expands. Then comes a sudden shower. The cold rain causes the rock to shrink so fast it cracks. Daring mountain climbers make a yearly close-up inspection of the faces to detect cracks and seal them against moisture.

HOW TO LOSE A MOUNTAIN

Without constant care, Mount Rushmore would suffer the fate of other mountains. When water which has seeped down into cracks and crevices between rocks freezes, it expands in volume. Like a giant wedge or crowbar, the frozen water cracks open small rocks and pries loose slabs of rock from sheer mountain cliffs, sending them crashing into canyons below to form a slope of broken rocks at the base of the cliff.

Rocks pried loose by frost-wedging (alternate freezing and thawing) often build up a huge rock pile called a talus slope at the base of a mountain. "Talus" is the Latin word for "ankle," and the foot of the mountain makes a good ankle for the piles of broken rocks.

Many times rocks split open by frost-wedging are held in place by ice and do not tumble down until the spring thaw. That is why mountain driving and travel along roads bordered by steep cliffs can be dangerous in the spring of the year.

A SIZZLING HAMBURGER FOR LUNCH!

What is the difference between a hamburger just out of the refrigerator and one just out of the frying pan? Answer—the molecules in the cooked hamburger are moving faster!

A molecule is defined as the smallest particle of a substance that still acts like that substance. A molecule of water is the tiniest bit of water. A molecule of salt is the tiniest bit of salt.

The molecules in your chair, your pencil, or in your shoes are always in motion. If we could look into this tiny world of molecules, we would find motion everywhere.

Heat is a form of energy caused by the motion of molecules. The faster the molecules in a substance move, the more heat it contains. The heat energy contained in any body is the sum of all energy in all its many molecules. Things that we call cold are objects that have less heat than other objects.

When things get hot, they expand. This is not because the molecules themselves get bigger. They simply move farther apart.

A PICNIC BUS

Heat, remember, does not make molecules grow bigger. It simply speeds them up. They jostle against each other harder and move farther apart. When one cubic centimeter of water evaporates or turns into steam, it expands about 1,700 times.

The molecules of water in the liquid state are like a group of teenagers packed into a bus. Their motion is limited. Their kinetic energy is low. When the bus unloads at the picnic grounds, the teenagers tumble forth from the bus and run all over the landscape. They are like molecules of water jumping from a liquid state to a gaseous state. Their individual size is the same, but they occupy an area 1,700 times that of the bus. They are warmer. They have more kinetic energy.

WILD HORSES AND FOOTBALL PUMP

Get a football or basketball pump. Push down on the plunger vigorously several times. You may notice that the bottom part of the pump is quite warm. Some of the heat is produced by friction of the plunger in the pump, but most of the heat

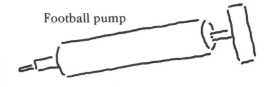

Football pump

comes from the compression of the air in the pump. You force the air molecules into a smaller space, thus causing the walls of the cylinder to be bombarded more often.

Pushing a great number of air molecules into a smaller space is like chasing wild horses into a small corral. So many madly galloping mustangs are herded into a small space that they continually bump into the sides of the corral. The more horses you cram into a corral, the more often the walls will be bombarded by flying hooves and thumping bodies.

Cup of coffee

A CUP OF STEAMING HOT COFFEE

What has more heat—a cup of steaming hot coffee or the Mississippi River at St. Paul on a cold day in winter?

The separate molecules in the coffee are moving very fast, so they have a high temperature. The molecules in the cold river are moving slowly, so they have a lower temperature; but there are many millions of times as many molecules in the river as there are in the cup. For that reason, all of the river molecules taken together will have more heat than the coffee.

FOURTH OF JULY SPARKLER

Sparkler

A Fourth of July sparkler is a good example of the difference between heat and temperature. A warning stamped on the side of the sparkler box says: "Danger! Do Not Touch Glowing Wire."

Why will the glowing wire burn your hand while the glowing sparks won't? Even though the glowing wire and the sparks have the same temperature, the sparks have little heat because they are so small. They have little mass, or weight. The wire has more heat, even though it has the same temperature, because it has more mass, more weight. There is more material in it.

BACK RUB

Many years ago I worked as an orderly in a large hospital in St. Louis. One of my jobs was to rub the backs of patients with rubbing alcohol. As soon as the rubbing alcohol hit their backs, some patients complained that the liquid was "too cold." In reply, I told them that the bottle of alcohol had been sitting on the shelf at room temperature. Who was right?

To help you appreciate the viewpoint of the patients, try the following: pour a few drops of rubbing alcohol on the back of your hand. Wave your hand in the air a few times. The liquid will vanish. Your hand will feel "cool."

In order for the molecules of alcohol to become "airborne" they have to acquire enough energy to jump from the liquid state into the gaseous state. They do this by "stealing" heat from your hand, thus cooling your skin.

WE CAN'T DEPEND ON OUR SKIN!

Since we can't depend on our skin to tell us what the temperature is, we use a thermometer. The common thermometer is made of a slim glass tube with a bulb at the bottom. The bulb is usually filled with mercury. Sometimes alcohol or some other liquid, such as toluene, is used.

Since molecules move faster and spread farther apart when heated, the mercury increases in volume and rises in the tube when the temperature is high. It may be marked with the Fahrenheit scale, abbreviated F, or with the centigrade scale, abbreviated C.

WHAT IS ZERO FAHRENHEIT?

What does zero stand for on the Fahrenheit scale? How cold is zero? If you ever helped to make homemade ice cream, you may have poured salt into a pail of ice to get the temperature down to zero.

In 1724 when Gabriel Fahrenheit invented the thermometer that now bears his name, the coldest temperature that could be obtained experimentally was reached by mixing equal parts of salt with ice or snow. Fahrenheit decided to call this temperature zero.

Fahrenheit put the 100° mark on his thermometer to equal what he thought to be the normal temperature of a healthy human body. Later, more accurate measurements found that the body temperature is usually 98.6°.

On the Fahrenheit scale the temperature at which water freezes is 32°. Water boils at 212°. The temperature at which water freezes and the temperature at which water boils are known as the fixed points on a thermometer.

COLDEST SPOTS

The temperature of the coldest spot in the United States, this side of Alaska, was recorded in Yellowstone National Park. The temperature fell to -66°F on February 9, 1933. A record low world temperature of -126.9°F. was recorded at the Soviet Antarctic station Vostok on August 24, 1960.

HOTTEST SPOTS

On July 10, 1913, in Death Valley, California, the temperature in the shade rose to 134°F. The hottest day ever recorded was on September 13, 1922, in Azizia, Libya, North Africa. The mercury rose to 136.4°F.

GREATEST CHANGES

The greatest temperature change in one day took place at Browning, Montana, on January 24, 1916. The temperature fell from 44°F to -56°F, a total drop of 100°F. The greatest yearly changes in temperature are in Siberia. At Olekminsk the summer temperature has soared to 113°F. In the winter, temperatures have dropped to -76°F—a total range of 189°F.

THE COLD SAHARA

Perhaps you think of the Sahara desert as torrid. The strange thing is that the climate of the Sahara is one of extremes. It can reach a high of 133°F in the daytime. At night, it may drop as low as 11° above zero.

ENTER THE CENTIGRADE SCALE

In 1742 Anders Celsius, a Swedish astronomer, invented a thermometer using the centigrade scale. On the centigrade scale, zero is considered as the temperature at which water freezes and the boiling point of water is 100°.

On the centigrade scale there are 100 degrees between the freezing and boiling points of water. On the Fahrenheit scale there are 180 degrees between the freezing and boiling points of water (212°-32°).

HOW TO CHANGE SCALES

To change from one scale to the other is simple if you keep the following comparisons in mind:

BETWEEN FREEZING AND BOILING

—on the Fahrenheit scale are 180 degrees.

—on the centigrade scale are 100 degrees.

This gives us a relationship of 180/100, or 9/5.

In other words:

THERE ARE 9 MARKS ON THE F (Fahrenheit) SCALE FOR EVERY 5 MARKS ON THE C (centigrade) SCALE.

Also keep in mind that on the F scale the freezing point is 32 degrees higher.

TO CHANGE A CENTIGRADE READING TO FAHRENHEIT

Multiply the centigrade reading by 9/5 and add 32.

This gives us the formula: $F = 9/5C + 32$

TO CHANGE A FAHRENHEIT READING TO CENTIGRADE

Subtract 32 from the Fahrenheit reading and multiply by 5/9.

This gives us the formula: $C = 5/9(F-32)$

HOW HOT IS A "DOG DAY" IN CENTIGRADE?

On a hot "dog day" in August your thermometer reads 86°. What would this reading be on the centigrade scale?

Take the formula:	$C =$	$5/9(F-32)$
Put in the value of the Fahrenheit reading:	$C =$	$5/9(86-32)$
Solve:	$C =$	$5/9(54)$
	$C =$	$5(6) = 30$ degrees

WOULD YOU BE COMFORTABLE AT 80 DEGREES CENTIGRADE?

Take this formula:	$F =$	$9/5(C) + 32$
Put in the value of the centigrade reading:	$F =$	$9/5(80) + 32$
Solve:	$F =$	$9(16) + 32$
	$F =$	$144 + 32$
	$F =$	176 torrid degrees Fahrenheit!

CHANGING TEMPERATURES

Change –40°F to degrees on the centigrade scale:

$$C = 5/9(F - 32)$$
$$C = 5/9(-40 - 32)$$
$$C = 5/9(-72) = -40$$

It is interesting to note that –40°C is also –40°F.

Change 45°C to degrees Fahrenheit:

$$F = 9/5(C) + 32$$
$$F = 9/5(45) + 32$$
$$F = 81 + 32$$
$$F = 113°$$

Change 41°F to degrees centigrade:

$$C = 5/9(F-32)$$
$$C = 5/9(41-32)$$
$$C = 5/9(9)$$
$$C = 5°$$

Which do you prefer—a temperature of 50°F or 10°C?

HEAT BY CONDUCTION

The transfer of heat from molecule to molecule by collision is known as conduction. If you have a toy train you will be able to demonstrate this method of heat transfer. Hook about six cars behind the locomotive. Now push the locomotive back and forth. The motion will be transferred from the locomotive to the coal car, then down through the other cars in the freight train to the caboose.

Let the cars represent molecules. You can see how the motion of the first molecule (the locomotive) is transferred down to the last molecule (the caboose). Molecules that transmit heat by means of conduction move only very short distances. They pass energy along by bumping into neighboring molecules.

GOOD AND POOR CONDUCTORS

Metals are the best conductors of heat. The motion of molecules is easily passed along in such substances. Pots and pans are usually made of metal. The metal conducts heat from the flame into the food.

Wood, wool, cloth, paper, plastic, and feathers conduct heat slowly. They are, therefore, poor conductors. Have you noticed that cooking utensils, electric irons, and soldering irons usually have wooden or plastic handles? Materials that are nonconductors of heat make good insulators. The word comes from the Latin "insula," meaning "island."

Porous materials that have many air cells or pockets make good insulators because gases and liquids are poor conductors of heat. A cigarette smoker has a miniature furnace glowing some 2 inches from his nose, yet the burning tobacco does not burn his nose or scorch his lips.

The following table gives the relative heat conductivity of metals and insulators:

SUBSTANCE	HEAT-CONDUCTION RATING
Silver	100
Copper	92
Aluminum	50
Brass	28
Iron	11
Lead	8
Glass	0.20
Water	0.12
Paper	0.013
Sawdust	0.012
Cotton wool (tightly packed)	0.010
Air	0.005

COLD TILE

On a crisp winter morning when you walk barefoot across the bathroom rug and then step on the tile floor, you say that the tile is cold. If you place a thermometer on the rug and on the tile, you will find that they both have the same temperature. The tile feels colder because it conducts heat away from your feet faster than the rug does.

Rug

Tile floor

CONVECTION

Water is a poor conductor of heat, yet it is possible to boil water. This is done by convection, the second method of heat transfer. Convection comes from a Latin word that means "to bring together" or "carry." It is the transference of heat by moving masses of matter.

Conduction is the transfer of heat **FROM MOLECULE TO MOLECULE**.

Convection is the transfer of heat **BY THE TRAVELING OF MOLECULES** from one point to another.

Water and air molecules pass along very little heat by bumping into each other. They transfer energy by moving along in a group.

SUN KISSED

Stretch out your hand on a warm summer day and shake hands with a beam of sunlight. The heat you feel is not due to conduction. The air on top of you is a poor conductor. Neither is it due to convection. Hot air does not travel downward. The heat is produced by radiation, the third method of heat transfer. The word radiation comes from a Latin word that means "to emit rays."

Whereas conduction and convection depend on the presence of matter, radiation does not. Waves of radiant energy from the sun pass through space at the speed of 186,000 miles per second. They are packed with potential heat, but until the energy is absorbed by some substance it cannot properly be called heat. When the waves strike your hand or other objects the energy is imparted to the object and speeds up the motion of the molecules.

Radiant energy can travel through a vacuum without warming it. It can also pass through such substances as glass and air without warming them appreciably. Radiant energy travels rapidly through space, sometimes over great distances. Conduction and convection transfer heat slowly over relatively short distances.

RADIATE YOURSELF!

Stand by a radiator in January. If the radiator is not too hot, you may gently place your hand on it and be heated by **CONDUCTION**.

Hold your hands over the hot radiator in the path of the rising warm air. You are being heated by **CONVECTION**.

Stand about three feet to one side of the radiator. The heat that reaches you is coming directly by **RADIATION**.

PUT THE SUN TO WORK

A radiometer consists of a glass bulb in which four vanes pivot on a needle-point. Only about 1 percent of normal air is left in the bulb at the time of manufacture. One side of each vane is made of highly polished metal. The other side is black.

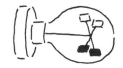

Radiometer

When radiant energy from the sun or a warm object falls on the vanes, the black sides absorb more energy than the polished sides. The air next to the black surfaces is heated by conduction. As these air molecules acquire more kinetic energy, they push against the dark surfaces, causing the vanes to rotate in the near vacuum.

Place the radiometer in direct sunlight, then in partial light. Notice the results.

THERMOS BOTTLE

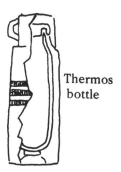

Thermos bottle

A thermos bottle from which you can remove the bright, silvered interior flask is a useful demonstration unit. The silvered walls of the flask reflect the heat back into the liquid, and thus prevent heat loss due to radiation. The vacuum between the double glass walls of the flask prevents heat loss due to both conduction and convection. Both these methods of heat transfer depend upon molecules. The few stray molecules that are left in the partial vacuum inside the walls of the silvered flask are not sufficient to transfer much heat.

About the only place for heat to escape by conduction is through the cork and the glass neck of the flask. Since both cork and glass are poor conductors, this heat loss is slight.

When you reassemble the thermos bottle, note that there is also a dead-air space formed between the glass flask and the outside walls of the container. Likewise, there is another dead-air space between the cork and the top of the threaded cup. All this helps to cut down on heat loss by conduction and convection.

REGELATION

Ice melts under pressure and refreezes when the pressure is released. This process is called regelation. In making snowballs, you squeeze the snow to create enough pressure to melt some of it. Then, when the pressure is relieved, the water refreezes, leaving a firm snowball. If the weather is extremely cold, however, it is impossible to make decent snowballs, because you can't apply enough pressure to melt the snow.

FREEZE-DRIED TOWEL

If you hang a wet dish towel outdoors on a very cold day, the water it contains will freeze solid. The towel will become as fragile as ice. You have to be careful not to poke your finger through it. Nevertheless, the towel will dry after a while. The ice leaps from a solid into a gas.

HOW TO CHANGE THE SIZE OF THINGS

Though the molecules in solids are close together, they need more "running space" when they warm up. The amount of expansion due to increases in temperature, and of contraction in the case of cooling, depends upon the material. Various substances have different rates of expansion. The fractional increase in length of a given material for each degree rise in temperature is known as the coefficient of linear expansion. The following table lists the coefficients of linear expansion for several common solids, indicating the increase per unit of length per centigrade degree.

RATES OF EXPANSION OF VARIOUS SUBSTANCES

SUBSTANCE	COEFFICIENT OF LINEAR EXPANSION
Aluminum	0.0000240
Copper	0.0000168
Steel	0.0000110
Cast iron	0.0000106
Platinum	0.0000090
Soft glass	0.0000085
Pyrex glass	0.0000036
Invar (a nickel steel)	0.0000009
Quartz	0.0000004

As the table indicates, the increases in dimensions for a single degree are so small as to be negligible. However, an engineer who designs a bridge several thousand feet long, to be erected in a place where temperatures vary from far below zero to over 100 degrees, must know how much change in length can be expected in order to provide for expansion and contraction.

A hot summer day in San Francisco makes the cables of the Golden Gate Bridge stretch. As a result, the towers lean in and the road sags as much as 16 feet.

In Duluth, Minnesota, one cold January night, police received many calls from persons suspecting prowlers in their homes. The noises were discovered to be the buildings cracking from the cold.

UNUSUAL SUBSTANCE

In my home town of Butte, Montana, the temperature would sometimes drop to –40°F. The mercury in the thermometer on our back porch would shrink all the way down into the bulb at the base of the tube, then freeze into a tiny solid sphere.

Most substances are like mercury. They shrink as they grow colder. A notable exception to this is water. At room temperature water expands when it is heated. It contracts when it is cooled until it reaches a temperature of 4 degrees centigrade (39.2°F). At this point, it reaches its maximum density of 1 gram per cubic centimeter. Further cooling makes its volume increase. When water freezes into ice it becomes even less dense. Ice is about ⁹/₁₀ as dense as water. It floats on the surface.

HOW MANY SENTINELS IN YOUR HOME?

Thermometers that measure extremely high or extremely low temperatures are usually made of two strips of metal soldered or welded together. This bimetallic strip is frequently made with brass on one side and iron on the other. Since brass expands one and one-half times as much as iron, this bimetallic strip bends with changes in temperature, rotating a pointer that indicates the temperature.

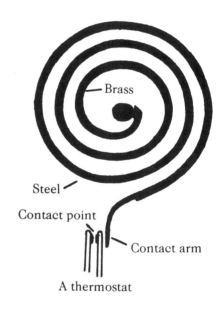

A thermostat

If this temperature is connected to an electric circuit and operates a switch, the thermometer becomes a thermostat. This common device uses the expansion and contraction properties of materials to do its job. Thermostats in your home do a number of jobs. They control electric irons, hot-water heaters, ovens, furnaces, toasters, and air conditioners.

How does the thermostat in your refrigerator keep food fresh? When the bimetallic strip gets warm, it bends in such a way that it closes the electric circuit. This causes electricity to flow to the motor. As the temperature falls back to the desired level the strip bends in the opposite direction. This turns off the motor in the refrigeration unit.

Perhaps you know a person who will give you an old wall thermostat that was used to control the temperature in a home. This makes a wonderful demonstration unit. You can see for yourself that the length of time the furnace stays on is determined by the distance between the contact points. These can be adjusted by setting the dial to any desired temperature.

A LIFESAVER

The thermostat in your hot-water heater is a "lifesaver." When the temperature of the water reaches a certain point, the bimetallic strip expands and breaks contact, thereby shutting off the heat to the water. Otherwise, the water would get so hot it would turn to steam. It might explode and take you and your house along with it!

DOES YOUR OVERCOAT KEEP YOU WARM IN WINTER?

Strictly speaking, no. Your body furnishes the heat. All the coat does is to prevent heat loss by conduction and convection. The coat contains untold millions of dead-air pockets. Your coat thereby prevents the warm air from leaving your body.

DEAD-AIR PIGEONS

How do pigeons use dead-air space to keep warm in winter? Just look at them and find out. They puff out their feathers, thus "trapping" more air. This trapped air acts like a "blanket of insulation" to keep the warm air from their bodies from leaving them.

HOW TO MAKE WEATHER

Every wind, whether it is a gentle breeze or a giant wind that shrieks down from the north, is caused by convection. As the blazing sun beats down upon the equator, the earth and the air above it are heated to a higher temperature than elsewhere. The warm air expands and rises. Cooler air from regions north and south of the equator moves in to take the place of the warmed air.

If the earth did not rotate, the warm air would divide high in the air. It would then move toward the poles. Slowly it could cool and sink. A surface wind of cold air, from the north in the northern hemisphere and from the south in the southern hemisphere, would blow over the land. Since the earth does rotate, there are trade winds which move from northeast to southwest near the equator. Farther north or south, the river of falling air becomes the prevailing westerlies.

PAINT IT WHITE

White, silvered, and polished objects reflect energy. Refrigerators are commonly given a coat of smooth, white enamel so they will not absorb heat from the room. Long steel bridges receive a coat of aluminum paint. The paint reflects the heat and prevents the bridge from expanding as much as it otherwise would. Steelworkers often wear helmets painted with aluminum. Aluminum foil is nailed to the rafters to keep houses cool in summer. Some ironing boards have a surface of aluminum foil material. It reflects heat back into the cloth you are pressing and so speeds up the ironing job.

When our astronauts walked on the surface of the moon they wore suits with a shiny, reflective surface to keep the intense rays from the sun from cooking them.

BLACK IS THE ANSWER

In early winter you may notice an interesting thing. During the night a snowfall of one or two inches covers the landscape. Within a few hours after sunrise the snow on the blacktop highway melts away, but the snow on the grass and trees remains. The reason the snow melts so rapidly on the blacktop highway is that black is an excellent absorber of heat.

YOUR FIREPLACE IS A RADIATOR

Any heated body sends out rays or beams of radiant energy. The hotter the body, the more energy it emits per second. An ordinary fireplace heats a room almost entirely by radiation. For this reason it might be called a radiator. It is far from efficient, however. Most of the heat goes up the chimney with the convection currents. Practically no heat goes out into the room by conduction.

WE LIVE ON A RADIATOR!

Do you know that we live on a radiator? By day the earth absorbs heat from the sun. At night the earth radiates this heat back into space. Because a cloud blanket will reflect the radiated heat back to earth, cloudy nights are not the coldest.

YOU ARE A RADIATOR!

You, too, are a radiator. Your body continually absorbs or radiates heat. When a radiator is colder than its surroundings, it absorbs heat. When it is warmer, it radiates heat. Heat always passes from a warm body to a colder body. The warmer material loses energy and the cooler one gains energy. The transfer continues until both objects reach the same temperature.

LONGER RAIL TRIPS IN SUMMER

Have you ever noticed that concrete highways have gaps filled with tar and that space is left between the individual sections of rail when railroads are built?

These spaces allow for expansion and contraction. Bridges are frequently anchored securely only at one end. The free end can slide back and forth on roller supports. In hot weather concrete roads and railroad rails fit tightly at the joints. In cold weather there is space between adjacent rails. On the Canadian National Railway, for example, the steel rails are about 40 inches longer per mile in summer than they are in the winter. Despite all precautions rails sometimes buckle in extremely hot weather and snap in cold spells.

GREENHOUSE

A greenhouse allows radiant energy from the sun to pass through its glass roof and walls. Once inside, the light falls on soil and plants. They convert the radiant energy into heat waves. Since glass is a good insulator against loss of heat by conduction, the temperature inside a greenhouse may be quite high even though it is cold outside.

WHY 50 MILES PER HOUR?

Have you ever wondered why one is advised not to drive a new automobile over 50 miles per hour for the first 500 miles? The bearings on a new car are fitted to a perfection of 1/1,000 of an inch, with allowance made for expansion. Friction will eventually wear down moving parts and allow for greater expansion. If you drive too fast at the start, when the bearings fit snugly, it is possible that enough heat may be generated to burn out or melt the metal in the bearings.

HOW TO SHRINK A BRIDGE

In downtown Chicago there are numerous bridges that carry motor traffic and pedestrians across the Chicago River. In order to allow passage to big boats on the river, each bridge "breaks" in the middle. Powerful motors tilt each half of the bridge into a vertical position. Sometimes on very hot days in summer, the upended bridge sections stretch so much they cannot be put back into proper position again. They are too long.

How, then, can you "shrink" a bridge back to normal? The answer is simple. The fire department comes and sprays cold water on the bridge.

TEETH AND ELECTRIC LIGHTS

Did you ever stop to think of the tremendous amount of research and scientific skill that make possible things we take for granted, such as fillings in teeth and light bulbs? Just think of the problems due to expansion and contraction. If a filling were to expand more rapidly than a tooth when heated, the tooth could be shattered. If the filling cooled off and shrank at a faster rate than the tooth, the filling might fall out while you were eating ice cream.

Now look at a light bulb. Note that the glass fits snugly into the threaded metal base. Suppose that the glass expanded faster than the metal base. The bulb would shatter. If the glass shrank faster than the metal, the bulb would fall out of its threaded base. The coefficient of expansion of the metal and glass parts must match if the seal is to be perfect at all temperatures. Scientists found that an alloy (or mixture) of iron, nickel, and cobalt has the same rate of expansion as glass. Wires made of this alloy support the filament and connect it to the base of the lamp through the glass.

ARE YOU CRACKING YOUR TEETH?

What happens to your teeth when you take a drink of ice-cold soda pop, then bite into a red-hot hot dog? According to some scientists, such thermal shocks, or rapid temperature changes, make small cracks in the teeth. This may open the way to decay.

DOES YOUR HOUSE STRETCH?

Do you know why paint cracks and peels? It is mainly because your house stretches and shrinks with every change in temperature. As it works back and forth, the paint film works loose. One paint company now claims that it has a new paint that stretches and shrinks along with your house. A new formula gives this new paint four times the stretch power of other latex films.

SNOW MAKES GRAVEDIGGERS HAPPY!

I have a clipping taken from the *Wisconsin State Journal* a few years ago: "Gravedigger reports from around the state said the heavy snowfall during November provided protective insulation, which limited frost penetration. In

Columbia County there is no frost under the snow. The grass underneath the snow is green. By contrast, during the previous winter there was no snow cover. Gravediggers reported that the ground was frozen from 6 to 8 feet down."

CAMPERS BEWARE!

If you are going camping next summer, please keep this in mind. When water in wet rocks expands to 1,700 times its volume and becomes steam, the rocks of a campfire can blow up like a hand grenade, injuring or killing teenage weenie roasters.

EXPANDING CONCRETE

If you live in a city where the temperature soars on hot days in the summer, you may have seen sections of concrete expand so much that the pavement literally "explodes." I have seen strips of concrete as wide as two feet erupt and tear themselves apart.

HOW TO COOL OFF AN AIRCRAFT CARRIER

If you stood on the deck of an aircraft carrier and watched a jet plane roar off, you'd see the searing blast of the exhaust burn away at the deck surface. How, the Navy wondered, could the deck be protected most efficiently? They found the answer in aluminum. Placed in the carrier deck around launching catapults, these aluminum panels dissipate the heat from the exhaust blasts of jet planes much as a radiator cools an automobile engine.

DUST MAKES GRAIN ELEVATORS "TIME BOMBS"

According to the Department of Agriculture, highly explosive dust accumulating in grain elevators is a time bomb that can be touched off easily when conditions are right. There are about 3,000 grain explosions every year.

Wheat dust is about three times as explosive as coal dust. Soy dust is about the same, and flour dust is about fifty times as explosive as coal dust. The Secretary of Agriculture said that "grain dust is an occupational hazard" around elevators and that "any kind of spark can set it off" when conditions are right. Some authorities believe the danger is greater when the humidity in the atmosphere is low and static electricity is generated. Conveyor belts rubbing together, for example, sometimes produce heat and static electricity at the same time.

DANGER IN YOUR HOMES

On a hot afternoon in August a 40-year-old mother of three strolled through her backyard, tossed an empty bug-spray can on a wastepaper fire, and turned back toward her kitchen door. A dull explosion echoed through the neighborhood. A piece of flying metal from the torn can spun through the air and cut the woman's jugular vein. Fifteen minutes later, she was pronounced dead at the local hospital.

As more and more household products go into pressurized cans and bottles the opportunity for tragedies grows. The era of the great squirt began in the early 1940s with the first appearance of bug sprays in pressurized containers. In 1947, a handful of manufacturers sold 5 million cans. Today, more than 140 packagers sell more than a billion aerosol containers each year in the U.S. alone.

What many people do not understand is that even when the product is exhausted, there is still vapor left inside the container. All you need do to make a bomb out of that "empty" is to warm it up—on a trash fire, for instance. Rising temperature expands the remaining gas until the can explodes. Some of the most violent aerosol-container accidents are attributable to this single cause.

WHY DON'T FISH FREEZE?

When you look across a frozen lake or river do you ever wonder how the fish in it can stay alive? The answer lies in a unique feature of water. It expands when it freezes.

Most substances expand when heated and contract when cooled. Water at room temperature expands when it is heated and contracts when it is cooled—but just until it reaches a temperature of 4°C (39.2°F). At this point it reaches its maximum density of 1 gram per cubic centimeter. Further cooling makes its volume increase.

This abnormal property of water keeps lakes and rivers from freezing solid in cold weather. In the late fall, when cold air cools the top layer of water in a lake, this layer contracts, becomes more dense, and sinks to the bottom. The warmer water rises to the surface and is in turn cooled by the air. This circulation continues until all the water in the pond is at 39.2°F. Further cooling of the top layer of water causes it to expand and this layer remains on top because it is less dense. Finally, the layer freezes. The ice, about 9/10 as dense as water, floats on the surface. Since ice and water are poor conductors of heat, the thickness of the ice increases slowly. Fish and other types of life in the lakes and rivers are protected because the temperature at the bottom of deep lakes does not go below 39.2°F.

If water contracted regularly as other substances do, the colder water would sink to the bottom and freezing would begin there. A lake could freeze solid in the course of a few days of subzero weather.

Lake Tahoe, the highest lake on the North American continent, never freezes over because it is so deep. The surface water as it cools is continually replaced by warmer water from the bottom. By the time the lake is fairly well cooled off, it is spring again, and the surface begins to warm up.

ACTIVITIES

Tea kettle

Hot plate

Activity 1

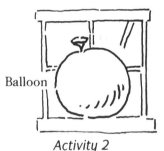

Balloon

Activity 2

Balloon

Activity 3

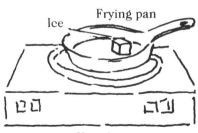

Ice   Frying pan

Hot plate

Activity 4

1. *PUT ON THE TEAKETTLE*   **Home**

To demonstrate how heat makes molecules move faster, put water into a teakettle or Pyrex flask and place it on an electric hot plate or gas burner. When the water heats up, some of the molecules will move fast enough to leap out of the flask or the spout of the teakettle as steam.

Strictly speaking, what you see coming out the spout of the teakettle is not steam, but water. Steam itself is as invisible as the water vapor above any body of water. As the invisible steam strikes the air, some of its molecules give up their heat and return to the liquid state. It is this condensed "steam" in the form of fine particles of water that we see. There generally is a clear space between the spout of a vigorously boiling teakettle and the cloud of condensing steam. This clear space is where you will find real steam.

2. *POP BALLOON*   **Home**

To demonstrate that a gas expands when it gets hot, simply blow up a balloon to maximum size and place it in a window in direct sunlight. What happens?

3. *OPERATION DEEP FREEZE*   **Home**

To demonstrate the opposite effect, the result of cold temperature, do the following. Blow up a balloon to maximum volume. Place it in a freezer. See what has happened to the size of the balloon four hours later.

4. *MAKE MATTER DISAPPEAR*   **Home**

Put an ice cube in a frying pan or a metal container. Place the pan on an electric hot plate or over a gas burner. The heat will turn the ice into water, then into steam. You will be left with an empty frying pan. The solid block of ice will disappear.

5. *ARE YOU A GOOD THERMOMETER?*   **Home**

Place three pans on the table. Fill the first with cold water and ice cubes. Fill the second pan with water as hot as you can stand it. BE SURE IT ISN'T HOT ENOUGH TO BURN YOU. Fill the third pan with lukewarm water.

Place your right hand in the ice-cold water. Place your left hand in the hot water. Keep your hands in the pans for about two minutes. Now place both hands in the lukewarm water. What do they tell you?

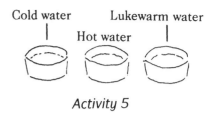

Activity 5

6. *BURN STEEL*   *Supervised Classroom*

Ordinarily we think of steel as "fireproof." We put precious documents and papers in safes to protect them. The reason the steel safe doesn't burn is the same reason it is hard to burn a Sears, Roebuck catalog. If you apply a lighted match to the cover of a Sears catalog you may burn a few of the outside pages, but the interior of the catalog will most likely remain untouched. If you wish to burn the entire catalog you will first have to tear out each page, crumple it, and make a big pile of crumpled pages so oxygen can get at each sheet of paper.

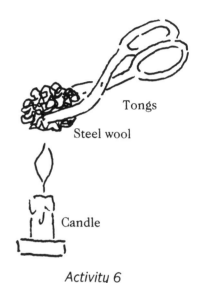

Activity 6

If you wish to burn steel, you have to do the same thing. Expose enough of it to oxygen. To demonstrate this, simply use tongs to pick up a wad of steel wool and hold it over a candle flame. The sparkling "stars" of burning steel wool result from tiny bits of steel combining with oxygen in the air. This "combining" of steel and oxygen (called oxidation) produces a compound called iron oxide.

To keep the steel in the body of your automobile from combining with the oxygen in the air (rusting or oxidizing), the car is given a coat of paint to keep it from making contact with oxygen. We paint steel, therefore, to prevent it from "burning up" or "rusting" or "oxidizing" by combining with oxygen. Rusting is slow oxidation. Fire is rapid oxidation.

7. *HOW TO STOP BURNING*   *Supervised Classroom*

To stop burning (oxidation) is simple. Shut off the supply of oxygen. To demonstrate this, hold a glass tumbler upside down over a candle flame. The smaller the glass, the sooner the flame goes out.

Activity 7

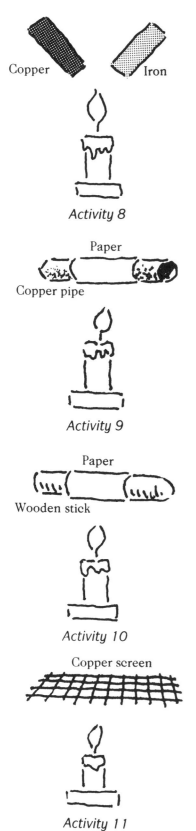

Copper   Iron

Activity 8

Paper

Copper pipe

Activity 9

Paper

Wooden stick

Activity 10

Copper screen

Activity 11

8.   *HEAT RACE*   *Supervised Classroom*

Get a strip of copper and a strip of iron, each about half an inch wide and 4 inches long. Pick up the iron with your right hand. Pick up the copper with your left hand. Hold the far ends of the metals in a candle flame. Which metal conducts the heat to your fingers first?

In this experiment you did not see heat travel through the metal. You did not see any motion of the molecules. But there was motion, for heat is the speeding up of molecules. The higher the temperature, the more rapidly the molecules of a substance move.

The candle flame speeded up the motion of the molecules at the tips of the metal strips. These bumped into molecules next to them hard enough to set those molecules into more rapid motion. The second group of aroused molecules bumped into other molecules farther down the strips. This increased motion passed along the strips until at last the molecules touching your fingers were moving rapidly.

9.   *PAPER WON'T BURN!*   *Supervised Classroom*

To demonstrate the conductivity of copper, get a copper pipe about 6 inches long and 1 inch in diameter. Wrap a piece of paper snugly around the middle of the copper pipe. Be sure to use only one thickness of paper and keep it as tight as you possibly can. Hold this paper directly over a candle flame. It may blacken, but it won't burn if the single layer of paper fits tightly around the copper. The copper absorbs the heat from the candle, conducts it through the length of the pipe, and radiates it into the air so fast that the paper can't get hot enough to burn.

10.   *NOW IT BURNS!*   *Supervised Classroom*

Repeat the previous experiment, only this time wrap the paper around a wooden stick instead of a copper pipe. A sawed-off portion of an old broomstick makes a good stick. Since wood is a poor conductor (or good insulator), it does not take the heat away. The heat stays where it is. Result—scorching!

11.   *COPPER SCREEN IN A FLAME*   *Supervised Classroom*

Get a piece of copper screen like that used for screen doors. A piece about three of four inches square will do nicely. Using tongs, gently lower the copper screen into a candle flame. What do you notice?

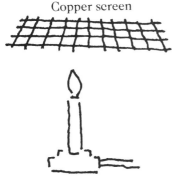

Copper screen

Activity 12

12. BUNSEN BURNER   Supervised Classroom

If you are lucky enough to have a Bunsen burner, you can perform an even more dramatic demonstration. If the gas is allowed to rise through the copper screen, and then ignited above it, the heat is carried away so rapidly by the screen that the gas on the bottom of the screen does not receive enough heat to catch fire.

Now hold an iron screen over the Bunsen burner and repeat the experiment. What happens?

13. LAZY CONDUCTOR   Supervised Classroom

To demonstrate what a poor conductor wood is, get a pan with a wooden handle. Put a little water in the pan. Place it on an electric hot plate. When the water comes to a boil you can still pick up the pan by the wooden handle—proof that wood is a poor conductor.

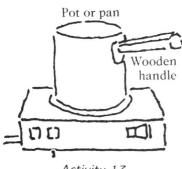

Pot or pan

Wooden handle

Activity 13

14. CONVECT A MARSHMALLOW   Supervised Classroom

Run a long stick through a marshmallow and hold it over the red-hot coils of an electric hot plate. It roasts by convection, by means of the hot air rising upward from the coils.

15. SAWDUST TRAIL   Supervised Classroom

To show how convection currents work, pour water into a glass coffeepot and mix some sawdust with it. Place the pot on a hot plate or stove toward one side of the burner rather than directly in the center.

As the water near the source of heat warms up, it expands, becomes less dense, and rises. You can see the particles of sawdust that are carried along by the current of water. The colder and heavier liquid settles to the bottom. This is in turn heated. It becomes less dense and rises. The sawdust keeps circulating. Finally, the water boils. Convection currents brought about the transfer of heat by the circulation or movement of the heated parts. Convection occurs only in gases and liquids where molecules are free to move in a group.

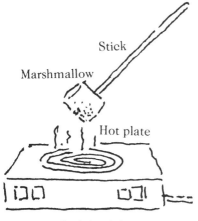

Stick

Marshmallow

Hot plate

Activity 14

Glass coffeepot

Hot plate

Activity 15

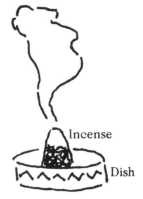

Activity 16

Activity 17

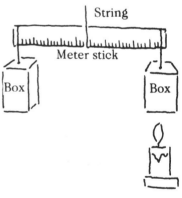

Activity 18

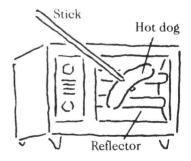

Activity 19

16. INCENSE   *Supervised Classroom*

Place incense in a dish and light it. The convection current rises gently like a white cloud. Smoke coming from chimneys and smokestacks also demonstrate convection currents. The biggest convection currents of all are those from forest fires and volcanoes.

17. CONVECTION ENGINE   *Supervised Classroom*

Get a piece of stiff paper. Draw a spiral on it about half an inch wide. Cut out the spiral and suspend it by a string run through a pinhole punched in the top of the spiral. Hold the spiral over a radiator when the heat is on and watch the results. You may also try holding it over a 100-watt lamp. Note what happens.

18. HOT BOX   *Supervised Classroom*

Get two empty half-gallon cardboard milk containers. Cut off the tops. Turn each box upside down. Punch a hole in the bottom of each box with a big pin. Through this hole run a string. Secure the string with a knot on the inside of the box so the box won't slip down. Suspend each milk container from the end of a meter stick which is balanced by a string tied on the 50-centimeter mark. When the entire unit is balanced, place a lighted candle under the open end of the box on the right-hand side. What happens?

19. RADIATE A HOT DOG   *Supervised Classroom*

To cook a hot dog by radiation, impale a frankfurter on a wooden stick and hold it in front of an electric heater that has a reflective metal behind it. Some electric room heaters are built with a concave reflector behind the coils. If so, hold the hot dog at the focal point of the concave reflector and cook it by radiation.

Note that the hot dog is NOT being cooked by CONDUCTION. (Air is a poor conductor.) The hot dog is NOT being cooked by CONVECTION. (Hot air rises.)

The rays from the electric heater are traveling through space to heat the meat. Rays from the sun travel through space to heat the earth in much the same fashion.

20.   *SPOTLIGHT ON RADIATION*   ***Supervised Classroom***

Place a radiometer on one side of a piece of glass. Place a heat lamp or spotlight on the other side of the glass. Shine the light from the lamp through the glass onto the radiometer. It begins to spin immediately.

The heat coming to the radiometer can't be due to conduction. The glass and the air are poor conductors. The heat reaching the radiometer also can't be due to convection. Convection currents travel up, not sideways.

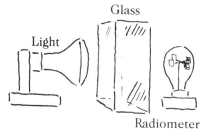

Activity 20

21.   *COOL GLASS*   ***Supervised Classroom***

If you don't have a radiometer, simply place your hand on the other side of the glass behind which you have placed a heat lamp. Notice how it is warmed by the rays coming through the glass.

Now turn off the lamp. Place your hands on the glass. You may be amazed to find that the glass is not even warm.

Radiant energy can pass right through a transparent object without heating it.

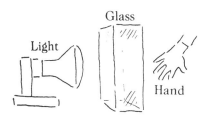

Activity 21

22.   *COOL ALUMINUM*   ***Home***

Place your hand 4 or 5 inches in front of a heat lamp. You will soon have to move it. Your hand is too close to the lamp for comfort.

Now wrap your hand in a sheet of aluminum foil, or simply place your hand in an aluminum-lined sack like those used to bring ice cream home from the store. Place your aluminum-wrapped hand in front of the heat lamp. This time your hand does not get as hot. The bright, shiny surface of the aluminum reflects the radiant energy.

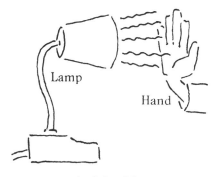

Activity 22

23.   *CRAZY QUILT*   ***Home***

If you have some old, worn-out clothes, or rags of various colors, cut them into squares about 3 inches on each side. Try to get as many different colors as possible: red, blue, green, black, white, purple, yellow, etc.

After a freshly fallen snow, gently place the squares of different colored cloth on top of the snow. Place them so shadows from

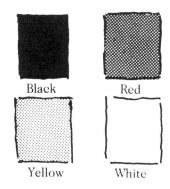

Black   Red

Yellow   White

Activity 23

houses or trees won't cover them for several hours. After three hours, carefully examine the cloths to find which one has sunk the greatest distance into the snow and, therefore, melted the most snow. What do you find?

Pop bottles

Activity 24

24. HOT-WATER BOTTLES   *Home*

Get two empty bottles such as catsup bottles or pop bottles. Fill one with clear water. Fill the other with muddy water. Leave both bottles in the sun for two hours. Then note their temperature. You will conclude that a dark substance absorbs more radiant energy than a clear one.

25. REGELATION   *Home*

To demonstrate that ice will melt under pressure and freeze again when pressure is released, do the following:

Wrap the ends of a very thin copper wire around the middles of two pencils. With the pencils serving as handles, place the wire loop on the top of an ice cube and bear down hard on the pencils.

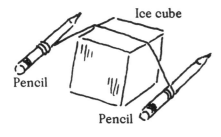

Ice cube

Pencil

Pencil

Activity 25

As the wire presses against the cube, the ice will melt and then freeze again once the wire has passed through. The ice cube will be left as solid as when you began. Pressure causes the ice to melt directly beneath the wire. As the ice melts, it takes heat from the wire. The wire, in turn, takes heat from the water directly above it. This water above the wire, no longer under pressure, freezes when it gives up its heat. This process of melting under pressure and refreezing when the pressure is released is called regelation. The word itself comes from Latin roots and means "to refreeze."

Big glass bowl

Dry ice

Activity 26

26. AN AMAZING CENTERPIECE   *Supervised Classroom*

Some years ago I was asked to suggest a centerpiece for a luncheon for the Mothers' Club associated with Campion High School. I suggested putting a one-pound block of dry ice in a big glass punch bowl about ¾ full of water.

Dry ice is carbon dioxide in a solid state. It evaporates directly from a solid to a gas. It does not go through the liquid state. Dry ice is about 80 degrees colder than ordinary ice but weighs only half as much. Since it leaves no messy liquid by melting, dry ice is quite popular for refrigerating ice cream and various foodstuffs for delivery.

Use gloves or tongs when you handle dry ice. It could cause frostbite if you pick it up with bare hands. Don't keep it in a glass bottle or any closed container. It can develop enough pressure to explode. Since dry ice is solidified carbon dioxide, you could suffocate if you were together in a small closed room.

If the opportunity comes your way, be sure to place a big chunk of dry ice in a large glass dish ¾ filled with water. Describe what happens.

27. *BOIL IT*   *Supervised Classroom*

Every year I'm amazed to discover how few students have ever taken time out to observe all the interesting things that take place when a flask of cold water is brought to a boil. If you have a Pyrex coffee pot of clear glass, fill it about ¾ full of cold water. Place it on a hot plate or stove and describe what happens.

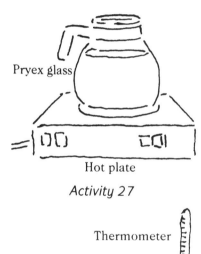

Pryex glass

Hot plate

Activity 27

28. *WARM UP*   *Supervised Classroom*

Heat is motion, the motion of molecules. Therefore, a rise in temperature means an increase in molecular activity. Each molecule needs more "elbow room" as its activity increases. Almost every material expands when heated.

To show how fast a liquid can expand, throw the beam of light from a lamp on a thermometer. (DANGER! Don't expose the thermometer to the heat too long.) For this experiment I use a thermometer with colored alcohol because it is easier to see than mercury.

If you have a thermometer made of Pyrex glass, you may now plunge the thermometer into cold water. Watch the rapid change in the volume of the liquid.

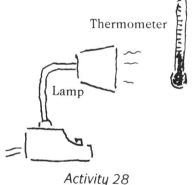

Thermometer

Lamp

Activity 28

29. *AMAZING COPPER WIRE*   *Supervised Classroom*

Stretch a 6-foot copper wire between insulators fastened to support stands. Connect the ends of the wires, through a switch, to a 6-volt battery. Turn on the current. What happens? Switch off the current and notice what happens. (CAUTION! DON'T touch wire when current is running through it.)

Insulator

-Copper wire-

Switch

Support stand   6-volt battery   Support stand

Activity 29

Glass jar

Activity 30

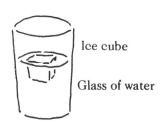

Ice cube

Glass of water

Activity 31

30.   EXPANDING WORLD   Home

During the coldest days of winter you may be able to demonstrate how water expands when it turns into ice. Fill a bottle with water and leave it outdoors overnight. The following morning you can see the results for yourself.

31.   ICE CUBE   Home

Find out for yourself how much of a block of ice floats beneath the surface. Put an ice cube in a glass half full of water and note what happens.

HIGHLIGHTS OF THIS CHAPTER

● Heat is a form of energy caused by the motion of molecules. The faster the molecules in a substance move, the more heat it contains. The heat energy contained in any body is the sum of all the energy in all its many molecules.

● When things get hot, they expand. This is not because the molecules themselves get bigger. They simply move farther apart.

● When water turns into steam, its volume expands by 1,700 times.

● Temperature is a measure of the speed, or kinetic energy, of individual molecules. The more rapid the motion of the molecules, the higher the temperature.

● The temperature at which water freezes and the temperature at which water boils are known as the fixed points on a thermometer.

● The fixed points on the Fahrenheit thermometer are 32 and 212 degrees.

● The fixed points on the centigrade thermometer are 0 and 100 degrees.

$$F = 9/5(C) + 32$$
$$C = 5/9(F-32)$$

● Conduction is the transfer of heat from molecule to molecule.

● Convection is the transfer of heat by the traveling of molecules from one point to another.

● Radiation is the transfer of heat by means of wave motion.

● Regelation is the process of melting under pressure and refreezing when the pressure is released.

● The fractional increase in length of a given material for each degree rise in temperature is known as the coefficient of linear expansion.

Multiple-Choice Questions

1. Most things expand when they get hot. This is because:
    a. the molecules increase in size.
    b. the molecules increase in K.E.
    c. the molecules move farther apart.
    d. the molecules move faster.

2. A quart of boiling water and a gallon of boiling water both have:
    a. the same heat.
    b. the same P.E.
    c. the same total K.E.
    d. the same temperature.

3. The best conductor of heat among the following is:
    a. aluminum.
    b. copper.
    c. iron.
    d. lead.

4. Among the materials listed here, the one with the smallest coefficient of linear expansion is:
    a. invar.
    b. platinum.
    c. aluminum.
    d. steel.

5. The space between the fixed points on a Fahrenheit thermometer is divided into:
    a. 100 equal marks.
    b. 120 equal marks.
    c. 132 equal marks.
    d. 180 equal marks.

True or False Questions

1. A reading of –40 degrees on the Fahrenheit thermometer is the same as a reading of –40 degrees on the centigrade thermometer.

2. You know how much heat is in a cup of coffee when you know its temperature.

3. On a chilly winter morning the tile on the floor of your bathroom feels colder than the rug because the tile is a better conductor.

4. When you breathe, convection currents help to keep you alive.

5. Regelation means that ice goes directly from a solid state into gas.

Chapter 11

HOW OFTEN DO YOU SEE THINGS THAT ARE NOT SO?

Your Eyes Are Photoelectric Cells that Change Light into Electricity

A most amazing phenomenon took place during the last year of World War II. An American sub was on routine daytime patrol in the South Pacific. Intelligence had reported that there were no Japanese ships closer than Formosa Strait several hundred miles to the north. The crew was given the day to relax.

The men were on the deck of the sub, enjoying the sunlight and acquiring a tan. Suddenly a sailor jumped up, excitement almost choking him. "Look," he shouted. "The Japanese fleet is coming at us!"

The officers stared in amazement as a convoy steamed into view. Quickly all hands were ordered below. The sub submerged and moved in toward the target. For two hours the sub tried to gain on the convoy. At last, in mad desperation, the captain gave the command to surface.

The phantom convoy had vanished into thin air!

That night Intelligence reported that there had been a convoy. "It was our convoy, but you couldn't have seen it. It was 100 miles away from your sector." The officers and crew had been victims of nature's light bending. Beams of light, bouncing off ships far over the horizon, had been bent so a "picture" or "image" of the fleet was projected on the surface of the water in the sub's line of vision.

MORE MIRAGES

If you local library has back copies of the *Scientific American* magazine, you may find it interesting to look up the issue for January 1976. The main article is on mirages. It is illustrated with many fascinating photos.

COLD NOSE ASTRONOMERS

If you dislike working in a cold room, don't become an astronomer. Observatories are not heated. Rising currents of warm air would bend the beams of starlight and make it difficult to get a good picture. In order to reduce the bending of a beam of starlight due to the air, astronomical observatories are often built on the top of high mountains.

At the present time (1987) astronomers from four nations are working on one of the world's most important observation sites, on top of Mount Mauna Kea, Hawaii. After testing many places around the world, many astronomers believe that conditions for looking at the stars are better here than anywhere else in the northern hemisphere. The top of Mount Mauna Kea is 13,796 feet above the sea, so high that clouds hardly ever pass over it.

BLACK SKY OVER THE MOON

Light is truly a "dark subject," as is proven when you look up and see the golden moon high in the sky. Light from the sun cascades through space all around the moon, but the moon is the only thing we see. It is the only thing in the sky that "bounces" or "reflects" the light from the sun back to us. Moonlight is "bounced" sunlight.

When there is no moon, the sky is dark, even though light from the sun is still passing through it.

The first photos of the American astronauts on the moon show that its "sky" is black. There is no air to scatter and reflect the light.

WHAT IS IT?

According to some people, light is something—and at the same time it is nothing! Two beams can pass through each other as if they never existed. The exact nature of light is still a mystery, even though great scientists from Galileo to Einstein have tried to fathom it. One thing is known for sure—light has a dual nature. It has "two faces." Depending on the circumstances, light can have the characteristics of waves of energy or it can have the characteristics of particles, or electrons.

Light zips through space at the speed of 186,000 miles a second. This is equal to a trip around the earth in $1/7$ second!

Light is a form of electromagnetic energy that radiates in straight lines or rays. Light also travels in a wave form like the ripples on water when a stone is dropped into a pool.

Light is truly a "dark subject." Despite long years of study and research, we are still "in the dark" concerning its exact nature!

YOUR BRAIN IS LOCKED IN SILENT DARKNESS

You are somewhat like a king who lives inside the stone walls of a castle and who depends on messengers to bring news about the great wide world that stretches beyond the castle walls. Your brain is locked up in silent darkness behind the bony walls of your skull and it depends on the five senses to bring information about the great wide world that surrounds you.

Centuries ago a very wise man named Aristotle said, "Nothing is in the brain unless it has first been in the senses." Only through our senses—seeing, hearing, smelling, tasting, and touching—do we gain knowledge of ourselves and the world around us.

THE GIFT OF SIGHT

The most important of our senses is sight. Try this. Close your eyes and then, very slowly and carefully, try to walk across the room. If you are like most people, you will feel uneasy with your eyes shut. In a few minutes you will feel such a great need to see that you can no longer keep your eyes shut. You open your eyes with a rush of joy to find yourself once again in contact with the things around you.

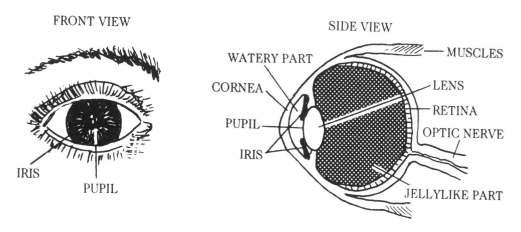

FRONT VIEW

IRIS
PUPIL

SIDE VIEW

WATERY PART
CORNEA
PUPIL
IRIS

MUSCLES
LENS
RETINA
OPTIC NERVE
JELLYLIKE PART

If you look sideways into a mirror, you may be able to see the clear, plastic-like covering that bends, or bulges out, at the front of your eyeball. This clear tissue is called the cornea. The cornea is like a tiny glass window on the outside of your eye.

Because the cornea is curved like a half-circle, it helps to bend beams of light. A healthy cornea is one of the clearest tissues in the body.

Look into the eyes of a friend. Perhaps her eyes are brown, blue, or hazel. The circle of color you are looking at is the iris. Its job is like a shade on a window—it controls the amount of light that comes into the eye.

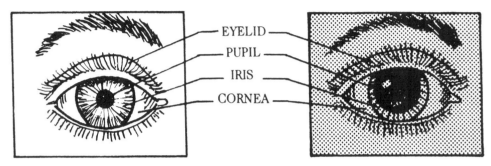

In bright light the pupil is smaller.   In dim light the pupil is larger.

In the center of the iris is a round black spot called the pupil. It is really not a separate part, but it is the opening in the iris through which the light passes. The pupil seems to be black because it leads into the inside of the eye. In much the same way, the window of a distant building, even though clear, sometimes appears black in bright sunlight.

I mentioned that the iris might be thought of as a shade on a window, but it does much more. It is also an automatic light meter that measures the amount of light falling on it and then opens or closes the pupil to let just the right amount of light enter into the eye. On a bright day the iris makes the pupil very small. On a cloudy day, or in the evening, the iris makes the pupil much bigger.

To show how fast the iris can change its size to control the amount of light entering the eye, try this experiment. In the evening stand by a bright lamp. Use a hand mirror to see how small the iris is. Now walk into a dimly lit corner of the room. Again look into the mirror and see what has happened to the iris.

Before you take a picture with an expensive camera, you must first adjust the diaphragm, or opening in front of the lens, to admit the proper amount of light. The iris of your eye is a combination light meter and self-adjusting diaphragm.

When you walk from a darkened room into bright sunlight, the iris expands to cover more of the pupil, making the pupil smaller. In the evening, the iris contracts, or grows smaller, increasing the size of the pupil to let in more light.

Behind the pupil of your eye is the lens. Its purpose is the same as the lens in a camera—to make a clear, sharp picture or image, to bring things into focus. When we say a thing is in focus, we mean that its image or picture inside the eye—or inside a camera—is sharp and clear. There are, however, some big differences between the lens in a camera and the lenses in our eyes.

The lens in a camera is a solid piece of glass made into a convex or bulging shape. The lens in a camera may be moved forward or backward until a clear, sharp picture or image is made on the film.

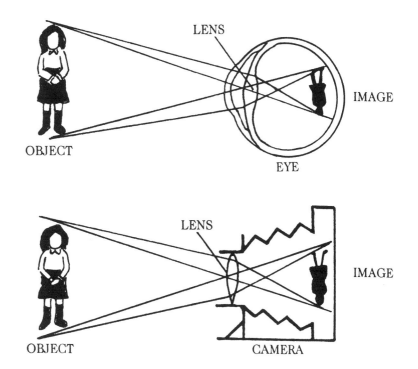

The lens in your eye is soft, like jelly. It is held in place by a broad sheet of material that reminds you of a sheet of plastic. Unlike the lens in a camera, the lens in the eye does not move forward or backward to get a clear picture. It changes its shape. This change in the shape of the lens of the eye is brought about by the pull of a ring of muscle called the ciliary muscle, which is attached to the sheet that holds the lens in place.

If you have normal vision you can look at a nearby object, such as this book, and then at a distant object, such as a tall building six blocks away, and both will be in focus.

Eye muscles act very fast to change the shape of the lens in your eye so you always have a clear view of the world around you. As you read this page, the lens

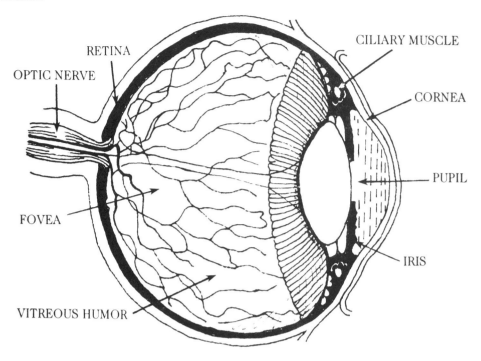

must thicken to focus the print onto the retina, the back part of your eye. When you watch a high-flying wedge-shaped band of geese honking their way south in the autumn sky, the lens becomes thin. When you look at distant objects the muscles around the lens are relaxed, or at rest.

If you read for a long time or do other kinds of close work, the muscles become tired. Be kind to your eyes and rest them now and then by looking at distant objects or by closing them for a short time.

The space in back of the lens in the eyeball is filled with a clear, jellylike material through which the light passes on its way to the retina. This clear, colorless material is called the vitreous humor. "Vitreous" is a Latin word meaning "glass-like." "Humor" is a Latin word meaning "fluid."

When you take pictures with an ordinary camera, you must keep it supplied with fresh film. After the film is exposed, it must be developed and printed before you have a picture. You don't have to supply your built-in camera, your eye, with film. Your brain interprets the image on the retina in an instant. As you let your eyes travel around the room, the retina responds to one image after another. You never have to replace any film. New images are formed as old ones fade away. The retina in the eye is like the film in a camera, but it is far better than any film.

The retina is a living tissue of about 130 million cells sensitive to light. When light hits them they go to work. There are two kinds of cells—rods and cones, so named because of their shape.

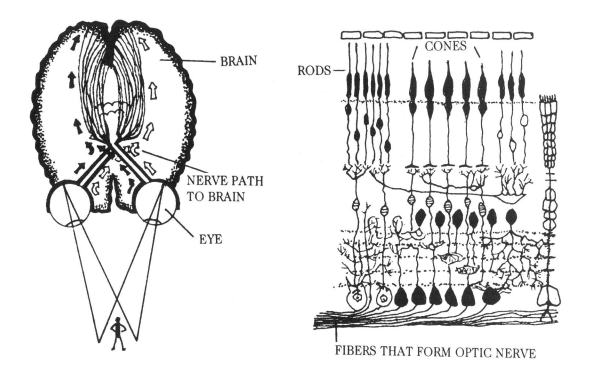

Cones work in daylight and give us color vision. Rods give us only black and white. Cones are most numerous at the fovea, a very small pit or tiny spot in the retina where the eye gets its sharpest images.

The rods and cones are connected to the optic nerve. The optic nerve may be compared to a telegraph cable that gives the brain a private line to what is going on in your world. The place where the optic nerve enters the retina is called the blind spot. Any image formed on this spot cannot be seen.

Oddly enough, the brain itself never directly experiences the form of energy we call light. The brain rests in darkness inside your skull. Your eyes change the energy of light into electrical signals that are sent along the optic nerve to the brain. When this electricity reaches your brain, your brain interprets, or translates, these electrical signals into what we call sight.

REFRACTION BLAMED FOR DROWNINGS

Refraction is sometimes named the culprit responsible for people drowning. First-time visitors to a strange lake put on their swimsuits, then walk out on the pier. When the visitors look down into the lake, the water looks shallower than it really is. The visitors jump in to cool off, only to find the water over their heads.

DON'T LET A JUG OF WATER SET YOUR HOUSE ON FIRE!

Some people have a hobby of collecting empty bottles of fascinating shapes. They fill these bottles with colored water. They place these containers on a shelf by the window for the joy of seeing sunbeams sparkling through the transparent liquid.

Unfortunately, any bottle that is shaped like a lens, be it a goldfish bowl or a gallon jug, can set a house on fire. These convex lenses focus the sun's rays to a focal point. They become "burning glasses." Here are some actual accounts of jugs that have started fires.

Lewiston, Montana: "Two buildings were set on fire within two weeks here when the sun's rays shone through two different jugs of water igniting the sides of the structures."

Wellington, Kansas: "A bottle of distilled water started a fire here Friday. The bottle was on the front seat of a car parked by Mrs. John Allen. The bottle focused the rays of the sun onto the seat.

"When Mrs. Allen returned from an errand, she found the seat on fire and the car filled with smoke."

"FAT" LENSES

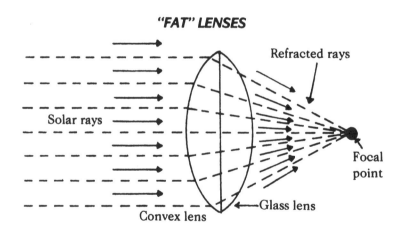

If a lens is thicker at the middle than at its edges, it is a convex lens.

If a convex lens bulges out on both sides it is a double convex lens.

If it is flat on one side, it is a plano-convex lens.

If it curves in on one side, it is a concavo-convex lens.

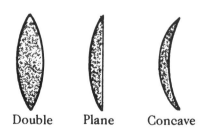

Double   Plane   Concave

"THIN" LENSES

Concave lenses are thicker at the edge than in the center. Concave lenses spread apart or diverge parallel rays of light that pass through them.

If a concave lens is shaped like an hourglass, it is a double-concave lens.

If it is flat on one side, it is a plano-concave lens.

If it curves out on one side, it is a convexo-concave lens.

CONCAVE

Double   Plane   Convex

"BENT IN" AND "BENT OUT"

The sketches at the right show the main difference between convex and concave lenses.

Parallel rays of light that go through a convex lens are "bent in," or "converge," and "come together" at the focal point.

Parallel rays of light that go through a concave lens are "bent out" or "diverge."

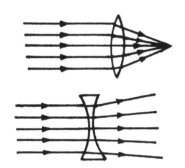

ARE YOU FARSIGHTED?

Some people can see things that are far away more clearly than nearby objects. In these farsighted people the distance between the lens and the retina is too short, or the lens may be so flat that it does not bend the light beams enough.

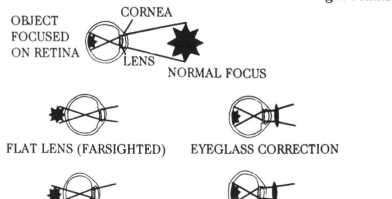

Enlarged convex lens

Farsightedness can be corrected with convex lenses. The curved surface of a convex lens pulls the light rays together so the images of nearby objects are focused on the retina.

ARE YOU NEARSIGHTED?

Some people can easily see things that are near to them but can't see distant objects. In these nearsighted people the eyeball is too long, or the lens is so thick that light rays from distant objects come together or converge to make an image in front of the retina instead of on it.

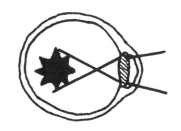

LONG EYEBALL (NEARSIGHTED)

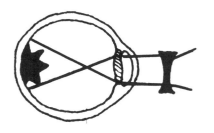

EYEGLASS CORRECTION

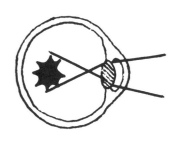

THICK LENS (NEARSIGHTED)

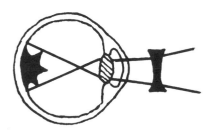

EYEGLASS CORRECTION

How can we make the image move back onto the retina? Nearsightedness can be corrected with concave lenses. A concave lens curves inward like the bowl of a spoon. This caved-in lens scatters, or throws apart, the beams of light that go through it. A concave lens is a diverging lens that pushes the beams of light apart.

When a person wears concave lenses, the curved-in surface spreads apart the light rays before they enter the eye. As a result of this spreading of the rays of light, the image is formed at a greater distance from the lens of the eye and is brought to focus on the retina.

Enlarged concave lens

ASTIGMATISM

Besides nearsightedness and farsightedness there is another defect of the eye called astigmatism. It is the failure of the eye to see different parts of an object distinctly at the same time.

ASTIGMATISM (OFF FOCUS)   EYEGLASS CORRECTION

The curved shape of the cornea acts as a converging lens. If the surface of the cornea does not have the same amount of curve in all places, light rays will be bent more in one part than in another. A blurred, fuzzy image is thrown on the retina. Unequal curvature of the surface of the cornea causes astigmatism. This word comes from the Greek words "a" meaning "not" and "stigma" meaning "spot." Special lenses are used to correct astigmatism.

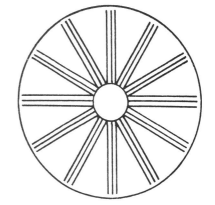

Look at this wheel with one eye at a time. If you have astigmatism, some of the spokes in the wheel will be clear and in focus while others will be less clear and out of focus.

WHAT IS A LUMINOUS OBJECT?

What is it that you never see, yet it makes other things visible?

Your sister may be pretty as a picture, but in a deep coal mine no one could appreciate her beauty without a flashlight or a match to produce light. When light strikes an object that has no light of its own, the light is reflected or bounced back to the eye so you "see" the object.

A lighted flashlight is a "luminous" object. It gives off light. The word "luminous" comes from the Latin word "lumen," meaning "light." A campfire, a firefly, a burning candle, the sun and stars are other examples of luminous objects. Most of the objects we see are nonluminous. They merely "bounce" or "reflect" the light that is thrown upon them.

IN WHAT RESPECT IS A LIGHT BEAM LIKE A RUBBER BALL?

Remember how a rubber ball bounces when you throw it against a wall or a sidewalk? If you hurl the ball straight forward or straight down, at an angle of 90 degrees (perpendicular) to the surface, it will jump back at the same angle. Light bounces in much the same way.

If you throw a ball against a wall at an angle of 45 degrees, it will not bounce back to you. Instead, it will bounce from the wall in a direction away from where you stand. It will bounce at the same angle of 45 degrees.

MIRRORS THAT CURVE IN AND OUT

Mirrors may curve in or out. Those that bulge out at the center, such as the back of a spoon or the side of a coffeepot, are convex. Those that curve in, such as the hollow of a spoon, are concave. The word "convex" comes from a Latin word "convexus," meaning "arched" or "rounded." The word "concave" comes from a Latin word "concavus," meaning "hollowed out."

The image in a convex (rounded out) mirror is small and erect (right side up). It covers a wide area. Rearview mirrors used outside truck windows enable the drivers to see a large section of the highway behind them. When a beam of light consisting of parallel rays is reflected from a convex mirror, the rays spread apart. That is why one can see a wide area in such mirrors.

Some gardens have a beautiful ornament consisting of a large, highly-polished sphere. Next time you see one, take a good look at this fascinating convex mirror and note the view.

CONCAVE MIRRORS

Concave mirrors, which curve in at the center, may form two types of images. If you stand close to a concave mirror, or hold it close to you, your image is enlarged and erect. Stand at a distance from a concave mirror, though, and your image will be small and upside down.

Dentists and physicians use small concave mirrors to concentrate light in the mouth, the throat, or in the ears of a patient. Big concave mirrors in amusement parks may make you look like a dragon. Convex mirrors reduce you to the size of a midget.

WHAT PUTS THE SPARKLE IN DIAMONDS?

The critical angle for water is 48.5°. This means that when a beam of light hits the under-surface of the water at an angle greater than 48.5° the beam of light cannot escape from the water into the air. The beam is reflected back into the water. This is called total internal reflection.

The diamond owes its brilliance to the fact that it has a low critical angle of 23.7°. Most of the light that enters is reflected back and forth inside the stone, giving the sparkling effect.

In what is sometimes called "piped illumination," light moves around curves in a lucite rod because it strikes the sides of the rod at angles greater than the critical angle and is totally reflected.

CIRCLE AROUND THE MOON

Sometimes you may notice a circle around the moon. This is still another example of refraction. Moonlight coming through the upper atmosphere is bent by tiny ice crystals that sometimes form high in the sky.

WATCH FOR A MIRAGE ON A SUMMER DAY

Mirages seen by a thirst-maddened desert nomad are caused by refraction, but you don't have to ride a camel across the sands of the Sahara to see a mirage. "Mirage" comes from a French word that means "to look at carefully, to aim."

The next time you are cruising down a highway on a hot summer day, you may see "wet" spots or "pools of water" that mysteriously disappear when you approach. This optical illusion is caused by air in contact with the highway that becomes heated and therefore less dense than the air above it. Rays of light passing through this air are refracted or "bent" and you see "pools" that may be called "patches of sky fallen down from on high." Or, to be less poetic, they are simply beams of light that have been bent.

DASHBOARD

Perhaps your family car has a tiny light on the dashboard to indicate whether or not the headlights are on. A bundle of flexible, plastic fibers run from the headlight to the dash. When the headlights are on, light is bounced through the fibers and emerges as a tiny light on the dashboard.

LOOK INSIDE YOUR STOMACH?

Fiber optics make it possible for a doctor to look inside your stomach. A tube containing a great number of plastic fibers can be inserted down your throat into your stomach. Some of the fibers are used to carry light down into the stomach. A tiny lens on the end of the tube then focuses the illuminated stomach lining onto the remaining fibers. The fibers receiving light from the lens transmit the light along the tube so the same image appears on the other end of the tube. All that remains is to magnify that image, and the doctor can see the lining of your stomach.

EARTHSCRAPER

During the long winter months Minnesota is blasted by subzero temperatures and snowed in for days. In the summer the state is at times subjected to 100-degree heat. Such changes in temperature present a challenge to architects and engineers. Minnesotans have taken a cue from the state's mascot, the gopher, and are building underground.

While single-family houses in Minnesota and other places with cold climates have been built partly or completely underground for years, the new Civil and Mineral Engineering building at the University of Minnesota in Minneapolis quite literally goes further than any of its predecessors—seven stories into the earth. At that depth, 110 feet below the surface, it takes very little energy to heat the rooms regardless of what is happening on the surface. The reason—at that level, the building is embedded in sandstone with a constant temperature of 55 degrees Fahrenheit.

Among the earthscraper's more intriguing innovations are those intended to "pipe in" the daylight world so workers and students do not become claustrophobic. The most remarkable of these is the Ectascope remote-view optical system—possibly the largest periscope in the world. It runs down a shaft to the seventh floor, where a television-like screen projects a sharp outside view of a lecture hall surrounded by lawn and trees.

More than just a view is transmitted to the lower floors. An experimental solar lighting system in an above-ground cupola follows the sun with moving plastic mirrors, collecting sunlight that is focused and relayed by lenses and other mirrors down a shaft running alongside the periscope system. The sunlight emerges through a glass panel in the ceiling of the seventh floor to provide illumination.

If your library keeps back issues of *Discover* magazine, you can see pictures and diagrams of this passive solar lighting system on pages 74–77 of the February 1984 issue.

ACTIVITIES

Pencil

Glass of water

Activity 1

1. *BENDING LIGHT*   Home

If you want to bend a beam of light, try this experiment. Put a pencil in a drinking glass about ¾ full of water. Where the pencil meets the water, it appears to be broken. In fact, you may even think that there are two separate pencils. One stops at the level of the water. The other begins there.

How can we explain the illusion of the broken pencil? The answer is that light that passes from a less dense medium or substance, like air, into a denser medium or substance, like water, is bent, broken, or refracted. "Refract" is a Latin word that means "to break." Refraction, or the bending of a light beam, takes place because light travels more slowly in a dense substance such as water.

2. *WHICH WAY THE BEND?*   Home

Place three pencils in a wide-mouthed glass. Hold the container at eye level. Rotate the container slowly. What do you notice?

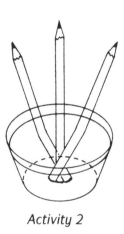

Activity 2

Eye

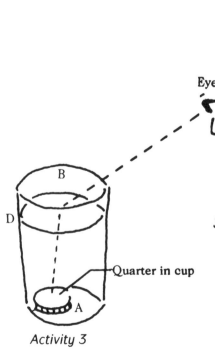

B

D

Quarter in cup

A

Activity 3

3. *MAGIC QUARTER*   Home

Place a quarter in the bottom of a cup as shown in position A at the left. Place the cup on a table. Now stand back a few feet from the table so the quarter becomes invisible when you look over the edge of the cup.

Without moving your head or the cup, pour water into the cup. If this is too difficult, have a friend pour water into the cup for you. What happens? Why?

4. CAN YOU TOUCH THIS STONE?   **Home**

If you are walking along the shore of a clear lake or stream, try this experiment. Take a long stick and try to touch a stone submerged on the bottom of the stream about seven feet away. The first time you try, you will most likely miss. The stone is not where you can see it.

You think that your vision continues from A to B as shown by the dotted line. In truth, as shown by the solid line, the beam of light is bent at position C when it goes from air in water.

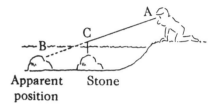

Activity 4

5. PAUL BUNYAN FIST   **Home**

Get a clear, glass gallon jar. Fill it about ¾ full of water. Place the jar on the table. Submerge your fist in the jar of water. What do you notice?

6. GOLDFISH BOWL PICTURE   **Supervised Classroom**

In this experiment, use a water-filled spherical goldfish bowl. Place a clear 40-watt bulb on the far side of the bowl and look at it through the bowl. Notice how gigantic the filament appears to be.

Now take a piece of white paper on white cardboard and move it back and forth on the side of the goldfish bowl opposite the lamp. You may be surprised to see a picture of the filament on the cardboard.

If the day is bright and sunny, hold the goldfish bowl in your right hand when you stand by a window. In your left hand move the white cardboard back and forth until you have a picture of the outdoors.

You may never have thought about it, but a goldfish bowl that is spherical in shape is a convex lens. A lens is defined as a transparent material with at least one curved surface that can be used to bend a beam of light. "Convex" is a Latin word that means "curved" or "rounded." Convex lenses are thicker in the middle than at the edge.

Gallon jar

Activity 5

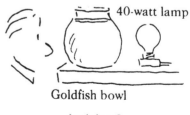

40-watt lamp

Goldfish bowl

Activity 6

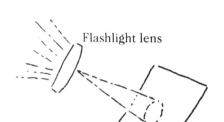

Activity 8

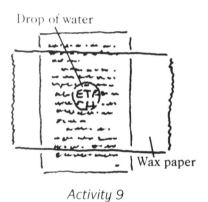

Drop of water

Wax paper

Activity 9

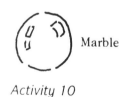

Marble

Activity 10

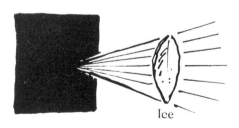

Ice

Activity 11

7. EYEGLASSES   Home

If you wish to experiment with concave lenses, perhaps a friend will let you borrow some eyeglasses. Concave lenses are used in eyeglasses for nearsighted people.

Using your friend's concave lenses, try to throw a picture of the sun on a sheet of paper. The light rays spread out or diverge as they pass through the lens. There is no real picture. The images produced by concave lenses are called "virtual."

8. FIND THE FOCAL LENGTH   Home

If you can borrow a reading glass or the lens from a flashlight, try this experiment. Stand in the sunlight and move the lens back and forth until you see a small, sharp picture of the sun on a sheet of paper. The distance from the dot of light on the paper to the center of the lens is the focal length.

What is your conclusion from using different lenses?

9. SEE BIG WITH WATER   Home

The ancient Romans are said to have used drops of water to magnify things. You may do likewise. Place a drop of water on a piece of clear, waxed paper. Underneath this waxed paper slip a page of fine print. Note how beautifully the drop of water magnifies.

10. MARBLES = MICROSCOPES   Home

A clear glass marble makes an excellent simple microscope. Experiment with various sized marbles. What do you notice?

11. START A FIRE WITH ICE   Supervised Classroom

Can you use a piece of clear ice to start a fire?

Yes, if first you shape the ice into a convex lens. Take a piece of strong, heavy-duty aluminum foil and mold it into a convex shape. Fill it with water and put it in a freezer.

In order to avoid having your lens melt while you are using it, wait for a cold but bright day in January. Take the lens outdoors and focus the rays of the sun on a rough, black piece of paper.

12. *CAN YOU SEE LIGHT?*   **Home**

On a dark, cloudless night when there is no moon, shine a flashlight directly up into the sky. If the air is clear and free of dust, you will not be able to trace the outline of the beam of light. Try the experiment again when there is a dense fog.

Strange as it may seem, we do not see light itself directly. We see things that give off light (the sun, a lamp) or things that reflect light (the moon, an apple). Far above the earth's surface, where there is no air, there are no particles of dust or air to reflect light. The sky is black even though it is high noon and light from the sun is going through it.

13. *IS THE FLASHLIGHT ON?*   **Supervised Classroom**

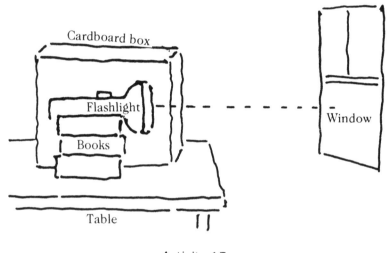

Activity 13

"Can you tell whether or not my flashlight is turned on?" This is a question I toss out every year.

On my lecture table I place a cardboard box about 2 feet long and 2 feet tall. On the side of the cardboard box facing me, I place three books on top of one another. On top of the books I place my flashlight in a horizontal position so it is aimed out the open window. I open the window so the students will not be able to see the reflection of the beam of light from the windowpane. I perform this demonstration on a bright day when there is no fog or dust in the air. I place my left hand on the flashlight so I can flick the switch on and off. I ask the students to tell me when the light is on. To their amazement, they cannot. There is nothing to show the path of light.

Next I leave the flashlight turned on. I pick up two erasers from the blackboard and clap them together in the space between the flashlight and the window. The particles of chalk dust floating in the air make visible the path of the beam of light.

14. PRISM EXPLORATIONS   *Supervised Classroom*

If you have a triangular-shaped piece of glass called a *prism*, you can do three things with light.

Hold the prism directly in front of your face so one of its flat surfaces is facing you. You may be able to see yourself. The smooth surface is a mirror. It "bounces back" or "reflects" the beams of light that fall upon it.

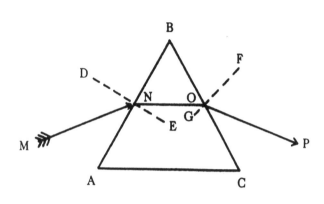

Activity 14

Slowly turn the prism. At just the right angle you may notice that you can see "to one side" or "behind your back." The glass prism is "bending" or "refracting" beams of light. In order to understand why the beams of light are "bent" or "broken" so much, let us consider the prism shown at the left.

Somewhere along the line or surface AB draw a dotted line that is perpendicular to the line AB. This perpendicular line is called the normal. It is represented by the letters DE. Draw another such normal FG that is perpendicular to BC. Now we are ready to follow the adventures of a beam of light, MN.

If the beam of light, MN, did not happen to hit the surface of the glass at N, it would have continued along its path in a straight line. However, when a beam of light goes from a less dense medium or substance (air) into a denser substance (glass), the beam of light is bent toward the normal. This means that the beam of light no longer keeps moving in a straight path. At position N it turns down toward the normal, DE. Its path is now NO.

If this beam of light were to continue in glass, it again would keep moving in a straight line, but when a beam of light goes from a dense material (glass) into a less dense substance (air), the beam of light is bent away from the normal. Its path is now OP. The path of the beam of light is MNOP.

So far we have seen how a prism can "bounce" or "reflect" light. It can also "bend" or "refract" light. Now let us find the most thrilling thing it can do.

15. A RAINBOW IN YOUR ROOM   *Supervised Classroom*

Stand by a window where the sunlight is pouring into the room. Hold a prism in a beam of sunlight. Turn it slowly. At a certain position you will be delighted to find that you can throw a beautiful rainbow on the opposite wall of the classroom. The prism has "dispersed" or "broken apart" a beam of light into its various colors. This breaking up of white light into colors is called dispersion.

You have just discovered the same thing that Sir Isaac Newton did when he placed a triangular glass prism in the path of a beam of sunlight. A beam of white light is separated or dispersed into a spectrum—a fan-shaped band of seven colors arranged according to their wavelengths. Red is at one end, violet at the other. These seven colors—red, orange, yellow, green, blue, indigo, and violet—are called pure colors. They cannot be separated into simpler colors.

You see colors when a beam of sunlight passes through a prism because the rays of light are bent or refracted unevenly as they pass through the glass. The rays that are bent the least are red, the longest wavelength. Those that are bent the most are violet, the shortest wavelength.

The figure here shows a beam of light going through a prism and being broken up into the colors of the rainbow.

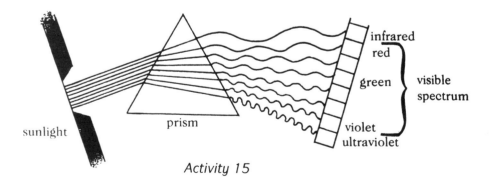

infrared
red
green   visible spectrum
violet
ultraviolet

sunlight   prism

Activity 15

16. "BOUNCING" LIGHT   *Home*

By using a flashlight and a mirror in a darkened room, you can demonstrate how light rays are "bounced" or "reflected." Stand about 6 feet in front of a mirror. Hold the flashlight at eye level. Shine it directly into the mirror at an angle of 90 degrees. The light will "bounce" or "reflect" straight back to your eyes.

Now move to one side. Shine the light into the mirror at an angle. (You will be able to see the rays more distinctly if you first burn incense in the room.) What do you notice about the reflected ray?

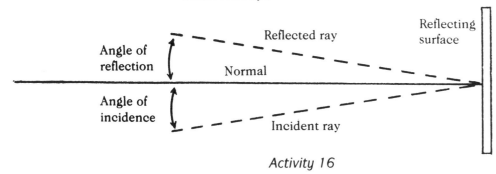

Activity 16

A ray of light striking an object is called an "incident" ray. "Incident" comes from a Latin word meaning "to fall upon."

The ray that bounces off the reflecting surface is the reflected ray.

The normal is a line drawn perpendicular to the surface. It enables one to judge the angle at which a ray strikes the surface and is reflected from it.

The angle between the incident ray and the normal is called the angle of incidence.

The angle between the normal and the reflected ray is the angle of reflection.

The basic law of reflected light rays is: THE ANGLE OF REFLECTION IS EQUAL TO THE ANGLE OF INCIDENCE.

17. FOLLOW THE LIGHT   *Supervised Classroom*

Here is a beautiful demonstration to show how light can be "bounced" and "bent." If you have the equipment, you too will thrill to "bouncing" and "bending" beams of light.

35 mm projector

Activity 17

I heap a generous supply of incense on a piece of burning charcoal until my lecture table and environs are "fogged in" under a heavy cloud cover. Now I'm ready for the "magic." I close the shutters on the windows and turn off the overhead lights. (If you have a smoke detector in your classroom, you may wish to turn it off during this demonstration.)

Now I turn on a projector (a 35-mm projector is excellent). The dramatic moment approaches. I pick up a big convex lens and place it in the path of the beam of light. Thanks to the smoke, the students can see how the lens bends the beam of light. I use a variety of convex lenses, big and small, and show that the greater the curvature of the lens, the greater is the converging or "bending" power.

Next I use concave lenses. Students are amazed to see the beam of light spread out.

Now comes the greatest moment of all. I insert a big prism 7 inches long and 3 inches wide in the beam. The students are amazed to see the light bent through 90°!

Then I take a plane mirror and "bounce" or "reflect" the light. With the smoke making the path of the light beam easy to follow, students can see quite vividly that the angle of reflection equals the angle of incidence.

I also place a water-filled, ball-shaped goldfish bowl in the beam. It acts like a convex lens.

Then comes the grand climax! I slip a 35-mm color slide into the projector. The picture is thrown on the wall. Then I insert the big prism in the beam coming from the projector. Behold! The picture is thrown on the ceiling! By turning the prism you may throw one picture on the ceiling and, at the same time, throw the same picture on the wall.

18. MIRROR MAGIC

Home

If you have a mirror on your wall, stand to the left of it. Ask a friend to stand on the right side of the mirror. Neither of you will see your own image. You will see your friend, and your friend will see you.

Activity 18

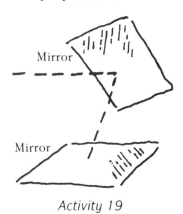

Mirror

Mirror

Activity 19

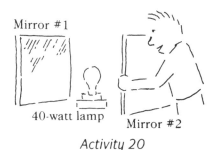

Mirror #1

40-watt lamp

Mirror #2

Activity 20

STAR

Activity 21

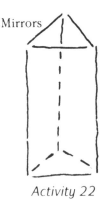

Mirrors

Activity 22

19. PERISCOPE   Home

To demonstrate the working principles of a periscope, place one mirror flat on a table. Now hold a second mirror about 2½ feet above it. Tilt this mirror so that by looking down into the mirror on the table you can see what is in front of you.

20. WATCH THE "BIG PARADE"   Home

Hold a mirror with its edge resting on the table. In front of this mirror place a 40-watt lamp. On the other side of the lamp place a second mirror parallel to the first mirror.

Lower your head until your eyes just skim over the edge of mirror #2 and look into mirror #1. What do you notice?

21. STAR = ?

Write the word STAR in big letters on a piece of paper. Hold the paper up to a mirror. What happens?

22. A MAGIC WORLD   Home

Get three plane mirrors, each about 6 inches or more in length and 4 inches wide. Arrange the mirrors with their bases resting on the table and their sides touching so they form a triangle with the reflecting surfaces facing each other.

Place a few coins inside the bottom of your tall triangle. Better yet, use a 40-watt lamp with a clear bulb for your "center-piece." This is such a delightful demonstration, you will want to share it with your friends. What do you see when you look inside the triangle?

23. A REVERSE LETTER   Home

Write a brief note to a friend. Hold the note in front of a mirror. Now copy this note as it appears in reverse. You friend will have to read this "reverse message" in a mirror to decode it.

24. WATER MIRROR   Home

You may know that the surface of a quiet pool of water acts like a mirror, but do you know that the under-side of the water surface does likewise?

To demonstrate this, place an aquarium on top of a wooden box about 1 foot high. Fill the aquarium almost to the top. On one side of the wooden box place a 40-watt lamp and on the other side, a mirror. Adjust the mirror until you see a reflection of the lamp.

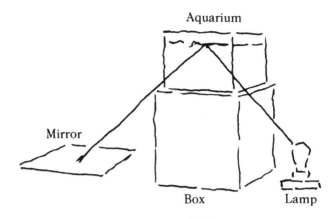

Activity 24

25. *LOOK UP TO SEE DOWN*   **Home**

An interesting variation of the above experiment is this. Remove the lamp and mirror. Rest your head on the table where the lamp was and look up at the under-surface of the water. Have a friend do likewise where the mirror was. You will be able to see each other.

26. *"DISEMBODIED" FINGERS*   **Home**

For a final demonstration with the aquarium, try this. Place your head on the table where the lamp was and look up at the under-surface of the water. Have a friend place her fingertips in the water. They will look like "disembodied fingers without a hand" wandering around in a sea of shining mercury. (Sounds incredible? Try it yourself!)

27. *REGULAR VERSUS DIFFUSE*   **Home**

Put some water in a pan or wide dish. The smooth surface of the water acts like a mirror in which you can see yourself. You have "regular" reflection. Now wiggle your finger in the water. The rippled surface makes it impossible for you to obtain a clear picture of yourself. This scattering of light by a rough surface is called diffusion or diffuse reflection. Diffusion may also take place when light passes through a translucent material. Sunlight going through fog, for example, is diffused.

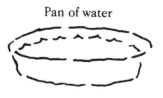

Activity 27

The word "translucent" means "to shine through." A translucent material, such as fog or frosted glass, admits the passage of light, but it scatters or diffuses the light so objects cannot be clearly seen.

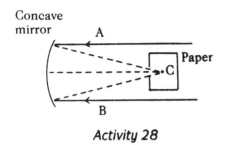

Concave
mirror

Activity 28

28. CONCAVE MIRROR   *Supervised Classroom*

Find the focal length of a concave mirror by focusing the sun's rays on a piece of paper. The distance from the center of the mirror to the intensely bright spot of light on the paper is the focal length.

In the diagram, both A and B represent incoming beams of light. These beams hit the curved surface of the mirror and are reflected to C, the focal point.

Concave mirrors are used to concentrate the powerful beams of spotlights, floodlights, and airplane beacons.

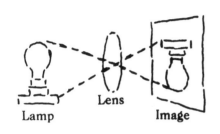

Activity 29

29. CONVEX LENS   *Supervised Classroom*

To show the variety of uses to which a convex lens may be put, do the following.

Mount a big, white square of cardboard on the wall to serve as a screen. The wall itself may serve as a screen if it is painted a light color. If possible, get a carbon filament lamp with clear bulb. I use a carbon filament since it is big and easy to see. If you don't have a carbon filament lamp, a tungsten filament lamp will be OK.

a. Place the lighted lamp on the far side of the room. Hold the convex lens at the distance of its focal length from the cardboard screen or wall. What type of image do you have? What is the lens being used for—a camera, a microscope, or what?

b. Bring the lamp to within about 3 feet of the lens. What type of image do you have?

c. Place the lamp so it is a distance of twice the focal length from the lens. Describe the image. How is the lens being used?

d. Place the lamp so it is between 1 and 2 focal lengths from the lens. Describe the image. How is the lens being used?

e. Place the lamp at the focal length from the lens. What happens?

f. Place the lamp between the focal length and the lens. What happens?

30. DRIVE-IN THEATER   *Supervised Classroom*

How does a theater get such a big picture on the screen?

It is because they use this formula:

$$\frac{\text{Image Size}}{\text{Object Size}} = \frac{\text{Image Distance}}{\text{Object Distance}}$$

To demonstrate this ratio, get a filament lamp with a clear bulb. Hold it between one and two focal lengths from a convex lens. Throw the image on a nearby wall.

Now throw the image on a more distant wall. You have a bigger image because the image distance is greater.

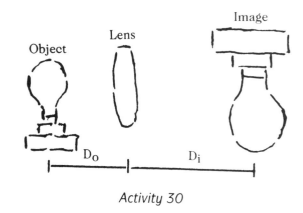

Activity 30

31. HEAD SHRINKER   *Supervised Classroom*

You may also use the previous formula to "shrink" a head!

If you have a 35-mm projector, throw a picture of a person on a large, white cardboard screen. Now ask a friend to take the cardboard and walk very slowly toward the projector. As the screen come toward you, keep the picture in focus. Notice that the closer the image is to the projector, the smaller the size of the image. You "shrink" the image by decreasing the image distance.

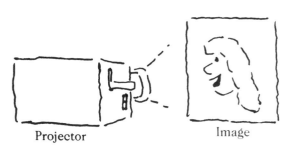

Activity 31

32. HOT DOG FOR EVERYONE   *Home*

Seeing is not always believing, as you may prove by some of the following demonstrations. Hold your index fingers together at arm's length in front of your face. Make your eyes look past your fingers. Focus on the distant sky or on the opposite wall. You may see a tiny "hot dog" stuck between your fingertips.

Activity 32

Activity 33

33. *BLIND SPOT* Home

To experiment with the blind spot in your eye, try this.

Hold this page about 20 inches away from your eyes. Close your left eye and look at the letter X with your right eye. You will still see the letter O in the corner of your eye. Slowly bring the page closer to your eyes. At a certain distance, the letter O will vanish.

This is the position where the image falls on the blind spot—the place where the nerves of the retina come together and go to the brain through the optic nerve.

Mailing tube

Activity 34

34. *A HOLE IN YOUR HAND?* Home

Get a long mailing tube such as calendars come in. With your right hand hold the tube directly in front of your face so you can look through the tube with both eyes. Place your left hand, palm up, against the side of the tube at a distance of about 20 inches from your face.

Now look through the tube at some distant object. Behold! You will find that you are looking through a hole in your left hand.

35. *WATCH YOUR THUMB JUMP!* Home

Hold your right arm out in front of your face and stick up your thumb. Now close your left eye. Line your right thumb up with a distant pole, tree, or doorjamb. Rapidly close your right eye and open your left eye. What happens?

36. *WHEN OUR EYES FOOL US* Home

Sometimes the brain makes a mistake in translating or decoding the electrical signals that are sent to it from the eye. In these cases we may say that our eyes fool us.

Part of what we see comes through the eyes, but much comes from the mind—past experiences, imaginings, desires, and other things that make illusions and often fill in parts of a picture that are not really there.

When we are fooled by our eyes, it is not because light bouncing off an object did not reach the retina. It is because the brain gets its signals mixed up. Optical illusions show that seeing is not always believing.

Does the black bottle seem **smaller than** the empty one? Empty **containers always** appear larger than **filled containers of** the same size.

Stare at the black **and white diagram** shown here. Do you **see gray dots in the** white lines where the black squares meet? If you do, look at **just one of them.** Do you still see it?

Home

How many cubes do you count? Turn the picture upside down and count **again.**

Which line is longer—AB or BC? Measure them.

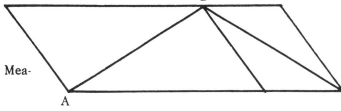

Does this book fold in or out?

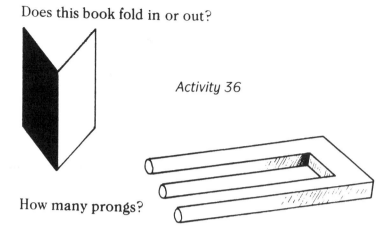

Activity 36

How many prongs?

37.   *MAKE YOUR OWN RAINBOW*   Home

Get a glass and fill it nearly full of water. Find a small mirror that will fit into the glass. Place the mirror at an angle in the glass. Make sure that the mirror is covered with water.

Stand the glass on a table. Turn the glass so sunlight strikes the mirror. As the beams of light enter the water, they bend. When the light strikes the mirror, it is reflected. The reflected beams of light are bent again as they travel through the water and the side of the glass. As a result of this dispersion the light breaks up into the colors of the rainbow. You can see this tiny rainbow when it strikes a sheet of paper.

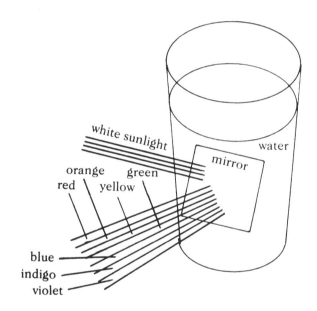

After a rainstorm nature provides her own prisms in the shape of tiny drops of water. These disperse or break up sunlight into all the colors of the rainbow.

As the rays of light enter the raindrop, they are broken or bent into separate colors. These colors are reflected from the inside back surface of the drop. You can see some of this light if you look toward the raindrop with your back to the sun.

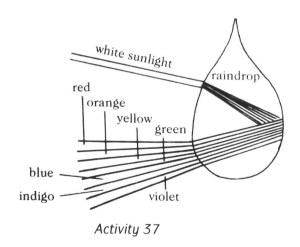

Activity 37

It isn't easy to see a rainbow. Bright sunlight must enter fairly large raindrops at a particular angle, and the reflected colored light from the raindrops must enter the viewer's eye at a particular angle. Rainbows will even give you an idea of the time of day. The higher the rainbow is, the lower the sun is.

38. A SCUBA DIVER'S VIEW

Imagine you are a scuba diver and you find yourself in a lake with crystal-clear water on a day when no wind ruffles the surface, you could treat yourself to a variety of views.

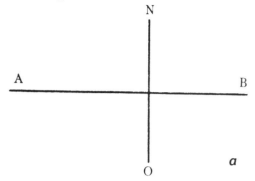

a

Let line AB represent the surface of a lake. Line NO is a normal—a line drawn perpendicular to the surface of the lake.

a. If you are at position O and look straight up to see a bird flying at N, will the bird appear to be where it really is?

b. Now look up at an angle as shown by line OC in drawing *b*. When the beam of light leaves the water, it will not continue in a straight line. Could you still see the bird flying directly over your head?

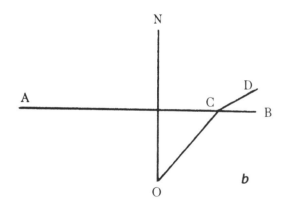

b

c. Now imagine looking up at the under-surface of the water at a still greater angle, as shown in drawing *c*. What would you see?

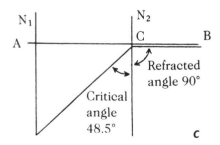

c

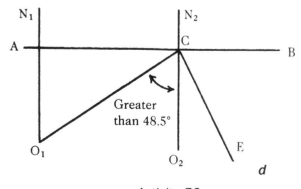

d

d. Now look up at the under-surface of the lake at an angle greater than 48.5°, as shown in drawing *d*. What do you see?

Activity 38

HIGHLIGHTS OF THIS CHAPTER

- The bending of a beam of light as it travels from one medium or substance to another is called refraction.

- A lens is defined as a transparent material with at least one curved surface that can be used to bend a beam of light.

- Convex lenses are thicker in the middle than at the edges.

- Concave lenses are thinner in the middle than at the edges.

- The focal point is the *place* where the rays of light come together.

- The focal length is the *distance* from the optical device to the focal point.

- Dispersion is the breaking up of a beam of light into its colors.

- Luminous objects are those that give off light.

- A normal is a line drawn perpendicular to a surface.

- A ray of light striking a surface is called an incident ray.

- A ray of light that bounces off a reflecting surface is called a reflected ray.

- The angle of reflection is equal to the angle of incidence.

- The reflection of light from rough surfaces is called diffuse reflection.

- The critical angle for water is 48.5°.

Multiple-Choice Questions

1. Which of the following statements is true?
   a. A convex lens curves in on both sides.
   b. A convex lens spreads apart or diverges parallel rays of light that pass through it.
   c. A convex lens is thinner in the middle than at the edges.
   d. A convex lens causes rays of light passing through it to come together at the focal point.

2. If you shine a narrow beam of light at a sharp angle on the surface of the water in an aquarium, the beam of light will:
   a. be reflected.
   b. be bent toward the normal.
   c. be bent away from the normal.
   d. continue through the water in a straight line.

3. Which of the following is true?
    a. A concavo-convex lens is thicker in the middle.
    b. A convexo-concave lens curves in on both sides.
    c. A convexo-concave lens curves out on both sides.
    d. A double-convex lens bulges in on both sides.

4. The critical angle is:
    a. the angle of incidence for which the angle of refraction is 90°.
    b. the angle that produces total internal reflection.
    c. 48.5° for a diamond.
    d. 23.7° for water.

5. A rainbow is due to:
    a. refraction.
    b. total internal reflection.
    c. dispersion.
    d. reflection.

True or False Questions

1. A translucent material is one that admits light, but you can't see through it.

2. A ray of light "bounces" off a surface at the same angle it "falls" on it.

3. The higher the rainbow in the sky, the higher the sun is.

4. Total internal reflection occurs when the angle of incidence is greater than the critical angle.

5. Stars appear to twinkle due to refraction.

Chapter 12

SOUND OFF

How to Catch Ideas Running Around in Your Head and Put Them into Your Friend's Head

In January, 1964, Astronaut John Glenn launched himself into Ohio politics when he decided to run against Senator Stephen Young for the Democratic senatorial nomination.

Then, just four days before he was to retire from the Marine Corps, Glenn, then 42 years old, slipped, fell, and cracked his head against the bathtub in a Columbus apartment. He began to hear ringing in his ears. He had dizzy spells and nausea whenever he moved his head. Postponing his retirement, Glenn checked into a San Antonio military hospital.

Three months later he was still there, flat on his back most of the time. He was unable to walk at all unless he tilted his head forward at a 45° angle. If he kept his head perfectly still he could shuffle along with his feet spread far apart.

His doctor, Earl W. Brannon, said that the bathtub blow hit just slightly above Glenn's left ear. This sent shock waves crashing into his inner ear, possibly causing swelling and some hemorrhaging. "He botched up his equilibrium center to a pretty good degree," said Dr. Brannon.

In September of 1964, John Glenn's photo appeared in newspapers. Beneath the photo of Glenn in a special cot were these words, "Seven months after leaving hospital, Astronaut John Glenn is still grounded by inner ear injury." The reason the doctors could do nothing positive to help John Glenn came down to this: ignorance!

There are so many unknown things about the workings of the inner ear that doctors feared that if they tampered with Glenn's inner ear they might only make things worse. They waited for nature to heal in its own slow way.

NOW I LAY ME DOWN TO SLEEP

We may close our eyes to sleep, but we can't close our ears. They are always on the alert, as I discovered when I visited an ancient palace in Kyoto, Japan.

A concerned emperor of long ago did not want an enemy sneaking into his bedroom in the middle of the night to kill him while he was deep in sleep. The "Safety First" plan invented by the emperor is fascinating. The emperor had his palace built so the only approach to his bedroom was a long, wide room or corridor. The floor of this long room is made so when anyone walks or even tiptoes across it, the floor vibrates and sends out a high-pitched warning. No matter how lightly I tried walking on this "singing floor" it "broadcast" my approach in a series of shrill notes.

COOL EARS

Some animals use their ears for more than collecting sound waves. The biggest ears of all belong to the African elephant. This massive creature spends much time in hot, sun-drenched areas in Africa. It needs to cool off. The large area offered by the outside ear, or pinna, of the African elephant provides it wuth a built-in "air conditioner." As the elephant's blood circulates through the great ears, it loses heat to its surroundings. This helps to keep the elephant cool.

Asian elephants, by contrast, spend more time in shady, moist jungles. They do not need such a huge "air-conditioning system." Their ears are smaller.

THE MOON IS QUIET AS A BROKEN BAGPIPE

The moon is as quiet as a broken bagpipe. Even if you stood on the rim of the moon's Bay of Rainbows and shouted at the top of your lungs to your friends only five feet away, they would not hear you. On the moon there is no air to carry the sound. Unlike light, which can travel through a vacuum, sound needs a medium or material through which to travel.

ALL THIS TO SAY "I LOVE YOU"

How do I get an idea from my brain into yours? First I fill my lungs with air. Then I vibrate vocal cords in my throat. Next I make "mouths" and shake the air. The air shakes a pair of little drums on the sides of your head. These vibrating drums shake groups of bones called the ossicles. The rapidly moving stirrups of the ossicles hit against still other drums called the oval windows. The rattling oval windows send pressure waves racing through small, snail-like shells called the cochleas.

Inside the cochlea the pressure waves of the liquid push against tiny hairs. The hairs are connected to nerve cells that change pressure waves into electric signals. These electric signals or impulses race along the acoustic nerves to the brain. Only when the brain "translates" these electrical signals do you get the idea that was on my mind. What a roundabout way to say, "I love you."

SOUND BEFORE LIGHT

At various medical centers around the world, experiments have been under way to answer two questions. What do newborn children know when they come into this world? How do they begin organizing and using that knowledge during the first few years of life?

According to researchers, a newborn baby is unable to see more than a blur, but its eyesight develops rapidly. Newborns start by looking at the edges of things, exploring. At eight weeks, newborns can tell the difference between shapes of objects and colors. At first they prefer red, then blue.

Unlike the eyes, the baby's ears worked even before birth. Tests as far back as the 1960s indicated that babies go to sleep faster to the recorded sound of a human heartbeat or any similarly rhythmic sound. More recent studies indicate that by the time they are born, babies already prefer female voices. Within a few weeks, they recognize the sound of their mother's speech.

ROCK 'N' ROLL MUSIC MAY DAMAGE HEARING

In trying to track a suspected Soviet submarine, the Swedish Navy had difficulty finding sailors who could hear well enough to operate listening devices. The hearing of vast numbers of young people, a Navy captain said, apparently has been damaged permanently by years of listening to loud rock music.

Similar hearing losses have been noted among American high school and college students who listen to rock music or go to discotheques. A Japanese survey showed hearing losses among high school students described as "headphone addicts." These students listened to stereo headphones more than 24 hours a week at volumes that equalled the noise level of rush-hour traffic.

To illustrate what noise can do to hearing, compare the inner ear to a recently seeded lawn with many tender shoots of grass. If you walk across a plot of new grass once, it will bounce back with time. If you trod over the same spot repeatedly, the grass will die.

Within the cochlea there are thousands of hairlike cells. These cells produce nerve impulses that are sent on to the brain, where the electric "signals" are "translated." The hairlike cells can "bounce back" after one encounter with high-intensity sound, but repeated noise exposure can produce permanent loss.

DO YOU HAVE A SOUND EDUCATION?

Do you owe most of your education to sound or sight? If all you had to do to be educated was to read a book, you would not have to attend school. You could stay at home and take a correspondence course by mail.

Why, then, do Americans spend millions of dollars for a tremendous school system that covers grade school, high school, college, and university? The answer is simple. The most simple and direct way to deliver thoughts from one person to another is through the spoken word. Another advantage is that students may ask questions concerning things that are not clear. Teachers, in turn, get feedback from students that helps them to know whether or not their presentation has struck home.

Human language is based on sound. Human thought is connected to the sound world in a way in which it is not connected to any other sensory field.

THE PRICE OF SOUND

To help you appreciate what sound means in our lives, think for a moment of the amount of money people pay every day for such delightful sounds as music. Think of all the radios, records, and tape recorders that are in use around the clock. Think of the thousands of musical instruments used in bands and orchestras across America and the world.

Recently a violinist by the name of Ani Kavafian was so fascinated by the "gorgeous, gorgeous sound" of a violin made by Antonio Stradivari more than two centuries ago that she sold everything she had and went in to debt to buy the Stradivari violin that had been made in 1736. The price, $250,000.

DIZZY SPINS

If an airplane goes into a spin, the pilot may become dizzy and lose control of the plane. Yet professional ice skaters, such as the stars of the Ice Capades, do not become dizzy when they go into a spin.

The Air Force wondered, why don't skaters get dizzy but pilots do? An investigation was conducted in an attempt to find the reason. As so often happens in scientific investigations, the reason behind all this was not discovered, but some interesting findings were turned up.

The skaters spun in a counterclockwise direction (opposite to the motion of the hands of a clock). When the skaters tried to spin clockwise (the same direction as the hands of the clock), they became dizzy. Investigations also showed that skaters going into a spin automatically focused their sight on some spot in the ceiling. If the skaters closed their eyes, even though they continued to spin on a counterclockwise direction, they became dizzy and fell down.

THREE BONES THAT NEVER GROW

Do you know that you have three bones in your body that never grow? They stay the same size throughout your life. These bones are the ossicles—the hammer, anvil, and stirrup—in your ears.

YOUR "INSTANT ALERT" SENSE!

Even though you may not be looking, you know when someone pops a balloon, toots a horn, hammers a nail, saws wood, rings a bell, or uses a pencil sharpener. While helping to dry the dishes, a plate slips through your hands. Without even looking down at the floor, you know when the plate breaks.

Even though a number of your friends are talking in another room, you can pick out the voice of your sister. Once you know the sound of a person's voice, you can tell when he or she is talking. The sound of a human voice is like a fingerprint. It belongs to one person only.

WHAT MAKES SOUND?

When you hear the hum of a mosquito or fly, or the buzz of a bee, do you ever wonder how they make those sounds? They do it by moving their wings back and forth. This back-and-forth motion is called vibration. The vibrating wings of the insect push the air into motion.

Drum

The beginning of all sound is something that vibrates, or moves back and forth. When you pound a drum or ring a bell, you are making things vibrate. Vibrating objects are the sources of sound.

WHAT IS SOUND?

So far we have seen that **THE SOURCES OF SOUND ARE VIBRATING OBJECTS.** The next question is: **WHAT IS SOUND ITSELF?**

After a rain you may have seen puddles along the sidewalk or in empty lots. Perhaps you threw a small rock or pebble into the puddle and saw something interesting. Ripples or waves formed in tiny circles around the spot where the pebble hit the water, then spread out into ever-larger circles until the small waves reached the rim, or edge, of the puddle.

PENNY IN PAN OF WATER

You don't have to wait for the next rain to have a puddle if you wish to do this experiment. Simply close the drain in the kitchen sink and turn on the cold water. Put about one or two inches of water in the sink. Instead of using the sink, you may use a big pan with one or two inches of water in it. Drop a penny in the water.

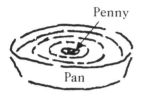

When the penny hits, it pushes against the water. This push, this disturbance or motion going through the water, is called a wave. It goes out in all directions.

WATCH THE BEAVER POND

If ever you are walking through the mountains and have an opportunity to toss a small rock into a quiet beaver pond or lake, notice what happens. The lily pads, stray pinecones, twigs, and leaves that float on the surface of the water are not washed ashore by the waves. They stay where they are, simply rising up and down. Only the disturbance (the wave) travels. The substance or material through which the wave moves is called the medium.

TRANSVERSE WAVES

Water waves are transverse, which means that they vibrate at right angles to their path or direction of travel. Transverse comes from a Latin word that means "to turn across."

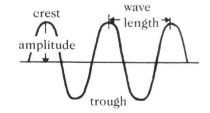

The peak or upper curve of a transverse wave is known as the crest. The depression or channel is called the trough. The wavelength is the distance from crest to crest or from trough to trough. The vertical distance from the top of the crest to the normal position of the rest of the water is the amplitude of the wave. On September 12, 1961, a sea wave of 67 feet in amplitude was recorded in the North Atlantic.

REACH FOR THE BIRDCAGE

Spring

Bird cage

Sound waves are somewhat different from transverse waves. They do not travel at right angles to their direction of travel. Instead, their motion is in the same direction as the wave progresses. This type of wave is described as a compression or longitudinal wave. To compress means to "squeeze" or "pack together." Longitudinal means "running lengthwise."

Perhaps you have a birdcage that is suspended by a spiral spring. To give yourself an idea of how sound waves travel, do the following. Pull the birdcage down a few inches toward the floor and then let it go. As the cage moves up and down, notice that the spring is first compressed, then it is stretched in the same direction as the motion of the cage. The moment you release the cage a compression leaps forward in the spring and then turns backward creating a rarefaction, or region where the turns of wire are farther apart.

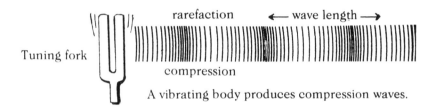

A vibrating body produces compression waves.

In order to understand for yourself the action of a single sound wave, visualize what happens when you swing a baseball bat. As you swing it to the right, the advancing surface forces the air ahead of it and squeezes it into a compression. Now swing the bat to the left. What was a moment ago the advancing surface of the object now becomes the retreating surface. It leaves the air behind it thin, or rarefied. The pressure on the air particles is released. The air returns to its normal position. This is the action of a single vibration that passes on its energy to the air and produces a sound wave.

The compressions and rarefactions of the longitudinal waves correspond to the crests and troughs of the transverse waves. A wavelength is equal to the distance between two adjoining compressions or rarefactions. Because it is difficult to draw longitudinal waves, a sound wave is frequently represented by a wavy line after the fashion of a transverse wave.

SLINKY TO THE RESCUE

An excellent way to illustrate how sound travels is to use a long coiled spring called a Slinky. Place the coil of wire on top of a table. Ask a friend to hold one end of the Slinky on one side of the table. Take the free end of the Slinky and pull it across the table to your side.

Slinky coil

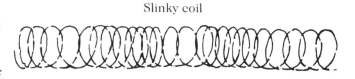

Keep a good hold on your end of the Slinky and quickly move your hand forward about three inches. What do you see? When you move your hand forward, you push against the coil and squeeze it. This push, or squeeze, keeps on moving through the coil to the other end.

Now move your hand forward and backward rapidly. You will send a great number of pushes, or vibrations, running through the coil. The faster you move your hand, the more vibrations a minute.

The distance between the vibrations in the coil is called the wavelength. As you can see, the faster you move your hand and the more vibrations you send out, the shorter the wavelength will be.

This experiment with the Slinky is a good one to help you understand that sound is a disturbance, or vibration, in the air or some other medium (liquid or solid) that travels in a wave motion.

WHERE IS THE JET?

Did you ever hear the roar of a jet airplane and look up into the sky only to find that the jet was not where the sound seemed to be? Why is the sound so far behind the jet? Why is it that sometimes, when you see a flash of lightning, you hear the roar of the thunder immediately and at other times the thunder does not come for a long time after the flash? The answer is that sound travels slowly compared to light. Light moves, or travels, 186,000 miles in one second. Sound moves through air at a speed of 740 miles an hour, or about 1,100 feet a second when the temperature is 32 degrees, or just at the freezing point. In warmer air sound travels faster. For each degree rise in temperature the speed of sound goes up about 2 feet in one second.

CHECK THAT LIGHTNING FLASH!

For a fast and easy way to check on the distance to a lightning flash, you may use 1,000 feet a second for the speed of sound. Your answer won't be exact, but it will be close enough to give you an idea of the distance to the lightning. If you see a flash of lightning and then, one second later, you hear the roar of the thunder, you know that the lightning is about 1,000 feet away. If five seconds go by between the time you see the flash and then hear the noise, you know that the lightning is about 5,000 feet, or about a mile, away.

Next summer see how many seconds you can count between the time you see the flash of lightning and then hear the roar of the thunder. If you count higher than 20, you probably won't hear the thunder at all. Do you know why? If I stood on top of the mountain behind my home in Butte, Montana, and shouted your name, you would not hear me. The sound would fade away, die out, and be absorbed by the air. That is why you wouldn't hear the thunder if you had to count more than 20 seconds between the lightning and thunder.

Lightning is a giant spark of electricity that may jump from one cloud to another, or from cloud to earth. Lightning flashes between a cloud and the ground may be 3 miles long. Flashes between two clouds may be as long as 10 miles. Although the path of the spark is long, it is narrow. It may be as thick as your thumb or as thin as a hair on your head.

The great flash of the lightning bolt gets the path of air through which it travels so hot that the air pushes out and expands, or explodes with great power. It is this push or air wave hitting your eardrum that makes the sensation we call thunder.

FOURTH OF JULY

If your city puts on a special Fourth of July fireworks display, you may notice that you can see a skyrocket break into many colors before you hear the sound of the explosion. The light of the flash reaches you almost at once. The sound takes longer to make the trip.

SONIC BOOM

An airplane moving at less than the speed of sound pushes, or squeezes, the air ahead of it. This pushed air moves away in all directions at the speed of sound—approximately one-fifth of a mile in a second, or about 760 miles per hour when the temperature is around 70°F. When the plane is moving faster than the speed of sound, the squeezed air cannot move ahead of the plane. Instead, this squeezed air fans out behind the plane. When this cone-shaped wave of air hits the ground, we hear a noise called the sonic boom.

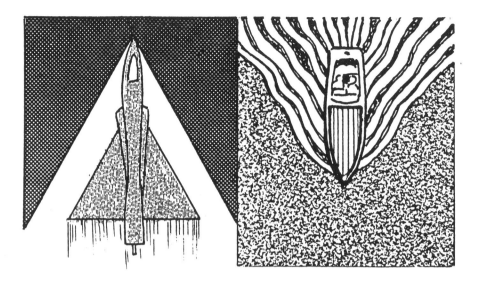

Just as the water waves from a fast-moving motorboat can be heard when they slap against the shore, so the air wave sent out by the supersonic jet is heard when it hits our ears. By the time the sonic boom reaches our ears, the plane that caused it may be 50 miles away. Any object exceeding the speed of sound can make sonic booms—a bullet, artillery shells, or missiles. A sharply cracked whip makes the same sort of sound.

BOUNCING SOUND

Throw a rubber ball against a cement sidewalk. It will bounce back. If you throw the ball into a pillow, it does not bounce back. Sound does much the same thing. It will "bounce back" or be reflected from hard surfaces such as walls of concrete, brick and rock. When sound hits a soft surface such as curtains, rugs, and cloth draperies, it does not bounce back.

If two sounds reach your ear as much as one-tenth of a second apart, you can tell that they are different. Two sounds that reach your ear closer together than one-tenth of a second mix together and become one sound. In one-tenth of a second sound travels about 110 feet. This means that the surface that bounces the sound back must be at least 55 feet away if the bounced sound is to be heard as an echo.

Echoes are produced when a reflecting surface is sufficiently far away that we can distinguish the reflected sound from the direct one.

WHAT HAPPENED?

If you were ever in a gym when it was empty, you may have noticed an interesting thing. If you shouted or sang as you walked down the middle of the gym from the back wall to the front wall, the echo was not always the same. Can you guess why?

HOW CLOSE IS THE SHORE?

Long before the invention of radar, steamship captains were able to tell by means of echoes how far they were from the shore. Caught in a thick fog, the captain would give a sharp blast on the foghorn and then listen for the echo. If four seconds took place between the blast of the foghorn and the return of the echo, how far away was the shore?

SINGING IN THE BATHROOM

What would happen if you were in a small room where there was no furniture and you threw a rubber ball against a wall? The ball would bounce back from the wall to the floor. After hitting the floor, the ball might bounce up again to hit another wall. After bouncing off this second wall to the floor again, the ball might bounce up once more to hit another wall.

Much the same thing happens when you are in a small room and talk loudly or sing. The sound of your voice bounces from one wall to another. This is why some people like to sing in the shower or bathroom. The smooth walls and ceiling of the room bounce the sound waves many times. This bouncing of the sound waves is called reverberation. A reverberation is the re-echo of a sound. "Reverberate" comes from a Latin word that means "to strike back." Sound waves in a small room bounce back from the walls and ceiling so fast they make the original sound stronger. It also lasts longer. No wonder that in such circumstances your soaring voice reminds you of Luciano Pavarotti.

LINGERING SOUNDS

The length of time a sound can be heard after it is made is called the reverberation time. In a small room reverberation may improve the sound of a speaker's voice by making it stronger with bounced or reflected waves. If the reverberation time is too long, sound waves may bounce back from a wall just in time to completely mix up, or scramble, the next words of the speaker.

EXAMINE ACOUSTICAL TILE

It is the job of sound engineers to control both echoes and reverberations. Soft cloth draperies cut down on echoes by soaking up or absorbing sound waves. Acoustical tile is often used for ceilings and walls. It has many small holes on the surface that catch the noise. Around the inside of the holes is a mineral wool lining that soaks up or absorbs the sound.

AND NOW, THE EAR!

So far we have seen that the sources of sound are vibrating objects. Sound itself is a disturbance in a medium. The process of perceiving sound is hearing. It is complicated.

Your ear is a sensitive and complex instrument. It has the important job of receiving and transmitting to your brain all the sounds around you—the voices of those you love, the rhythm of music, the mighty peal of thunder, the whisper of the wind among the trees on a lofty hill.

YOUR OUTER EAR

The outer portion of your ear is like a combination antenna and funnel. It captures sound waves and leads them toward the middle ear. The fleshy outer part of your ear is called the pinna. (Pinna is a Latin word that means "feather.") The pinna has the job of collecting sounds and leading them into the opening that goes to the middle ear. The pinna is also called the auricle.

YOUR EARDRUM

The visible part of your ear, the pinna or auricle, performs only a minor role in hearing. It merely concentrates the sound and delivers it to the ear canal. The canal condenses the sound waves and conveys them to the tympanic membrane or eardrum. The word "tympanic" comes from a Latin word meaning "drum." The eardrum is just that—a tiny, drum-like skin, or sensitive membrane. Sound waves striking the eardrum cause it to move back and forth or vibrate.

THE MIDDLE EAR

The middle ear is well named. On one side of it is the outer ear. On the other side of it is the inner ear. Within the middle ear there are three very small bones called ossicles. "Ossicles" is a Latin word meaning "little bones." These little bones also have Latin names: malleus (hammer), incus (anvil), and stapes (stirrup). These bones are so named because they are shaped somewhat like a hammer, an anvil, and a stirrup.

The hammer is attached to the inner side of the eardrum. The anvil is attached on one side to the hammer. The other side is attached to the stirrup, and the stirrup is attached to a membrane, the oval window, which separates the middle ear from the inner ear.

A MOVABLE BRIDGE

The three little bones in the inner ear form a movable bridge. The hammer is attached to the eardrum. It picks up sound vibrations that are then conducted to the inner ear by way of the anvil and stirrup.

THE INNER EAR

Inside the inner ear is a somewhat snail-shaped tube, the cochlea. "Cochlea" is a Latin word meaning "snail shell." The cochlea contains a fluid and the tiny hairlike nerve endings of the auditory nerve.

As the stirrup vibrates against the membrane and the inner ear, the vibrations are passed to the fluid in the cochlea. The endings of the auditory nerves "feel" the movements, which are changed into electrical impulses or signals and sent to the brain. When these electrical signals reach the brain, they are interpreted as sounds.

HOW TO HEAR BETTER

You can increase the collecting power of your pinnae by pushing them forward and cupping them with your hands. Even better, get a megaphone and hold the small end over your ear. You may also make your own megaphone by rolling a newspaper into a cone shape. Put the small end of the cone next to your ear and listen.

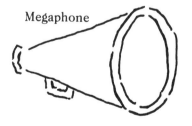
Megaphone

HOLES IN YOUR HEAD?

The middle ear is like a very small room with no floor. Instead of a floor there is an opening that marks the beginning of the Eustachian tube. (In 1563 an Italian scientist, Bartolommeo Eustachio, achieved fame by describing the air tube that leads from the middle ear to the throat.) The purpose of the Eustachian tubes is to equalize air pressure on both sides of the eardrums.

DO YOUR EARS POP?

Our ears "pop" nearly every time we swallow, although usually so gently that we hardly notice. The popping opens the Eustachian tubes, which supply air to the middle ear. This "popping" equalizes the air pressure in the middle ear so it has the same air pressure on both sides.

RIDE WITH AN OPEN MOUTH

Have you ever noticed a popping or ringing in your ears when you go up in an elevator, or take off in an airplane, or go up a steep mountain in a car? These sensations are due to changes in air pressure on the outside of your eardrums. You can help make the pressure equal by opening your mouth, yawning, or chewing gum. Soldiers firing big guns open their mouths so the sudden blast of air on the outside will not push on their eardrums hard enough to injure them.

WHEN YOU HAVE A COLD

You may have found that your hearing was impaired when you had a cold because the Eustachian tubes were swollen partly shut. Doctors inform us that many earaches are caused by germs and bacteria that travel from the throat up the Eustachian tubes to the middle ear where they may cause painful infections. Take it easy whenever you blow your nose. If you pinch your nostrils, a sudden blast of air may back up in the tube causing a rupture of an eardrum.

The eardrum is easily injured. Never try to remove wax or any foreign matter from your ear by using a pencil, toothpick, hairpin, or any sharp, pointed instrument. You should never shout into a person's ear. A loud sound can make the eardrum vibrate so much it may cause damage. You should never strike anyone on the side of the head. Any sudden change in pressure can injure the eardrum. If you use ear plugs when you swim, always take them out slowly. If you pull them out like a cork from a bottle, you make a low pressure area on the outside of the eardrum. The air pressure on the inside of the drum could rupture it. If you are a skin diver, remember that the deeper you go, the greater the pressure on the outside of your eardrums. Some divers have suffered permanent damage to their hearing because they neglected this fact.

HEARING AIDS

This air-conduction hearing aid goes into the ear. This actual-size drawing shows that the hearing aid is about the size of a marble.

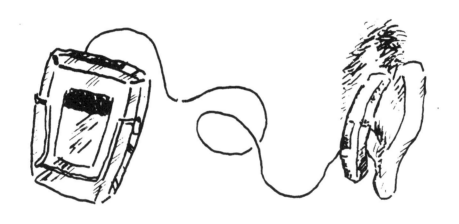

In the bone-conduction hearing aid the receiver is clamped to the bone behind the ear.

Many people who are deaf or hard of hearing are helped by hearing aids. The hearing aids have a small electrical device that mades sound louder. In the air-conduction hearing aid, the receiver is put into the outer ear and sends increased vibrations to the middle ear.

In the bone-conduction hearing aid, the receiver is clamped to the bone behind the ear. Vibrations are sent through the bones of the head into the inner ear. Bone carries sound better than air.

YOUR "DOUBLE-DUTY" EARS!

Your ears do far more than hear. They do "double duty" by also controlling our sense of balance. They tell us whether we are standing up or sitting down. They tell us whether we are in motion or at rest, turning or moving in a straight line. The mechanism that does all this is in the inner ear. It consists of three small tubes shaped like semicircles and set together in such a way that they resemble a distorted pretzel. These semicircular canals help maintain our sense of equilibrium.

The semicircular canals are filled with fluid. This fluid flows back and forth in the canals, bending sensitive nerve endings in the direction of the movement. The nerve endings send messages—"I'm turning left," for example—to the brain. The brain, in turn, sets up reflex actions such as turning the eyes and head to adjust to the movement.

DIZZINESS

When disease or injury disrupts the complex inner-ear mechanism, extreme dizziness called vertigo results. "Vertigo" is a Latin word meaning "dizziness." To the vertigo victim it seems as though the walls and floors are heaving and buckling. Vertigo victims cannot even sit up in bed without the dizzying sensation that the entire world is tumbling about them. Loss of hearing, ringing or buzzing noises in the head, and nausea and vomiting can result from disturbances of the inner ear.

SEASICKNESS

In normal activity, the inner ear usually performs flawlessly, but certain types of motion place quite different stresses upon it. The rolling motion of a ship, a plane, or even a car in very sensitive individuals cause the fluids of the inner ear to bend the nerve endings in an abnormal fashion. The brain reacts with feelings of nausea and sometimes vomiting, the dread symptoms of seasickness.

Some people today prefer to call these symptoms "motion sickness." This term was coined to admit the fact that ships are not the only means of travel that upset the stomach. Lawrence of Arabia, for example, got motion sickness while riding camels across the shifting sands of the Sahara.

In 1938 my first teaching assignment took me to the Red Cloud Indian School on the Pine Ridge Reservation in South Dakota. At the start of the school year I drove a big truck around the reservation to pick up students who were coming to board at the school. Alas, every trip had its quota of young Sioux who suffered from motion sickness.

Despite the number of people who experience motion sickness while riding in a car or airplane, the fact remains that ships are the number one source of nausea. In fact, the word "nausea" comes from the Greek word "naus" which means "ship."

One sign of seasickness that cannot be hidden is vomiting. No wonder that for many years the stomach was considered to be the seat of seasickness. The incredible thing, however, is that people who have had their stomachs surgically removed can still become nauseated.

William James, the Harvard psychologist and philosopher, seems to have been the first to suggest the true cause of seasickness. In 1882 he published an article entitled, "The Sense of Dizzyness in Deaf-Mutes." His findings were later confirmed by investigations of other scientists.

YOUR EARS MAKE YOU SEASICK!

Seasickness has to do chiefly with the ears. A person who is deaf due to damage done to the organs in the inner ear does not get seasick. James noticed that when a number of such deaf people had been exposed to rough weather at sea, not one of them had become seasick.

There are tremendous differences in how likely people are to get seasick. Not even the so-called experts have a hard and fast explanation. There are indications that some people's inner ears are simply more sensitive to motion than others. Infants less than two years old are usually immune. Children from two to twelve are most susceptible. From twelve onward, susceptibility declines with age.

Two to three days at sea is long enough for most people to get their sea legs. Some folks, however, take much longer. Charles Darwin never did get his sea legs. He suffered almost constantly during the ocean portions of his five-year trip around the world.

A "BAND-AID" TYPE PATCH

The usefulness of antihistamines in preventing seasickness was discovered quite by accident. In 1949, when a pregnant woman started taking Dramamine by prescription to control an outbreak of hives, she discovered that she no longer got carsick.

A short time ago I was talking with a man who makes a boat trip every summer out into the Gulf of Mexico to fish for the big ones. He mentioned that on his last trip he tried a new drug, Scopolamine. This drug is administered gradually through the skin by means of a Band-Aid-like patch. This patch is applied directly behind the ear. It must be stuck into place several hours before you go to sea. Alas, this new drug sometimes produces a disturbing side effect—hallucinations. Fortunately, the hallucinations are rare. Scopolamine is still called "the most promising advance in the prevention of seasickness."

HOW MANY BELS IN YOUR HOUSE?

Engineers measure the loudness of a sound by a unit called the bel, named for Alexander Graham Bell, whose investigations into the nature of sound led to the invention of the telephone.

The smallest increase in loudness that the human ear can detect is one-tenth of a bel, or a decibel. In a gently breeze the rustle of leaves is approximately 10 decibels. If you have very good hearing you may be able to hear a very faint movement of leaves that measures about 2 decibels. A whisper that can be heard at a distance of 4 feet is at a level of 20 decibels. The intensity level of ordinary conversation is 65 decibels; a vacuum cleaner is about 70 decibels. Traffic on a noisy street may be 75 decibels. A nearby clap of thunder may register as high as 125 decibels. A jet engine taking off may reach 150 decibels.

An accelerating automobile is about 85 decibels. A highway truck is just below 90. A motorcycle hits about 90 decibels. A rock and roll band reaches 120 decibels. Sounds registering above 90 decibels may damage the sensitive cells deep inside the ear. Some hearing loss may result over a period of time.

HOW MANY V.P.S.?

The normal range of human hearing is from 20 to 20,000 vibrations per second (V.P.S.). At frequencies between 1,000 and 4,000 per second, a normal ear is marvelously sensitive. Vibrations of less than 20 times per second are called *subsonic*. Those over 20,000 times per second are called *ultrasonic*. These sounds cannot be heard by the human ear.

In this respect dogs are superior to humans. They are capable of perceiving sounds of up to 35,000 vibrations per second. Special dog whistles are made to vibrate more than 20,000 times per second. If you were to blow such a whistle, your dog would hear it but you wouldn't.

ACTIVITIES

Pop bottles

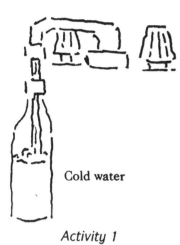

Cold water

Activity 1

1. POP BOTTLES   Home

Get a few empty pop bottles. Fill them with different amounts of water. The space left without water is full of air. Blow across the open ends of the bottles. You will find that the bottle with the longest column of air in it has the lowest frequency. The bottle with the shortest column of air has the highest frequency.

Now place an empty bottle under the cold water faucet. Turn on the water and, as the water rises to the top of the bottle, you will hear the frequency becoming higher. As the water replaces the air, the air column shrinks. There are more vibrations per second.

2. SPEAKING TUBE   Home

Here is a way to keep sound from spreading out in all directions so you can't hear it over great distances. Get a long cardboard tube such as those used for mailing big calendars. If you can't find such a tube, perhaps you can use a short garden hose.

Hold one end to your ear. Have your friend whisper into the other end. Be sure he whispers, or the sound will hurt your ears. Then let your friend listen while you whisper to him. Notice how clearly the sound comes through the tube. The walls or sides of the tube keep the sound from going out in all directions.

Some apartment houses have speaking tubes so people living upstairs can find out who is at the front door before they let them in. The people on the outside of the door speak into an open hose or pipe that runs through the walls of the apartment and thus brings the sound of their voices to the people upstairs.

Tube

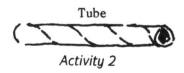

Activity 2

3. SOUND THROUGH WATER   Home

Sound travels about four times faster through water than it does through air. To prove for yourself how clearly sound travels through water, get a wide-mouthed gallon jar and fill it two-thirds full of water. Place the jar on top of the table close enough to the edge so you can place your ear firmly against the glass.

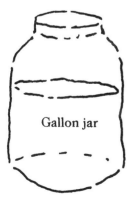

Gallon jar

Activity 3

Now ask your friend to take two marbles, two nickels, or any two things of about that size. Hold them under the water and click them together. You will be delighted to find how clear and sharp the sound comes through the water.

Activity 4

4.   ARE YOU A RATTLE-HEAD?   Home

When you talk, your tongue, vocal cords, and lips move back and forth, or vibrate, and set the air into motion. They even make your head rattle and shake. To prove it, simply place your hand firmly on top of your head and talk loudly or sing. You will feel your head shake, or vibrate.

Place your hand on your friend's head. Ask him to talk loudly. Does his head shake as much as yours?

5.   A STRING TELEPHONE   Home

You can find out how things that vibrate make sound by constructing your own simple string telephone. Get two empty coffee cans. Punch a hole through the bottom of each can with a small nail and a hammer. Get a long, heavy string or cord about 15 or 20 feet long. Push one end of this string through the hole in one of the cans and tie a big knot in the string so it can't pull out. Put the free end of the string in the other can and tie it the same way.

Empty can   Tight cord   Empty can

Activity 5

Ask your friend to pick up one can by the rim and walk away from you until the string is pulled tight. Hold your coffee can by the rim and speak into it while your friend holds the other coffee can next to his or her ear. When you talk, the sound of your voice makes the bottom of the can move back and forth. This motion is passed on to the string, which, in turn, makes the listening can vibrate. The vibrating metal of the listening can sets air into motion so your friend hears your voice.

A real telephone does not carry sound through the wires. What happens is this: when you talk, you set the air into motion. This moving air hits a small piece of metal inside the mouthpiece of the phone and makes it vibrate. The vibrations of this metal control the amount of electricity that goes through the wires. This changing flow of electricity makes another piece of metal in the receiving end of the phone vibrate the same way the first metal plate vibrated.

6. LISTEN TO YOUR ARMS   Home

Mosquitoes, flies, and bees can make sounds by moving their wings back and forth. Why can't you make sounds by moving your arms back and forth?

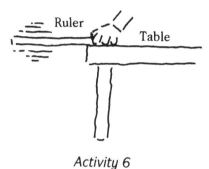

Activity 6

To find out why, get a thin wooden or plastic ruler or a long nail file. With your left hand hold one end of the ruler pressed firmly against the top of a table. Let most of the ruler come out over the edge of the table. With your right hand, hit the free end of the ruler. What happens?

Now bring more of the ruler back onto the table so the end sticking out over the edge is shorter. Hit the ruler again. What happens?

Now bring the ruler back onto the table still more, so only a small part sticks out over the edge of the table. Hit the free end again. What happens?

7. TICKLE THE IVORIES   Supervised Classroom

If you have a piano in your home or classroom, you may be able to experiment with frequencies. If you are allowed to pluck the wires in the piano, you will find that the longer and heavier the wire, the lower is the note, which means that its frequency is less. It vibrates fewer times in a second. The longest, heaviest wire vibrates at the rate of 27 times a second. The shortest, thinnest wire vibrates 4,096 times a second. The middle C on the piano has a frequency of about 264. In your experiment with the piano you may notice that the tighter the wires are strung, the faster they vibrate.

8. SOUND BOX   Home

Stretch four of five rubber bands across the top of an empty box or across the open side of an empty milk carton. Use a big, fat rubber band, a thin one, and some that are in between. What difference do you notice when you pluck them?

Rubber bands on empty box

Activity 8

9. RUBBER BAND   Home

Now place a rubber band over your thumbs. Have your friend pluck the band as you stretch it. What happens as you increase the pull on the rubber band and make it tighter? Use bands of different sizes and notice the difference.

10. MAKING MUSIC   Home

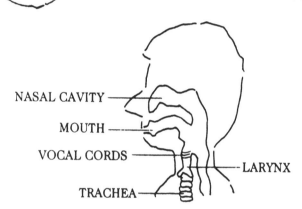

Guitar

Perhaps you have a guitar, or a friend who will lend you one to try this experiment. Pluck the string of the guitar with your right hand; then press the finger next to your thumb on the left hand across the different ridges, called frets, on the fingerboard. Does the pitch, or frequency, rise as you make the string shorter?

The most important musical instrument in the world is the one you carry around all day—your voice box, or larynx, and the vocal cords that are stretched across it.

You voice begins in the larynx, which is in your throat, at the top of the trachea, or windpipe. The vocal cords are two elastic tissues stretched across the top. You might compare them to thin rubber bands.

NASAL CAVITY

MOUTH

VOCAL CORDS

TRACHEA

LARYNX

Activity 10

When you speak, muscles tighten the vocal cords and air from the lungs causes them to vibrate. The tighter you stretch the vocal cords, the higher the frequency. Loudness depends upon the force with which they vibrate. If you place your fingers over your Adam's apple when you talk, you will be able to feel the vibrations of your vocal cords.

If you are to say words clearly, your tongue, lips, and teeth have to help your vocal cords. To prove this, hold your mouth wide open, keep your tongue on the floor of your mouth, and try to say such words as dentist, breakfast, snap, plop, and splash.

Clock

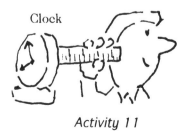

Activity 11

11. LISTEN WITH A RULER   Home

Get a stout wooden ruler. Hold one end of the ruler to your ear. Hold the other end against the back of a ticking clock. What do you notice?

12. KITCHEN TABLE   **Home**

Here is something to try when you are in the kitchen. Place your ear against one end of the table top. Ask someone to rap the other end of the table top with a spoon, pencil, or other object. What do you notice?

Activity 12

13. TAPE RECORDER   **Home**

If you haven't done so before, listen to a playback of your voice on a tape recorder. The first time you did, you most likely exclaimed, "Oh, no! That's not me! I don't sound anything like that!" You are correct. Even though you have been talking most of your life, you may have never heard your voice as others hear it. The sound of your own voice comes to you by bone conduction. Others hear you by air conduction.

14. TUNING FORK   **Supervised Classroom**

With a tuning fork, you can perform some interesting experiments. Hold the tuning fork at its base. Hit the prongs with a soft mallet or with the base of your open hand. While the prongs are vibrating, hold the tuning fork about half a foot from your ear. Listen to the sounds coming to you by way of the air.

Hit the prongs again. This time place the base of the tuning fork against the solid bone behind your ear. What do you notice? Hit the prongs of the tuning fork again. This time hold the base snugly against your forehead, then against the end of your elbow. What happens?

Tuning fork

Activity 14

15. MAKE A BIG SPLASH   **Home**

The vibrating prongs on your tuning fork may be moving back and forth too rapidly for your eye to follow the motion. If you want to see what is taking place, dip the tips of the vibrating tuning fork into a glass filled with water.

Tuning fork

Activity 15

HIGHLIGHTS OF THIS CHAPTER

- The sources of sound are vibrating objects.

- Vibrations less than 20 times per second are called subsonic.

- Vibrations more than 20,000 times per second are called ultrasonic.

- The frequency of stringed instruments depends on:

  > the length of the string or wire.
  > its weight (how thick and heavy the string is).
  > how tightly the string is strung (tension).

- Sound is a disturbance in a medium (gas, liquid, solid).

- Sound travels about 4 times faster through water than it does through air.

- Sound travels about 16 times faster through steel than it does through air.

- Echoes are produced when a reflecting surface is sufficiently far away so we can distinguish the reflected sound from the direct one.

- Reverberation time is the length of time a sound can be heard after it is made.

- The process of perceiving sound is hearing.

- The outer ear is like a combination antenna and funnel.

- The fleshy outer part of the ear is called the pinna.

- The eardrum is just that—a tiny, drum-like skin, or sensitive membrane.

- The middle ear is well named—it is between the outer ear and the inner ear.

- It contains three little bones called the ossicles (the hammer, anvil, and stirrup).

- The purpose of the Eustachian tubes is to equalize air pressure on both sides of the eardrums.

- Inside the inner ear are the cochlea, the "snail shell," and the semicircular canals. They look like distorted pretzels.

- Engineers measure the loudness of a sound by a unit called the bel. It is named after Alexander Graham Bell.

Multiple-Choice Questions

1. An ultrasonic wave is one that:
   a. creates a sonic boom.
   b. moves faster than 1,000 feet per second.
   c. travels with the speed of light.
   d. vibrates more than 20,000 times per second.

2. The speed of sound through water compared to air is approximately:
   a. four times as fast.
   b. twice as fast.
   c. three times as fast.
   d. sixteen times as fast.

3. A wavelength in a transverse wave is:
   a. the vertical distance from the top of the crest to the normal position of the water.
   b. the distance from crest to trough.
   c. the distance from crest to crest, or from trough to trough.
   d. the distance from the trough to the normal position of the water.

4. The frequency of a sound tells:
   a. how loud it is.
   b. how many times a second an object is moving back and forth.
   c. how big is the amplitude of its sound wave.
   d. how many bels it has.

5. The speed of sound through air:
   a. remains the same at all temperatures.
   b. decreases with an increase of temperature.
   c. decreases only until the temperature drops to 32°F and then remains the same.
   d. increases with an increase in temperature.

True or False Questions

1. A sonic boom can be produced by the fast-moving tip of a bullwhip.

2. If a tree fell in a forest where there was no one around to hear it, there would be no sound.

3. If we could move our arms up and down as rapidly as a bee moves its wings, we could listen to them.

4. In a sound wave, and also in a water wave, energy passes through a medium.

5. If a jet plane is speeding through the sky at 560 mph, it is supersonic.

Chapter 13

YOUR PRIVATE DETECTIVES
Your Chemical and Contact Senses

You can smell bacon sizzling in the frying pan, moth balls in your closet, or freshly cut clover in June because tiny particles or bits of matter called molecules jump up from these different things, then race through the air to punch you in the nose!

In the upper part of each nostril there is a flat membrane or piece of skin about the size of a postage stamp. Sticking out of the membrane, like so many lines on a telephone switchboard, are tiny hairs. When an odor reaches these hairs, they send an electrical signal or impulse racing along nerves that lead to your brain. Your brain translates or interprets these electrical signals as odors.

Our sense of smell can act as a lifeguard to warn us of gasoline fumes in the air or gas escaping from a leaky pipe in the basement. The smell of smoke—long before the smoke was seen—has warned families of hidden fires in attics.

Like your sense of hearing, your nose can operate in the dark. If you are walking through the woods at night, your sense of smell may tell you that a skunk has been around, even though you don't see it.

What accounts for our ability to smell? Science does not fully understand the olfactory organ, or sense of smell. Your nose can receive and sort out odors with a speed and exactness that no scientific instrument or machine can equal.

You notice that a young woman is wearing perfume. You may be smelling an amount of perfume so small that no machine known could find it or tell what it is. Scientists believe that the human nose can pick out as little as one-trillionth of an ounce of a strong-smelling chemical.

As far as we know now, there may be no limit to the number of odors the human nose can recognize or pick out.

Although our skill at picking out odors is good, some animals have an even better sense of smell. If the wind is right, a deer can smell a person more than 100 yards away.

It has been said that the nose, not the tongue, really enjoys food. Much of what people call tasting is really smelling. As you chew, you free odors that rise through the back of your mouth into the inner parts of your nose, where the olfactory nerve is located. If you have a head cold and your nose is stuffed up, you will have trouble tasting your food.

Thanks to your taste buds, each meal can bring delight to your day. Your tongue has 3,000 taste buds, each with its nerve connection to the brain. No one knows exactly how these taste buds work. Some scientists think that particles of food fit into them like light plugs into sockets, closing circuits and sending electrical impulses to the brain. The brain interprets the signals to mean: "The strawberry ice cream is delicious." "The lemon is sour." "The potatoes need salt."

Scientists know that the senses of taste and smell differ in one important way from the senses of sight, hearing, and touch. They are both chemical senses. Things that give us taste must come into direct contact with taste buds.

There are four generally recognized basic tastes: salty, sour, bitter, and sweet. The taste buds sensitive to these various tastes are distributed in a definite pattern on the tongue. Those buds most sensitive to sweet flavors are at the tip of the tongue. You may have noticed how candy tastes sweeter when you lick it than when you chew it farther back in your mouth. Salt-sensitive taste buds line the front of your tongue. A sour taste—lemon, for instance—is recorded by taste buds along the sides of your tongue. Bitter flavors are detected by taste buds on the back of your tongue.

Human taste sensitivity to different substances varies greatly. Scientists have found that most people can detect the bitterness of the medicine, quinine, if only one part of quinine is present in one million parts of water. Sugar, however, can't be detected unless there are less than 200 parts of water for every part of sugar.

Besides tasting, the tongue helps you eat by forcing the food against your teeth, where incisors (your front, cutting teeth) grind it under a pressure of 20 to 80 pounds per square inch. Then your tongue forces the food onto the molars (the back teeth with the flattened surfaces adapted for grinding) where the pressure rises to 130 to 160 pounds per square inch.

The tongue's nervous mechanism responds to the slightest pressure so it automatically clears out of the way of your teeth as you chew. Sometimes your dentist may have to give you an injection of xlyocaine or some other anesthetic to deaden your pain receptors. Alas, your tongue may become as numb as the pain receptors. Your dentist may caution you about chewing so you can avoid biting your sluggish tongue.

The tongue can create a lowering of air pressure that allows the atmosphere to force a malted milk up through a soda straw.

The pressure of your tongue across the top of your mouth when you speak is from 0.5 to 2.3 pounds per square inch. When you swallow, your tongue exerts a pressure of 2.0 to 4.6 pounds.

YOUR "CONTACT" SENSE

You are trying to find your way through a dark room. You reach out and happen to touch a hot radiator. Even though you can't see the radiator you know immediately that it is there.

Touch is the sense that puts us in the most direct contact with the world around us. Our eyes can see stars sparkling on the far side of the Milky Way galaxy. Our ears can hear the distant roar of a waterfall. Our nose can smell bacon frying. Our taste buds tell us about things that are mixed with the moisture on our tongue. The sense of touch, however, depends on direct contact.

Touch gives us a sense of love that no other sense can supply. According to scientists, love comes most of all from close bodily contact in the early months of life. Babies who are not given human contact, who are not hugged and picked up, suffer just as surely as if they had been starved.

The English language abounds in expressions that mirror the importance of physical contact in our lives. We lend others a "helping hand." If our friend does a good job, we give a "pat on the back." We experience kindness that "touches us."

It is interesting to realize that the word "tact" comes from the Latin word "tactus" meaning to touch. Tact, in its modern sense, was adopted from the French, and means "to delicately touch." By contrast, we say that a tactless man has a heavy touch.

YOUR TICKLISH NOSE

The nerve endings most sensitive to pressure are close together in the tips of the fingers, the bottom of the thumb, the palm, and the lips. The tip of your nose is also sensitive, as you know when you tickle it with a feather.

YOUR PAIN CENTER

Although much about the sensation of pain is still unknown, scientists have found that pain is a coded electrical signal or impulse sent to the brain from different parts of your body. The part of your brain that interprets these signals of pain is called the thalamus. This is a Greek word meaning "chamber."

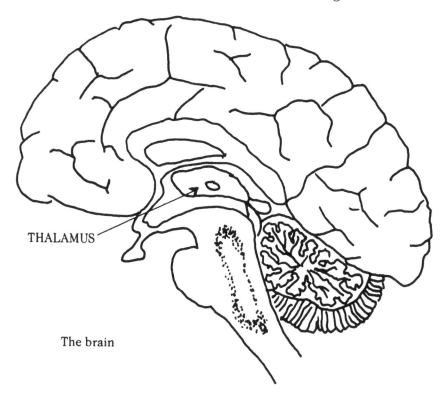

THALAMUS

The brain

WHEN YOU STUB YOUR TOE

Let's see what happens when you stub your big toe.

First, there are nerve endings in the skin called receptors. These nerve endings change the energy of impact when your toe hits something hard into a code of electrical nerve impulses. The nerve impulses are then sent by nerve fibers from the toe to the spinal cord. Some electrical messages race up your spinal cord at speeds up to 300 miles an hour. Your brain interprets or translates these electrical signals as pain.

NO PAIN

Strange as it may seem, some people are born without the sense of pain. They can be stuck with pins and plunge their feet into ice-cold water or steam and feel no pain.

This may sound wonderful, but it is really quite dangerous. Imagine placing your hand on a hot stove and not knowing that your flesh is burning. A pain-free boy wondered why he could not jump over a tennis net. He was found to have a broken thigh bone. A pain-free girl broke her ankle, but didn't know it until the ankle swelled so much she couldn't put her shoe on.

"DOMINEERING" MOLECULES

The molecules of some substances are more energetic and "domineering" than those of other substances. If you make the mistake of putting an unwrapped onion or slice of garlic in your refrigerator alongside a pitcher of water you want to cool, you will both smell and taste them when you drink the water. The active onion and garlic molecules will zip into the water.

ACTIVITIES

1.   *"TASTE" AN APPLE*   Home

The next time you eat an apple, note how the "taste" of the apple is a combination of the smell of the fruit just before you bite into it, the sensation recorded by the taste buds as you chew the apple, and the smell of the vapors released from the apple during chewing. These vapors enter the inner openings of the nose and stimulate the nerve cells responsible for the sense of smell.

2.   *BLINDFOLD TEST*   Home

Some afternoon you may wish to invite a few friends to your home for a tasting game. Before they come, cut a slice from an apple into small parts and put them in a cup. Do the same with a slice of potato.

When your friends arrive, blindfold them. While your blindfolded friends hold their noses shut, give each of them a small piece of apple to taste. Ask them to tell you what it is. Then do the same with a small piece of potato. Can your friends tell you what the foods are when their noses are blocked so they cannot smell them?

3.   *THE TASTE TELLS*   Home

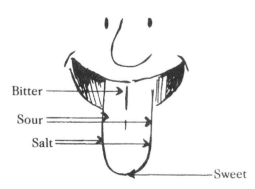

Bitter

Sour

Salt

Sweet

Activity 3

If you would like to find out what parts of your tongue are sensitive to different tastes, take a toothpick and put a drop of saltwater on different parts of your tongue. What parts are most sensitive to salt?

Take a fresh toothpick and repeat the experiment with sugar water. Then try lemon juice and bitter chocolate.

4.   *HOW FAR APART?*   Home

Here is an experiment to do when you are wearing a T-shirt or light clothing. Keep your eyes closed or wear a blindfold while a friend touches the points of two pencils at different spots on your back.

Without telling you how many pencils there are, your friend will touch your back with only one pencil at times. At other times your friend will use both pencils, keeping their points about one-quarter of an inch apart. Can you tell when you are being touched with one or two pencils?

Now let your friend keep increasing the distance between the pencils when touching your back with the points. How far apart do the pencils have to be before you feel them as two points?

5. *SCISSORS* Home

Here is an experiment for you to do yourself with a small pair of scissors such as nail-trimming scissors. Hold the scissors in your right hand with an opening of less than half an inch between the blades. Gently place the open end of the scissors on the tip of your tongue. Your tongue will immediately report that there are two distinct points of contact.

Now close your eyes and touch the open palm of your left hand with the points of the scissors. Finally, touch the back of your hand. What do you notice?

A spot on the end of your fingertip or tongue not bigger than the end of the eraser on your pencil may have over 100 receptors. A spot the same size on the back of your hand may have only ten.

6. *TOUCH AND TELL* Home

The sensation of touch can help tell what things are without looking. To prove it, get a big paper bag like those used in supermarkets. Into the bag put such things as a ping-pong ball, a marble, a rock, a piece of sandpaper, a piece of silk, and some nails. If you can't find these particular things, any assortment of things of different shapes and textures will do.

Blindfold a friend and ask him or her to reach into the bag and pull out one thing at a time, telling you what it is. How many times did they get the right answer?

HIGHLIGHTS OF THIS CHAPTER

- The sense of smell is located in the upper part of each nostril. It is a flat membrane or piece of skin about the size of a postage stamp. Sticking out of the membrane are tiny hairs. When an odor reaches them, they send an electrical signal to the brain.

- Much of what people call tasting is really smelling.

- Your tongue has 3,000 taste buds, each with its nerve connection to the brain.

- The buds most sensitive to sweet flavors are at the tip of your tongue.

- Salt-sensitive taste buds line the front of your tongue.

- Besides tasting, the tongue helps you eat by forcing the food against your teeth.

- Touch is the sense that puts us in the most direct contact with the world around us.

- The nerve endings most sensitive to pressure are close together in the tips of the fingers, the bottom of the thumb, the palm, and the lips.

- The part of your brain that interprets signals of pain is called the thalamus.

Multiple-Choice Questions

1. The taste buds most responsive to sweet substances are found:
   a. on the sides of your tongue.
   b. in the middle of your tongue.
   c. on the tip of your tongue.
   d. on the back of your tongue.

2. The number of smells the human nose can pick out is:
   a. 1,000.
   b. 1,500.
   c. 2,000.
   d. indefinite.

3. The number of taste buds on your tongue is:
   a. 3,000.
   b. 4,000.
   c. 2,000.
   d. 1,000.

4. Nerve endings in your skin, called receptors, send electrical impulses to your brain at the speed of:
   a. 1,000 ft. per sec.
   b. 186,000 mph
   c. 300 mph
   d. 680 mph

5. When you swallow, your tongue exerts a pressure of:
   a. 2.0 to 4.6 lbs. per sq. in.
   b. 0.5 to 2.3 lbs. per sq. in.
   c. 5.7 to 8.9 lbs. per sq. in.
   d. 11.2 to 13.4 lbs. per sq. in.

True or False Questions

1. A child who is born pain-free is lucky.

2. The most versatile organ of the human body is the tongue.

3. The tip of your finger has approximately ten times more receptors than the same area on the back of your hand.

4. The sensors that puts us in most direct contact with the world around us are our eyes.

5. Much of what people call tasting is really smelling.

Chapter 14

GREEN MAGIC

You Eat Sunlight for Breakfast!

How would you answer this question, "What is more wonderful, a Cadillac or a watermelon seed?" No doubt you would rather have a car in your garage than a seed in your pocket, but compare the two. You can't plant an axle in your garden in the hope that it will grow into a shiny new automobile; but if you plant the seed, the result will be green magic. The tiny seed sends roots down into the ground to seek water. The plant captures the energy of the sun and grows into a large vine. In time, you will have not one melon, but several. No automobile can perform this feat of multiplication.

Automobile factories don't use the same materials to build a car that you would use to make a dress or construct a sidewalk. It may seem strange, therefore, to learn that all living plants and animals are put together with the same building blocks.

BUILDING BLOCKS

Protoplasm is the living substance that is found in plants, animals, and human beings. "Protoplasm" comes from the Greek words "protos," meaning "first," and "plasma," meaning "form." Whether you refer to your own body, the huge hulk of a whale, or a stalk of celery, they are all made of protoplasm. Every living thing contains protoplasm.

Chemists who have analyzed materials found in both plants and animals have discovered that protoplasm is made up chiefly of hydrogen, carbon, oxygen, and nitrogen, together with limited quantities of phosphorus, sulfur, and other elements.

When seen through the microscope, protoplasm looks something like the white of a raw egg. It is liquid and can flow. No scientist has been able to tell what makes protoplasm live. Even if you had all the elements that make up such a small plant as a radish, you could not make a radish.

YOUR CELLS

All the activities that take place in your body are due to the protoplasm within, but you do not find this substance all heaped up in one spot. It is packaged in neat little units called cells.

One day in 1665, when he was examining a piece of cork under a microscope, Robert Hooke noticed that it was constructed of row upon row of tiny "rooms" that reminded him of the cells in a monastery. Although the cork that he was examining was dead, Hooke later discovered that thin slices of vegetables also had cells and that these cells were filled with juices. In the cork he had actually seen only the woody walls of cells. It had no protoplasm or living material.

Almost two hundred years later, Matthias Schleiden made a detailed study of plants. Theodor Schwann studied animals. Summing up their experiences and those of other scientists, Schwann concluded that "every living thing is composed of cells." Subsequent observations by other scientists confirmed this statement. Cells are the building blocks of all living things. Within these small units one finds the protoplasm that is characteristic of every living organism.

"ROOF" CELLS

Some of the simplest plants and animals consists of one cell only. Most living things, however, are made up of many different kinds of cells. There are millions of cells of varied shapes and sizes in your body. Each type of cell has its own job to do. Red blood cells might remind you of tiny pancakes or miniature life rafts. Their function is to carry oxygen from the lungs to all parts of your body. Skin cells look like shingles on a roof. They cover your body with a layer of skin that is stretchable and waterproof. Nerve cells are long and resemble branches of a tree. They are like telegraph lines. They carry messages faster than you can run.

THE "INSIDE" OF A CELL

Although cells may differ a great deal in shape and size, these building blocks have the same general structure. The wall of a cell, known as the cell membrane, forms a jelly-like wrapper that serves the same purpose as a bag or a box. The bulk of living material that fills the cell is a thin watery protoplasm called cytoplasm.

Within the cytoplasm, often near the center of the cell, is a dense mass of protoplasm called the nucleus. This rounded mass is the most important and complex portion of the cell. The nucleus controls not only the activities of the cell, but also the production of new cells.

THE "EMPTY SPACES" IN YOUR CELLS

Nonliving material in the cell includes specks of food, fat, coloring matter, wastes, and vacuoles. "Vacuole" is a Latin word meaning "empty." These spaces within the cytoplasm were called vacuoles because they were once believed to be empty. They contain liquid waste, gases, and sometimes cell sap.

AN "EXTRA WALL"

Plant cells have an extra outside covering, the cell wall. It is not a living part of the cell. It is made chiefly of cellulose, which is manufactured by the plant's protoplasm. You can't squeeze the trunk of an oak tree or the shell of a walnut as

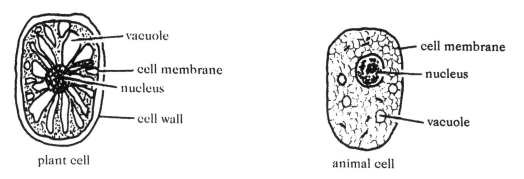

plant cell   animal cell

you can the flesh in your arm or the fur on a cat's back. The cell walls in plants offer resistance. Animal cells have only the cell membrane and thus change shape more easily. Of course the walls of some plant cells—leaves, flower petals, and strawberries, for example—are thin and easily crushed. They do not resume their original shape when pressure is removed.

UNIONS

A group of people who do the same type of work often belong to a union. Truck drivers are members of the Teamsters Union and people who work in automobile plants belong to the United Auto Workers.

Cells are organized along similar lines. Groups of cells doing special types of work are known as tissues. If you cut through the stem of a young plant you will see several types of tissue. Epidermal tissue forms the outer protecting layer. Conducting tissue transports material from one part of the plant to another. Embryonic tissue, composed of small and active cells, is found at the tips of roots, in buds on stems, and in the cambium layer of trees. During the growing season, embryonic cells divide to form new cells that mature into other plant tissue.

Animals have epithelial or covering tissue, nerve tissue that carries messages, muscle tissue that moves various parts of the body, and connective tissue that binds together and supports other structures. Groups of blood cells make up blood tissue.

ORGANS

Just as cells that have specific types of work to do form tissues, so groups of tissues act together to perform certain functions. Your heart is an organ. It has muscle tissue, nerve tissue, blood tissue, and epithelial tissue all working together to keep the blood in circulation.

Your eyes, ears, liver, lungs, arteries and veins, arms and legs are all organs. Many organs are usually required for the performance of special functions. A number of organs and tissues working together for one particular purpose form what is known as a system. The circulatory system, for example, is composed of the heart, arteries, veins, capillaries, and blood tissue.

LIVING ORGANISMS

The entire body of any living thing is called an organism. While scientists cannot fully explain what life is, they know that life requires protoplasm. Each cell in a plant or animal is a mass of this living substance. What do cells do, you may ask, and how many cells does it take to make a plant or animal?

THE SMALLEST ANIMALS

There are some living things that consist of one cell only. Included are the "wretched beasties" that Robert Hooke found in a drop of pond water. Protozoa— from the Greek words "proto," meaning "first," and "zoa," meaning "animals" —are found in water. Most of them are so small they can be seen only with the aid of a microscope.

An amoeba, one of the best known of the protozoa, is a one-celled animal that makes living look simple. At mealtime it simply flows around whatever food is available and stays there until the food is absorbed. You have lungs to take in oxygen. Your blood transports the oxygen to all parts of your body. An amoeba absorbs oxygen directly from the water in which it lives. It eliminates wastes directly into the water. Since it has no blood vessels, the amoeba doesn't need a heart. It reproduces by dividing in half and thus producing twin amoebas. The single cell carries on all life processes, including locomotion, digestion, respiration, excretion, and reproduction.

The amoeba is well named. The word comes from the Greek. It means "to change." The amoeba is always changing its shape by protruding portions of its body.

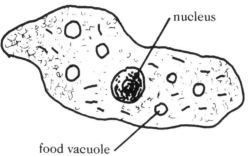

nucleus

food vacuole

DID YOU EAT SUNLIGHT FOR BREAKFAST?

As you are aware, you need energy to run, to play basketball, to study, and to work. Where does your energy come from? Did you ever stop to consider that our immediate body needs are cared for by shipments of energy from the sun? The radish you pull from your garden may be considered a "package of freshly minted sunshine." Just before you pulled it, the leaves of the radish were busy capturing energy from the sun and storing it for your use.

If you prefer a hamburger or steak, you depend on still another process. A white-faced cow on Pat Vinton's Spring Lake Ranch, just south of Gordon, Nebraska, obligingly ate the grass. Then, through the marvelous magic of the chemistry lab on hooves (the cow), the grass was turned into steaks. All the energy to do this comes from the sun!

Of all things on the earth, only plants can capture the energy from the sun and give it to us in the form we need to keep alive. Green plants carry on the most important manufacturing process in the world—making food.

The plant material that holds the key to this mysterious food-making process is chlorophyll, a green coloring matter. The word "chlorophyll" comes from a Greek word, "chloros," meaning "green." In the presence of sunlight it manufactures food.

BUILDING WITH SUNLIGHT

This process of manufacturing food with the energy from the sun is called photosynthesis. "Photo" is a Greek word meaning "light." "Synthesis" means to "put together" or "build." Photosynthesis is building with sunlight. When the golden rays of the sun "shake hands" with the green pigment or chlorophyll in a leaf, magic is in the making. The plant is packaging energy from the sun.

DEPENDENT MUSHROOMS

Not all plants have chlorophyll. Those that have no coloring matter are dependent on the green plants for food, just as animals are. Mushrooms and molds, for example, are dependent plants that secure food from other plants. Soil is full of organic compounds in the form of humus, which is the material resulting from the partial decay of plants and animals. The word "humus" is a Latin word meaning "soil."

TREES MADE FROM AIR AND WATER!

Plants capture energy from the sun, but what are the simple substances that plants use to make food?

Since plants are planted in the earth, it might be supposed that the basic materials come from the ground. To test this theory a Belgian scientist of the seventeenth century, Jan Baptista van Helmont, weighed a tubful of earth and a willow twig which he planted in the tub. Five years later the tree weighed over 160 pounds. Van Helmont dried the soil and weighed it, as he had done at the beginning of the experiment. The tub of dirt weighed just two ounces less than the original earth. Where did the tree get the 160 pounds?

Authorities tell us that the raw materials are carbon dioxide and water. Plants absorb water from the soil. The leaves take in carbon dioxide, a substance you exhale into the atmosphere. The green chlorophyll takes from sunlight the energy it needs to change water and carbon dioxide into sugar. As the sugar is formed, it dissolves in the water of the cells. Oxygen is given off by the plant during the process.

GREEN STOREHOUSES

In some plants, such as sugar cane or onions, the sugar is stored immediately in the stems and leaves of the plant. Most plants change the sugar into starch. This starch remains in the leaf until sundown, then much of it is again converted into sugar during the night and carried to all parts of the plant. Some of the remaining starch is stored as reserve food for the plant or is turned into proteins and oils, to be used immediately or stored.

THE APPLE YOU EAT MAY BE MADE FROM YOUR EXHALED BREATH!

How marvelous this process is. Carbon dioxide, which you exhale, combines with water to build an apple. Oxygen is returned to the air. We, along with animals, take oxygen from the air and exhale carbon dioxide. Plants absorb carbon dioxide and give off oxygen.

Animals and plants supply necessary substances for one another. When the sugar is oxidized in your body, the sun's energy is released for action, growth, or repair of cells. Whether you eat vegetables, fruit, meat, or fish, you take energy from the sun into your body. You are solar powered.

FOOD FACTORIES

Although a leaf may appear to be a solid green, you will find that it has airy spaces when you look at the inside through a microscope. The thin layer of cells on the upper side, called the upper epidermis, is transparent and colorless. Light passes through it to other layers of cells. "Epidermis" comes from two Greek words, "epi," meaning "over," and "derma," meaning "skin."

The lower epidermis or under side of the leaf has countless openings through which air enters and leaves the leaf. The openings are called "stomata," the Greek

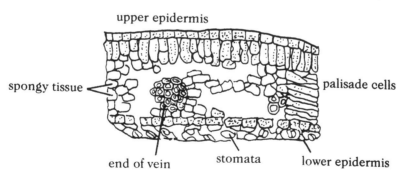

upper epidermis

spongy tissue

palisade cells

end of vein   stomata   lower epidermis

word for "mouths." Just below the upper epidermis are long slender cells that look like pillars or the poles of a palisade. They are palisade cells and are rich in chlorophyll, the green coloring matter.

The greater part of the leaf is filled with spongy tissue. Every cell is in direct contact with air. Water enters the plant through the roots and is brought into the leaf through the veins.

Plant cells are usually filled with water, which stretches them and gives plant tissues a certain amount of firmness. Less than 1% of the air that enters the leaf is carbon dioxide, yet this small amount is sufficient to supply plants with this essential material for food-building. Scientists have tried to produce sugar by uniting carbon dioxide and water, but without success.

Though some sugar and starch are always contained in leaves, they are not the best storehouses. You eat the fruit of the tomato plant, the seed of peanuts, the stem of celery, and the root of carrots.

ARE YOU SITTING ON A STEM OF A PLANT?

The answer is "yes" if you are sitting on a chair made from wood. The wood came from the stem of a tree.

WHAT ARE THE TALLEST STEMS?

The world's tallest trees are the California redwoods. The tallest of these is believed to be the Howard Libbey Tree in Redwood Creek Grove, Humboldt County, California. In 1964 it was announced that this tree was 367.8 feet high. In 1970 it was re-estimated at 366.2 feet.

WHAT ARE THE OLDEST LIVING THINGS?

At one time the most massive living thing on earth, a California "big tree" in Sequoia National Park, California, named "General Sherman," was also considered to be the oldest living thing. A ring count from a core drilled in 1931 showed the tree to be some 4,000 years old.

During 1963 and 1964, scientists found that the oldest recorded living thing is a bristlecone pine growing at 10,750 feet above sea level on the northeast face of Wheeler Peak in eastern Nevada. It is estimated to be 4,900 years old.

MIRACLE OF GROWTH

The seed of a "big tree," the California sequoia, weighs only 1/6,000th of an ounce. Its growth to maturity may therefore represent an increase in weight over 250 billion-fold.

WHAT IS YOUR BODY MADE OF?

Air and water make up from 95 to 96% of the materials used in the construction of your body. The other 4 to 5% comes from elements in the soil.

If you tip the scale at 150 pounds, then only about 6 pounds of your body are made of minerals from the soil. The other 144 pounds are chemical elements from air and water. If your body were completely consumed by fire, the 144 pounds of oxygen, carbon, hydrogen, and nitrogen would return to the air and water whence they came. The ashes that remained would be the 6 pounds of mineral elements derived from the soil.

IS THAT YOUR SAME FACE IN THE MIRROR?

If you dash over to your mirror, the face that stares back at you is not the same one that peered out at you twelve months ago. The molecules and cells that once made your face are all gone. New ones have fallen into line. Scientists used to tell us that we had a new body every seven years. Now we are told that we have a new body every few months. By this time next year you will have a new body.

Your body is constantly being repaired and rebuilt. Molecules are forever coming and going. Even as you read this print some 3 million red blood cells die per second in your body. They are replaced by fresh reserves from the bone marrow. Each time you sit down at the dinner table, you are collecting fresh molecules for a new body.

ACTIVITIES

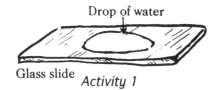

Drop of water

Glass slide   *Activity 1*

1. THE LIFE IN A DROP OF WATER   *Supervised Classroom*

Place a drop of water from a pond or aquarium on a glass slide and examine it beneath a microscope. Do you see any single-celled animals or plants?

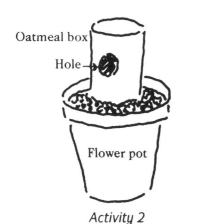

Oatmeal box

Hole

Flower pot

Activity 2

2. SEARCHING FOR THE LIGHT   *Home*

Plant a bean seed in a flowerpot. As soon as the plant breaks through the soil, cover it with an oatmeal box in the side of which you have cut a hole about the size of a quarter. What happens?

3. WHICH WAY IS UP?   *Home*

Plant a bean seed in a flowerpot. When the plant has grown to a height of 3 to 4 inches, turn the pot on its side. How does the plant grow?

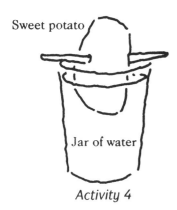

Sweet potato

Jar of water

Activity 4

4. SWEET POTATO   *Home*

Place one end of a sweet potato in a jar filled with water. Set it in a sunny window. From time to time you will have to add more water. You will be repaid with a luxuriant tangle of green. Explain how the plant obtained food and energy to promote such growth.

5. TREES ON HILLS   *Home*

Do trees grow on hills the same way they do on flat ground?

Keep your eyes open the next time you are in the woods. What do you notice?

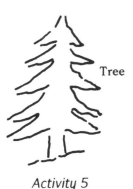

Tree

Activity 5

HIGHLIGHTS OF THIS CHAPTER

- Every living thing contains protoplasm. This living material is always packaged in tiny units called cells.

- Protoplasm is made up chiefly of hydrogen, carbon, oxygen, and nitrogen.

- There are million of cells in your body of varied shapes and sizes.

- The protoplasm in a cell is divided into cytoplasm and the denser nucleus.

- The entire package is surrounded by the cell membrane. Plants also have a cell wall.
    Groups of cells doing special types of work are known as tissues.
    Groups of tissues that act together, such as the heart or lungs, are organs.

- A number of organs and tissues working together for one particular purpose form what is known as a system.

- The single-celled amoeba divides into two animals. The cells of your body are constantly producing new cells.

- A green leaf—whether it is on an apple tree or a watermelon vine—has mystic powers in its fragile form. The little blade of green reaches out and absorbs carbon dioxide with cell sap brought up from the roots to form sugar.

- Each second of the day the sun sends out enormous amounts of energy, but only chlorophyll can manufacture food by solar energy. This process of building with light is known as photosynthesis.

Multiple-Choice Questions

1. Which of the following statements concerning protoplasm is false?
    a. When seen through a microscope, it looks something like the white of an egg.
    b. It is made up chiefly of hydrogen, carbon, oxygen, and nitrogen.
    c. It is found only in animals.
    d. It is a liquid and can flow.

2. The reason you can squeeze the flesh in your arm but not the trunk of a tree is that:
   a. our cells have only a cell membrane.
   b. our cells are filled with a thin watery protoplasm called cytoplasm.
   c. the dense mass of protoplasm in our cells is often near the center.
   d. the nucleus in our cells controls the activities of the cell.

3. Which of the following is false concerning an amoeba?
   a. It is composed of a single cell.
   b. Its cell wall is composed of cellulose.
   c. It multiplies by dividing.
   d. It flows around its food and stays there until the food is absorbed.

4. How many pounds of basic materials did van Helmont's 160-pound tree take from the soil?
   a. 100 lbs.
   b. 50 lbs.
   c. 25 lbs.
   d. Less than 1 lb.

5. Which of the following statements about a green leaf is false?
   a. The thin layers of cells on the upper side are transparent.
   b. The lower epidermis has openings through which air enters and leaves.
   c. The stomata are rich in chlorophyll.
   d. The palisades are long slender cells that look like pillars.

True or False Questions

1. Approximately 95% of your body is made from materials taken from air and water.

2. A redwood tree named General Sherman is the world's oldest living thing.

3. Robert Hooke discovered amoebas in a drop of water.

4. Red blood cells look like miniature life rafts.

5. Our lives depend on photosynthesis.

Chapter 15

WHAT MAKES ELECTRICITY?

How to Turn Your Head into a Broadcasting Station

What is the smallest thing you can name? The ancient Greeks came up with an answer. Their word "atom" meant "uncut" or "indivisible." The Greeks thought that the atom was the smallest "building block" that goes to make up all things in the universe. As years went by, however, scientists began to think of the tiny atom itself as having still smaller parts.

The simplest atom of all is hydrogen. In its center (or nucleus) is a positive charge of electricity. It is called a proton. Running in a circle around the proton is a negative charge of electricity. It is an electron.

HYDROGEN ATOM

Atoms are unbelievably small. For example, more than 3 million copper atoms could be placed on a dot the size of the period at the end of this sentence. Not one atom would need to touch another.

The only atom that has no neutrons in its nucleus is hydrogen. Neutrons are bodies that have approximately the same mass as protons. They have no electrical charge. A proton weighs 1,835 times as much as an electron. Almost the entire weight of the atom is contained in the nucleus.

Between the nucleus and the electrons there is a great deal of empty space. Since electrons whirl around the nucleus as planets do around the sun, the atom is frequently compared to the solar system.

ATOMIC NUMBER

On the next page, compare the hydrogen atom, which has 1 electron and 1 proton, with the helium atom. How do the nuclei of the two atoms differ?

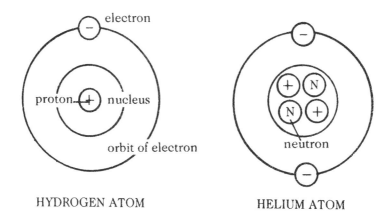

HYDROGEN ATOM   HELIUM ATOM

The nucleus of helium has two protons and two neutrons. The helium atom has two electrons whirling around the nucleus.

Other atoms are more complicated. Oxygen, for example, has eight protons, eight neutrons, and eight electrons. An atom of uranium has 92 electrons spinning around the nucleus in seven different orbits.

The number of protons that each element has is known as its atomic number. The atomic number of gold is 79. That of mercury is 80.

Add the number of neutrons in the nucleus to the number of protons. The result is the atomic weight. Hydrogen is the only element that has no neutrons in its nucleus. Its atomic number and atomic weight are both 1. The atomic weight of helium is 4. Oxygen has an atomic weight of 16.

There are 92 "original elements." Each of these atoms has one more proton than the one before it. The smallest is the hydrogen atom. It has only one proton in its nucleus. The next is helium with two protons. These two elements are not very abundant on the earth, but they account for 99% of all the matter in the universe. Vast clouds of hydrogen gas spread among the stars. The stars themselves are mostly hydrogen and helium.

WHAT DO YOU SEE IN THE MIRROR?

An atom is built somewhat like our solar system. It is almost all empty space. If you took out all the space in every atom in the body of a 200-pound man, he would be no bigger than a particle of dust!

Remember this the next time you admire yourself in a mirror. You are looking at the reflection of your body, which is almost 100% space. That is why x-rays, radio waves, and TV waves go through you.

PUT ALL THE PEOPLE IN A PEANUT SHELL!

Squeeze out all the space in the atoms in the 5 billion people on earth. They would fit into a peanut shell without losing an ounce of weight. A peanut shell full of spaceless humanity would be very heavy (almost 500 billion pounds). It would go through the rocky crust of the earth like a steel ball through snow.

HELP YOURSELF TO FREE ELECTRONS

It takes a very powerful force to take even one proton from the nucleus of an atom.

By contrast, it is easy to take away one or more electrons from an atom. The electrons that are taken away are called free electrons. Free electrons may attach themselves to other atoms of the same body. They may go into some other body. When you rub a comb through your hair, electrons jump from your hair into the comb. If a body picks up electrons from some outside source, it becomes negatively charged. A negatively charged body has more electrons than protons.

A neutral body is one that has the same number of electrons as protons. If a neutral body loses some of its own electrons, it is said to be positively charged. It has more protons that electrons. If a glass rod is rubbed with silk, some of the rod's electrons leave the glass. They go into the silk. The glass now has more protons than electrons. It is positively charged. The silk, which picked up the electrons, is now negatively charged.

THE GREEK WORD FOR AMBER

About 500 B.C. a Greek by the name of Thales found that when he rubbed a waxlike substance called amber with wool, it would attract pieces of straw, feathers, and other small objects. The Greek word for amber is "electron." By rubbing the amber, Thales had produced static electricity. Since static electricity is produced by friction, you can get into the act yourself.

CONDUCTORS AND INSULATORS

Metals are good conductors. They allow electrons to run through them. If 6.3 billion billion electrons run through a wire in one second, we have one *ampere* of current. A current of electricity is simply electrons in motion.

Under the same conditions, copper wire will allow more electrons to run through it than iron. Copper, therefore, is said to have a greater conductivity than iron. Conductivity is simply the ability to conduct an electric current.

Materials that do not let electrons pass through them with ease are called insulators or nonconductors. Dry air, shellac, paraffin, ebonite, rubber, porcelain, glass, mica, silk, paper, and pure distilled water are good insulators.

ACTIVITIES

1. *YOUR PERSONAL BROADCASTING STATION*   *Home*

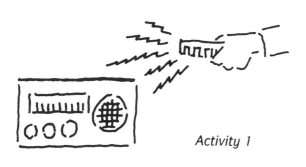

Activity 1

Here is an experiment you can do in your own home. All you need is your head—with hair on it—plus a plastic comb and an AM radio.

Your "program" will be better on cold winter days when the air in your home is very dry. Place your radio on the table. Spin the dial to a spot where there is no station. Turn up the volume. Now stand near the radio, and run a plastic or rubber comb through your hair.

As the comb rubs against your hair, it causes friction. This friction will make electrons jump between your hair and comb. Electrons are tiny bits of electricity. They have negative charges. The jumping electrons "broadcast" the fact that they are in motion. They send out radio waves.

Electromagnetic waves leap out from your head. They cut across wires in the antenna of your radio. In so doing, their energy is changed into electrical current. This current is then amplified or increased in volume and made to vibrate or move the diaphragm of the loudspeaker. The "program" you get is static. The faster and more ferociously you comb your hair, the greater the static.

Now find out how far you can broadcast. Start combing your hair while you are standing close to the radio. Slowly walk away from the radio. You will finally reach a distance where the broadcast fades out. The energy of your radio waves is absorbed by the air before it reaches the radio.

Static is caused by "untamed" electrons jumping around and giving out waves of untamed energy. When you run a comb through your hair, friction between your comb and hair causes electrons to hop around wildly.

In regular broadcasting, the electrons are "tamed." They are made to vibrate in step with the sound waves that push against the diaphragm of the microphone. The frequency of their jumps is timed to a woman's song or a sportscaster's rapid speech.

2. "SOS" WITH A RULER!   **Home**

Here is an interesting variation of the above experiment. Get a plastic ruler and a piece of fur or wool. Hold the ruler near the radio. Rub the ruler with the wool or fur. Each time you do, you will get a blast of static on the radio. By rubbing the ruler at proper times, you can control the static. The result will be a dot-dash effect. With a little practice, you may even use the Morse code to send an SOS.

3. PAPER-CATCHING RULER   **Home**

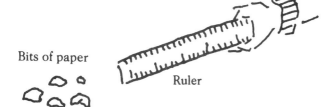

Bits of paper

Ruler

Activity 3

Here is a simple but interesting experiment. Tear some thin paper into very small pieces. Place these tiny pieces of paper on the table. Rub a plastic ruler with a piece of fur or wool. Hold the ruler near the small pieces of paper. What two things happen?

4. HOW TO "SEE" ELECTRICITY   **Home**

Since we cannot see electricity itself, we use a thing called an electroscope. It lets us see the effects of electricity. The word "electroscope" is a combination Greek word. The first part, "electro," stands for "electricity." The second part, "scope," means "to see."

To make a simple electroscope, take a page from a newspaper and cut out two strips. Make each strip about two or three inches wide and a foot long. Hold the top ends of the paper strips between thumb and forefinger of your left hand. With your right hand, pick up a woolen cloth or a piece of fur. Place the fur around the top of the strips of paper, just under your left thumb. Gently but firmly pull down the fur with your right hand. After two or three strokes, the "leaves" of your electroscope will spread apart.

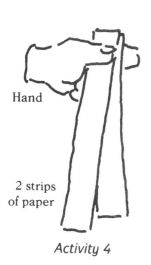

Hand

2 strips of paper

Activity 4

Please keep in mind that experiments with static electricity work best during the coldest months of winter. Then the air inside your home is warm and often very dry. In the summer, there is generally too much moisture in the air. The static electricity escapes to the ground.

Why do the leaves or strips of the electroscope stand apart? Friction between the fur and paper caused electrons to leap from the fur to the paper. Both strips of paper were "swarming" with electrons. Since like charges repel each other, the slips were pushed apart.

Now "shake hands" with the paper electroscope. Place your right hand between the leaves while they are spread apart. Notice how rapidly the strips swing over to "shake hands" with you. The negative charges on the paper strips are attracted by the positive charges on your hand.

Benjamin Franklin was the one who found two different kinds of static electricity. When Franklin rubbed a piece of rubber with fur, he found that both the rubber and the fur became charged. He decided to call the charge on the rubber negative, or minus (–). The charge on the fur he called positive, or plus (+).

5. KING-SIZE ELECTROSCOPE

Home

You can make a beautiful, interesting electroscope by doing the following. Tie two strings, each about two feet long, to the end of a yardstick. Tie an inflated balloon on the free end of each string. Now place the yardstick on the table. Briskly rub each balloon in turn with a piece of fur or wool. Now pick up the free end of the yardstick. What happens?

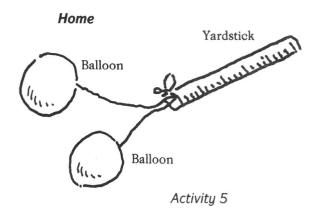

Activity 5

6. CHASING RULERS

Home

Two plastic rulers make an excellent electroscope.

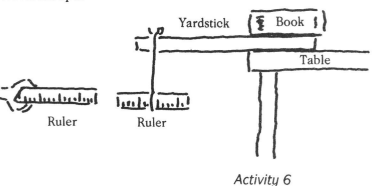

Activity 6

Place a yardstick on top of a table. Let two feet of the yardstick extend beyond the edge. Use a heavy book or other object to hold the yardstick in place. Tie a string about six inches long to the free end of the yardstick. Take the other end of this string and tie it to the middle of a plastic ruler. The ruler should be free to rotate.

Take a piece of fur or wool. Rub one end of the suspended ruler. Remember that friction causes the negative charges to jump from the fur to the ruler. Now rub one end of the second plastic ruler in the same manner. Bring the charged end of the second ruler to the charged end of the suspended ruler. What happens?

Instead of the second ruler, try a glass rod and a piece of silk. Rub the glass rod with the silk. Although you can't see them, electrons pass from the glass into the silk. The glass now has fewer electrons than protons. It is charged positively. What happens when you bring the charged glass rod to the suspended plastic ruler?

7.   *WATCH THE SPARKS*   *Home*

On a dark winter evening, stand in front of a mirror. Turn off the lights. Pull your sweater rapidly over your head. You may be able to see sparks.

8.   *GLASS BOTTLE ELECTROSCOPE*   *Home*

You may use an empty gallon jar or mason jar with a "lid" made from a heavy piece of cardboard to make an electroscope.

Push a bolt or big nail through the middle of the cardboard. Wrap a light wire around the free end of the bolt to serve as a stirrup. Through this stirrup insert a light strip of aluminum foil.

The glass bottle protects the foil from air currents. It allows you to see what is taking place. The glass and the cardboard keep the electrons from escaping too rapidly.

When the electroscope is neutral there are equal numbers of protons and electrons on the leaves of the foil. The foil strips hang straight down.

Touch the head of the bolt with a plastic ruler that has just been rubbed with fur or wool. Free electrons in the ruler pass into the head of the bolt. Because metal is a good conductor, the electrons will not remain on the head of the bolt. They will run down into the leaves. The leaves will fly apart.

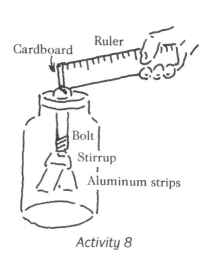

Cardboard   Ruler

Bolt

Stirrup

Aluminum strips

Activity 8

9. CHARGING BY INDUCTION   **Home**

In the previous experiment, you charged the leaves of an electroscope by touching the head of the bolt with the plastic ruler. The ruler had just been rubbed with fur. This time, bring the charged plastic ruler close to the head of the bolt but DON'T touch the bolt itself. Keep the end of the plastic ruler about an inch away from the head of the bolt.

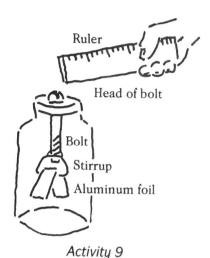

Note that the leaves of the electroscope spread apart. The "free electrons" on the ruler have "chased" or repelled the electrons from the head of the bolt into the leaves.

Around any charged body there is an area, or space, through which this electric force is exerted. This space or region is called the electric field. The experiment proves that a body (the electroscope) can be charged by bringing it into an electric field. This "remote-control" method of moving electrons is known as induction.

Activity 9

10. ANIMAL ELECTRICITY   **Home**

In 1786 an Italian scientist, Luigi Galvani, had a dead frog in a jar of salt water. The frog was hung by a copper hook tied to a string. Galvani picked up the string to place the frog on his lab table. By accident, one of the frog's legs touched a piece of iron. The frog kicked. According to Galvani, the frog jumped because of what he called "animal electricity."

Another Italian scientist of the time, Alessandro Volta, did not agree. He said that chemical electricity made the frog jump. This electricity was made apparent by the two different metals and the salt water. To prove his point, Volta made the first battery. He piled up small, circular plates of copper and zinc. Between each piece of copper and zinc was a cloth soaked with salt water. With this battery Volta could make a dead frog's legs jump at will.

11. ELECTRICITY FROM A LEMON!   **Home**

Get a new, clean penny and a new, clean dime. If you can't find new coins, clean old ones with steel wool. Cut two slits in a lemon about half an inch apart. Insert the coins in these slits. Now place your tongue on the coins. The tingle you may feel is electricity. You have made a voltaic cell. It is named in honor of Alessandro Volta.

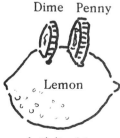

Activity 11

Your voltaic cell proves that all you need to manifest electricity by chemical means are two unlike metals and an acid. The metals are called electrodes. The acid is called the electrolyte.

12. *A WET CELL IN YOUR HEAD*   *Home*

The next time you have a freshly filled tooth, you can get evidence of the electricity in your mouth. Gently bite down on a strip of tinfoil from the wrapper of chewing gum, etc. The two different metals—the filling and the tinfoil—are the electrodes. The saliva in your mouth is the electrolyte. Result—a wet cell in your mouth. Electrons will be running around in your mouth—too many for comfort!

This is a compass galvanometer.

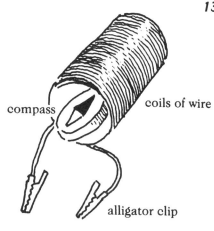

compass   coils of wire

alligator clip

Activity 13

13. *CURRENT DETECTOR*   *Supervised Classroom*

For some experiments you will need an instrument or device to let you know when a current of electricity is flowing through a wire. Such an instrument is called a galvanometer. The first part of this word, "galvano," refers to Galvani, the scientist who experimented with the dead frog. The second part of this word, "meter," means "to measure."

Perhaps you may borrow a galvanometer from your teacher. If not, you can make your own with a cardboard cylinder, such as one from the center of a roll of toilet paper. You may also use an empty cardboard salt container.

Wind 200 to 300 turns of number 24 insulated wire around the cardboard roll. (Number 28 enamel-covered wire also works very well.) Be sure to allow about five inches of wire to stick out from each end of the coil. You will need these "free ends" to make connections to your wet cell.

When you finish winding the wires on the cardboard, you may use tape to hold the wires in place. Place a small compass in the center of the cylinder. (You may purchase the compass in the toy department of a dime store.)

To attach the wires of your homemade galvanometer to the metals in a wet cell, fasten alligator clips to the ends of the wires. (Alligator clips are well named. Their sharp "teeth" give you a good "bite." You may purchase alligator clips in electronics stores.) Before you fasten the clips to the coil, be sure to scrape the insulation off the ends of the wires.

14. CHEAP ELECTRICITY

Supervised Classroom

Is it time to use the clean dime and penny again. Fasten the penny to one of the alligator clips and place it on the table. On top of this, place a small cloth soaked with salt water. On top of this, place the dime. Watch the compass needle. It will turn to show you that a current of electricity is flowing through the coil.

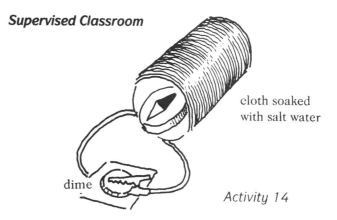

cloth soaked with salt water

dime

Activity 14

15. "ORANGE" ELECTRICITY

Supervised Classroom

For this experiment you will need a strip of copper and a strip of zinc. Each strip should be about four inches long and half an inch wide.

Connect one end of the coil to the copper strip by means of an alligator clip. Do the same for the zinc strip, connecting it to the other wire from the coil. Push the free end of the zinc strip into an orange. Now push the copper strip into the orange. What do you notice?

Push the ends of the metal strips into the orange for only half an inch. Then push the strips into the orange to a depth of two inches. Does this make any difference in the amount the compass needle turns?

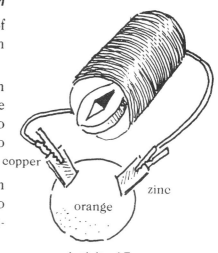

copper

zinc

orange

Activity 15

16. ELECTRICITY FROM COKE

Supervised Classroom

Use the same setup as in the previous experiment. This time put the strips of copper and zinc into a glass of Coke. Then try using 7-Up, vinegar, and salt water. Which gives the most electricity?

Place the metal strips at different depths in the liquid. Does this change the amount of electricity being made?

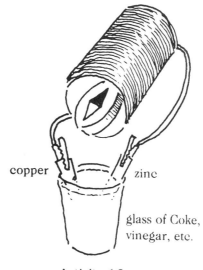

copper

zinc

glass of Coke, vinegar, etc.

Activity 16

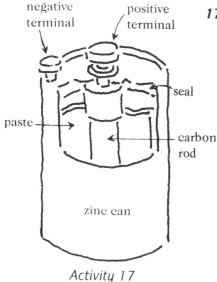

Activity 17

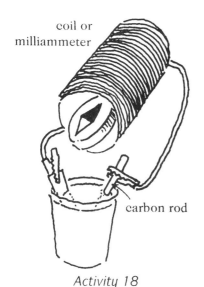

Activity 18

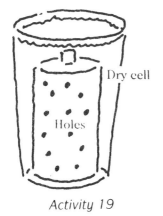

Activity 19

17. INSIDE A DRY CELL   *Supervised Classroom*

A wet cell is not convenient. The liquid (the electrolyte) can spill. We therefore use the so-called dry cell. To learn the "inside story" of a dry cell, perhaps you can find an old "dead" cell. Use a hacksaw to saw the cell in half lengthwise.

In the center of the cell is a black carbon rod. This is known as the positive terminal. The zinc can or container itself is the negative terminal. The acid used in making the cell is sal ammoniac. Ammonia may be familiar to you. It is the strong household chemical you use when you do housecleaning. It makes your eyes and nose smart when you smell it. Instead of pouring this liquid into the cell, it is mixed into a moist paste together with zinc chloride.

The zinc in a dry cell does two things. It acts as the container for the rest of the materials. It also gives the energy for the electric current. You may find many small holes in the zinc can. These are the places where the zinc was eaten away by the acid. The white powder surrounding the tiny holes is zinc chloride. The acid itself may have seeped out through the holes in the zinc.

A dry cell, then, is misnamed. It is really a non-spillable wet cell. The pitch seal at the top of the cell is to hold in the liquid. When the acid eats holes in the zinc and escapes, the cell becomes dry. As such, it is no good. It has no electrolyte.

18. FROM DRY CELL TO WET   *Supervised Classroom*

Take an old dry cell apart. Place the carbon rod and a piece of the zinc into a glass of vinegar. Use alligator clips and wires to hook the wet cell to a milliammeter or to your homemade "current detector."

19. LIFE FROM A "DEAD" CELL   *Supervised Classroom*

Get an old "dead" cell and punch holes in the zinc. To punch the holes in the zinc, use an ice pick or nail and hammer. When you have punched many holes in the zinc, place the old cell in a bottle or jar of vinegar, Coke, lemonade, or salt water. Connect the terminals of the cell to a milliammeter and see the results.

20. *ELECTROMAGNETIC INDUCTION* *Supervised Classroom*

So far we have seen that static electricity is made evident by friction. Electricity can also be manifested chemically by using two unlike metals and an acid. Most of the electrical current we use in our everyday lives is made in a power plant by spinning a magnet inside coils of wire. This puts electrons in motion and creates a flow of electricity. This method of making an electric current is called electromagnetic induction.

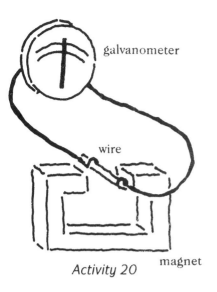

Activity 20

The following experiment will show you how to set electrons into motion. You will need a magnet, a wire, and a galvanometer to measure the current. If you wish, you may use the compass galvanometer described in Activity 13.

Get a short piece of copper wire about three or four inches long. Hook it up to the galvanometer with thinner copper wires, if need be. (Be sure to scrape the insulation off the wires whenever you want electric contact.)

Move the copper wire DOWN between the poles of the magnet. The needle of the galvanometer moves in one direction. Now move the copper wire UP. The needle goes in the opposite direction. You have made alternating current. Every time you change the direction in which you move the wire (down or up), the current changes direction.

Now hold the copper wire STATIONARY between the poles. You get NO current. Now move the copper wire BACK AND FORTH between the poles, but not across the magnetic lines of force that flow from the north pole to the south pole. Again, NO current.

This experiment shows that current is generated ONLY when:

1. there is MOTION of a conductor, and
2. the motion is at RIGHT ANGLES to the magnetic lines of force.

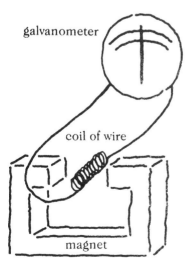

Activity 21

21. *MORE ELECTRICITY* *Supervised Classroom*

Repeat the above experiment, but instead of using a single strand of wire, use a coil of many turns of insulated wire. Move the coil through the magnetic field. You get much more current.

Note that you must move the coil perpendicular to the magnetic lines of force that travel from the north pole to the south pole of the magnet. The faster you move the coil across the magnetic field, the greater the current.

You have demonstrated that the amount of current generated depends upon the NUMBER of wires that cut the magnetic field and their SPEED through the magnetic field.

Now simply hold the coil stationary between the poles. You have both a magnet and a coil—but no current. Move the coil back and forth between the poles. Do NOT cut across the magnetic field. Move the coil parallel to the magnetic lines of force. Again, NO current.

By now, you must see that in order to get electrons into motion by electromagnetic induction (or, simply, with a coil of wire and a magnet), we need:

1. a magnet,
2. a coil of wire, and
3. motion across the magnetic field at a right angle to it.

The AMOUNT of the current will depend on:

1. the NUMBER of turns of wire in the coil, and
2. the SPEED with which the wires cut through the magnetic field.

HIGHLIGHTS OF THIS CHAPTER

- We do not "make" or "create" electricity. The electrons are already on the atoms. All we do is "shove the electrons along." We "get the electrons into motion." One way to do this is by rubbing, or friction. When rubber is rubbed with fur, the charge on the rubber is negative. The charge on the fur is positive. When we have electrons in motion we have an electric current. If 6.3 billion billion electrons pass a given place in one second, we have one ampere of current.

- In the center or nucleus of an atom we find:
    - Protons—which carry a positive charge.
    - Neutrons—which are electrically neutral.

- Running around the outside of the atom are the electrons. The negative charge of the electrons exactly equals the positive charge of the protons.

- The hydrogen atom is the only atom that does not have a neutron in its center or nucleus.

- Materials such as silver, copper, iron, and steel are conductors of electricity. They let electrons move through them easily.

- Dry air, rubber, glass, and silk are insulators. They block the flow of electrons.

- If a body has more electrons than protons, it is charged negatively. When electrons are taken away from a body, it is said to have a positive charge.

- Every charged body has an electric field of force around it.

- To make electricity by chemical means, you need two unlike metals and an acid. The metals are called electrodes. The acid is called the electrolyte.

- A galvanometer is an instrument to measure small amounts of electricity.

- A dry cell is really a non-spillable wet cell.

- To make electricity by means of electromagnetic induction, you need:
    1. a magnet,
    2. a coil of wire, and
    3. the coil of wire must be moved at a right angle to the magnetic field.

● The amount of the current you produce will depend on:

1. the number of turns of wire in the coil, and
2. the speed with which the wires cut through the magnetic field.

Multiple-Choice Questions

1. When you comb your hair with a plastic comb:
   a. you take protons out of your hair.
   b. you put protons into your hair.
   c. you take electrons out of your hair.
   d. you put electrons into your hair.

2. Which of the following is false?
   To make electricity by electromagnetic induction you need:
   a. a magnet.
   b. a coil of wire.
   c. motion of the coil perpendicular to the magnetic field.
   d. motion of the coil parallel to the direction of the magnetic field.

3. Which of the following is true?
   a. A proton weighs 1,835 times as much as the electron.
   b. The neutron rotates around the circumference of the atom.
   c. The electron is the biggest particle in the atom.
   d. The electron is in the nucleus of the atom.

4. The atomic number is:
   a. the number of protons in the nucleus.
   b. the number of protons plus neutrons in the nucleus.
   c. the number of electrons in the element.
   d. the number of neutrons in the element.

5. Which of the following is false?
   To make electricity by chemical means you need:
   a. 2 different metals.
   b. friction.
   c. acid.
   d. an electrolyte.

True or False Questions

1. The hydrogen atom is the only one that does not have a neutron in the nucleus.

2. When electrons are taken away from a body, it is said to have a negative charge.

3. The metals used in a wet cell are called electrodes.

4. The outside container of a dry cell is called the electrolyte.

5. When glass is rubbed with silk, the charge on the silk is positive.

Chapter 16

OUR ROMANCE THROUGH SPACE

We Are in a Spin

You are an astronaut! Your spaceship is the earth. This very moment you are speeding through space faster than any Saturn 5 rocket that took our astronauts to the moon.

To our eyes, our planet appears to stand solid and steady. It seems as unmoving as the Rocky Mountains. In reality, our spaceship is gliding across the vast ballroom of space. Even if you stay at home all day and never drop in at the nearest pizza castle, you are in a spin.

Our spaceship spins like a top. Every 23 hours, 56 minutes, and 4.1 seconds it makes one complete spin or revolution. The earth measures 24,903 miles around its "waist," or equator. This means our friends who live on the equator are truly in a spin. Our giant top turns east at the equator at a speed over 1,000 miles per hour. That is about 17½ miles per minute.

During the last 24 hours, you have gone around once with the world. If you live in San Francisco, your rate of travel was 13½ miles a minute. If you live in New York, you are heading east at this moment at the speed of 12¾ miles a minute. If you are a resident of our 49th state, living in Nome, Alaska, you are moving only 6 miles a minute.

THE SPIN THAT BRINGS SUNDOWN

According to a poet: "The light of the whole world dies with the dying sun." Actually, the sun does not die. It does not even have a heart attack. It keeps "blowing its top" in a series of hydrogen-bomb blasts. Each second some four million tons of the sun's mass or material explodes into energy.

When the earth turns so we can't watch the "hydrogen bomb" exploding over our heads, we call it night. The blackout is simply the shadow cast by the earth. As our great round spaceship continues to spin to the east, it once again brings the sun into view. We have "sunrise."

NO SUNRISE TOMORROW!

From the toplike motion of the earth there follows an alarming fact. There will be no sunrise tomorrow morning. Even though you stumble out of bed and squint at the candlelight of dawn glimmering on the eastern horizon, don't be fooled. The sun does not rise. It does not set. The sun stays fixed at the center of the solar system. It is like the hub or center of a wheel. The sun seems to turn around the earth, but in reality, the earth is spinning.

HOW FAST ARE YOU CRUISING THROUGH SPACE?

Our planet is not only spinning like a top, it is also galloping around the sun! The path followed by a heavenly body as it revolves or turns around a larger body is called its orbit. The earth's orbit or path around the sun is not a perfect circle. It is an ellipse, a sort of flattened circle. The mean or average distance from sun to earth is roughly 93 million miles. Since the earth's orbit is elliptical, the earth is sometimes as close as 91.3 million miles from the sun. At other times it is as far away as 94.5 million miles. In order to make one turn around the sun in one year, the earth must travel at a speed of 65,000 miles per hour.

To give you an idea of how fast you are galloping through space, think of this. The Saturn 5 rocket that brought our Apollo astronauts to the moon had a speed of 24,765 miles per hour. At this moment, you are rushing through space over twice that fast!

WHY DOES THE EARTH KEEP CIRCLING THE SUN?

Since our earth is traveling at such a tremendous speed, one might expect it to fly off into space. Why, you may ask, does the sphere on which we live whirl continually around the sun in an almost circular orbit?

Scientists explain it this way. The earth is bound and shackled to the sun with links stronger than iron yet as invisible as the air we breathe. A gasoline-powered model airplane is held in its circular orbit by guy wires in the hands of the "pilot" on the ground. In the same way, the earth is held in orbit by gravity. The huge sun is more than 1.3 million times the size of Earth. It reaches out through 93 million miles of space to hold the earth in orbit with its ever-present guy wires of gravity.

Our life truly "hangs in the balance." It is a balance between the gravitational pull of the sun and our forward speed. To replace the force of gravity the sun uses to hold us would take a steel cable 5,000 miles in diameter.

OUR NEAREST NEIGHBOR IN SPACE

Long before the Apollo astronauts began walking on the surface of the moon, people had some strange ideas concerning our nearest neighbor in space. You would become a lunatic, it was said, if ever you lifted your eyes to the evening sky and were overcome with the magic beauty and charm of the moon. "Luna" is the Latin word for moon. Lunatic means a person moon-struck, or affected by the moon. Years ago it was thought that light from the moon could make one insane.

HOW WIDE THE MOON?

The diameter of the moon is 2,160 miles. It does not quite match the width of the United States.

The moon is a satellite. This is a Latin word that means "an attendant." A satellite is an attendant body that revolves or moves around a larger one.

The moon moves around the earth much as the earth revolves around the sun. The sun holds the earth in orbit by gravity. In the same way, the gravitational pull of the earth holds the moon in its orbit.

HOW FAST THE MOON?

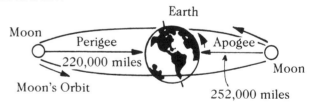

The moon speeds around the earth in a counterclockwise direction at a speed of 0.64 miles per second. (Counterclockwise is opposite the direction taken by the hands of a clock.)

The moon approaches as close as 220,000 miles to the earth. This is called its perigee. This word is from the Greek. "Peri" means "near," and "gee" means "earth." At other times the moon is distant from the earth by some 252,000 miles. This is called its apogee. "Apo" means "away from." The average or mean distance of the moon from the earth is 238,857 miles. This is often rounded out to 240,000 miles for easy reference.

MIRROR IN SPACE

The moon itself has no light. It is simply a huge rock or sphere. The light that seems to come from the moon began as bright light leaping from the flaming surface of the sun. In approximately 8 minutes it raced across some 93 million miles of space to strike the moon. Then it bounced back 240,000 miles to the earth in less than two seconds. Moonlight is "bounced" sunlight.

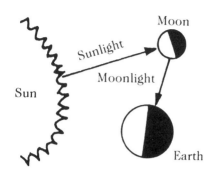

MOON MONTH

The time it takes the moon to circle once around the earth is called a lunar month. It is a period of 29½ days. The ancient Egyptians used lunar months in reckoning time. The Jewish people did also. For them it fixed the day of Passover and other feasts. The day of the new moon was the beginning of their month, which they celebrated as a holy day.

THE "FACES" OF THE MOON

The moon is like a person with a thousand faces. Sometimes its looks like a thin slice of silver melon. Again it is changed into a golden Chinese lantern aglow for a lawn party. Sometimes the moon vanishes. The world is wrapped in the darkness of night.

It may seem strange, but half of the moon is always flooded with sunlight. This is true except for those rare times when the earth gets between the sun and the moon. This occurrence is called a lunar eclipse.

You may be aware that you can see a full-faced moon beaming from the sky for only a few days each month. That is because the entire bright side of the moon

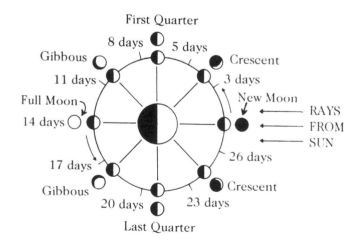

can be seen only when it is on the opposite side of the earth from the sun. At other times just a part of the bright side appears. Sometimes none at all can be seen. It all depends on the position of the moon in its flight around the earth. Every 29½ days the moon passes through what are known as phases. It goes from the usually invisible new moon, to quarter moon, to full moon, to quarter, and to new moon again. The new moon occurs when the moon gets between us and the sun. At these times the lighted half of the moon is on the wrong side for us to see it.

You will find something unusual in the diagram at the bottom of page 294. The earth is shown with the sunlight hitting it from the right-hand side. The inner circle of the moon shows that one-half of the moon is likewise hit by the sun. The outer circle shows us how the moon appears to us during a lunar month.

THE SHADOW FROM SPACE

Have you ever noticed how your shadow skips along ahead, behind, or beside you as you walk down a sidewalk? Anything in the path of the sun casts a shadow.

The moon casts a shadow too. It is a long, black one that trails to a point like an ice-cream cone or a dunce cap. When this cone-shaped shadow touches some spot on earth, there is an eclipse of the sun. "Eclipse" is a Greek word meaning "to leave out." "Solar" is a Latin word that refers to the sun. Whenever the moon is in a direct line between the earth and the sun, the sun is "left out." There is a solar eclipse. At the point where the moon's shadow touches the earth, the sun is darkened and an unearthly twilight begins.

The moon is only 2,160 miles in diameter. How can it blot out the sun, which has a diameter 400 times that size? To understand how this can happen, fix one eye on a distant building. Then hold a penny in front of your eye. The tiny copper piece prevents you from seeing the building. True, the diameter of the sun is 400 times that of the moon, but the sun is approximately 400 times as far away as the moon. It is like that distant building. The moon is like the penny that blocks out the view of the much larger object because it is closer to your eye.

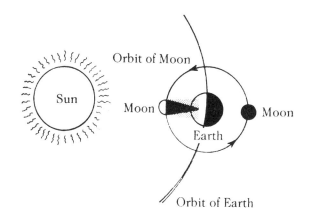

TOTAL ECLIPSE

A total eclipse of the sun takes place when the moon seems to cover the entire surface of the sun. The deep black shadow that the moon then throws on the earth is called an umbra. "Umbra" is a Latin word meaning "shade." The word umbrella means "little shade" or "little shadow." In India many folks carry umbrellas to make little shadows and thus shield themselves from the sun. They walk in the umbras of their umbrellas!

A total eclipse of the sun can be seen only from within the deep shadow called the umbra. This patch of deep shadow is never more than 170 miles in diameter. It travels across the face of the earth with amazing speed. The maximum time available to observe the eclipse is only about seven minutes. Usually the circle of deep shadow is less than 100 miles wide. A small umbra may last only two minutes.

ALMOST SHADE

Surrounding the circle of black shadow cast by the moon on the earth is a wider ring called the penumbra. This word means "almost shade." For people living in the area covered by the penumbra, the surface of the sun is only partly darkened. This is called a partial solar eclipse. Rays from the part of the sun that is not covered still reach the earth.

WHEN THE EARTH'S SHADOW SWALLOWS THE MOON

The earth casts a much larger shadow than the moon. When the earth is in a direct line between the sun and moon, this giant shadow swallows the entire moon. This lunar eclipse, as it is called, begins when the moon starts to enter the earth's shadow. It can be seen from half the earth's surface. It takes the blacked-out moon about an hour and 40 minutes to hurry through this deep shadow. If the

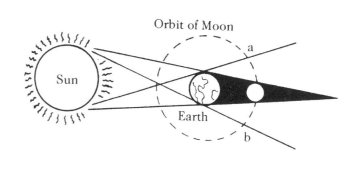

eclipse of the moon is partial, only part of the moon is in the shade of the earth's shadow.

There are never more than three lunar eclipses in a given year. There may be two, one, or none at all.

THE WANDERERS

The people of ancient times had only naked-eye views of the heavens, but they had sharp minds. When they looked up into the heavens, they saw two kinds of lights. Most of the bright lights stayed in their given place relative to each other. You could look into the heavens night after night and expect to find these lights in their right places. Each star in the Big Dipper, for example, stayed where it belonged, on the rim, or in the cup, or in the handle.

There were some lights, however, that wandered around. Sometimes these wandering lights even vanished from the sky for long weeks. To these lights the Greeks gave their word "planet," meaning "wanderer."

The "wanderers" known to the Greeks were five in number. The Romans named each of them after one of their gods or goddesses: Mercury, Venus, Mars, Jupiter, and Saturn. Sometimes the planets closest to the earth are called morning or evening stars. Although planets may look like stars, they have no light of their own. They reflect the light from the sun. If you look closely, you will see that planets shine with a steady glow while stars seem to twinkle. The stars are so distant they seem to be pinpoints of light. The thin rays of light from these distant stars are disturbed by air currents.

If you look at the planets through a telescope, they appear as small circles or disks of light. The light reflected from them is fairly steady because they are closer to earth.

SPEEDY

The ancient Romans were wide awake when they named the planet closest to the sun Mercury. Mercury was the speedy messenger of the gods. He is sometimes pictured as a young man with wings on his feet.

Why does the planet Mercury have to be speedy? To keep from being pulled into the flaming surface of the sun!

The closer a planet is to the sun, the greater is the pull of the sun's gravity on it. Tiny Mercury is only 36 million miles from the sun. In order to overcome the sun's powerful pull, Mercury has to gallop full speed ahead. It makes one trip around the sun in every 88 of our days. By contrast, we on the earth take 365 days to make our trip around the sun.

OUR LOVELY "TWIN"

Venus is called the earth's twin because both planets are about the same diameter. Venus is 7,700 miles in diameter. Earth is 7,913 miles in diameter.

Venus is the third brightest object in the sky, after the sun and the full moon. Venus can never be seen in the middle of the night. However, you may see the planet sometimes for as long as three hours or more in the early evening and early morning. This early-to-bed and early-to-rise habit led the Greeks to bestow two names upon Venus. When they saw Venus in the morning sky, they called it the Morning Star. (The Greek word is "Phosphoros.") When they saw it in the evening, they called it the Evening Star. (The Greek word is "Hesperus.")

It takes Venus 225 of our days to make one trip around the sun. Its speed forward is 22 miles per second. By contrast its twin, the earth, has a forward speed of 18.5 miles per second.

THE RED PLANET

Mars is named after the Roman god of war because of its angry red appearance in the night sky. It is the fourth planet from the sun, after Mercury, Venus, and the earth. Like these planets it has a mostly solid surface. By contrast, the outer planets are made mostly of gas.

Mars is just slightly more than half as large as the earth. Its diameter is 4,200 miles. Its speed around the sun is 15 miles per second. A day on Mars is 24 hours and 37 minutes. Its year is 686.98 Earth days, or 1.9 Earth years.

THE KING OF THE PLANETS

Jupiter is King of the Planets. It is so large it could swallow 1,300 earths. Its volume is 1½ times the volume of all the other planets put together. It has more than twice the mass or weight of all the other planets combined.

As befits a king, Jupiter does not "run" around the sun. Jupiter "walks" at a pace that takes 12 earth years to make one round trip. Its forward speed is only 8 miles per second.

Jupiter has an average diameter of about 86,800 miles. Compare this to the earth's 7,913-mile diameter.

Jupiter has a total of 16 moons orbiting it.

THE GOLDEN GLOBE

Saturn is the farthest planet that can be seen by the naked eye. It is some 886 million miles from the sun. Its volume is 815 times that of the earth. It takes Saturn 29.45 Earth years to make one trip around the sun. Its forward speed is about 6 miles per second. A day on Saturn lasts 10 hours, 39 minutes, and 26 seconds. Saturn is twice as far distant from the sun as Jupiter.

SATURN'S GLORY

Saturn's glory, one of the greatest spectacles of the solar system, is its rings. Before the coming of the space age, the rings seemed to be six in number. Photos sent back by the Voyager spacecraft showed that there are upwards of 1,000 rings. Until 1977, Saturn was believed to be the only planet encircled by rings. Now we know that both Jupiter and Uranus have thin, barely visible rings.

THE SEVENTH PLANET

Uranus is named for the god of the heavens. It is 1 billion, 782 million miles from the earth. It requires 84 earth years for Uranus to move once around the sun. Its forward speed is 4 miles per second. A day on Uranus is 10 hours and 45 minutes long. Its diameter is 31,000 miles. It has five known moons.

NEPTUNE

Neptune is nearly 3 billion miles from the sun. It takes Neptune 164.78 Earth years to make one trip around the sun. Its forward speed is about 3 miles per second. A day on Neptune is 15 hours and 48 minutes long. Its diameter is 28,000 miles.

THE LAST PLANET

The last planet to be discovered was Pluto. A Kansas man, Clyde Tombauth, made the discovery on February 18, 1930.

We know very little about Pluto. It goes around the sun once in 247.69 earth years. Its forward speed is 3 miles per second. Its diameter is about 1,500 miles. It spins on its axis once every 6.4 days.

THE "HAIRY ONES"

"Comet" is a Greek word meaning "hairy one" or "long-haired." The head of a comet is called the coma. Sometimes the coma has a very bright spot in its center. This brightest part of the coma is called the nucleus.

Some comets move around the sun in a "pushed-down" orbit or path. This type of orbit or path is called an ellipse. This is a Greek word that means "defect." The "defect" is that the path of the comet is not a circle. It looks more like a bike tire that has been pulled out on opposite sides. It is much longer than it is wide. Halley's Comet moves in such an elliptical orbit. It takes 76 years to make a round trip.

Comets may also move in another path called a parabola. This is from a Greek word meaning "shield." The path of the comet looks something like the shields the Greek warriors used on the field of battle. Comets that move in parabolic paths never return to the earth.

A DIRTY POTATO IN SPACE

In May of 1986, astronomers released the first detailed accounts of what was observed when five spacecraft flew past Halley's Comet in March, 1986. The scientists who took part in the Soviet and European experiments describe the nucleus as resembling a potato 9 miles long and 5 miles wide—roughly 10 times larger than expected.

The comet's surface features include at least seven spots that spew jets of dust and gas, primarily water vapor, toward the sun. The rest of its rolling "landscape," almost 40 square miles in area, is sooty black. It has an insulating layer that enables the surface to remain warm despite the underlying ice. The insulating layer on the comet, estimated to be less than one inch thick, is assumed to be the residue of many passages of the comet around the sun. Each trip around the sun drove off volatile gases and left behind dusty material.

HOT ROCKS FROM SPACE

Perhaps you have looked up into a clear night sky and seen a shooting star. Didn't it look like a bright, shining arrow shooting across the velvet-black sky?

In truth, the so-called shooting stars are not stars. They are small bits of matter. Some are tiny rocks about the size of a grain of sand. They bump into the earth's atmosphere at a height of about 50 miles. These particles plunge upon us at speeds of 40 miles per second. Friction with the air makes them glow white hot. Trails of gas from the burning rock make a bright, glowing ribbon of light.

The light itself is called a meteor. The word is taken from the Greek word that means "things in the air."

Before the tiny rock or grain of sand plunged into the air and made a streak of light it was called a meteoroid. A meteoroid is defined as a small, solid body traveling in the solar system.

FIREBALLS

Sometimes a rock crashing down from space is so big that the friction with the air does not burn it up. If the rock is about the size of your hand or larger, you may be in for a real thrill. As it speeds through the air, friction heats it up. The rock glows white hot. Sometimes it also gleams red, green, and yellow. This beautiful sight is called a fireball. If it explodes, it is called a bolide.

METEORITE

A rock from space that has lived through its long plunge through the air and has landed on the earth is called a meteorite. If this meteorite is seen coming down from the sky and is recovered, it is called a fall. If the rock is not seen falling from the sky but is picked up from the ground, it is called a find.

ASTEROIDS

There are more than 50,000 small planets called asteroids. "Asteroid" is a Greek word meaning "starlike." These small planets are also called planetoids, or minor planets. They roam around the sun in the space between Mars and Jupiter.

LUCKY MISS

During the week of May 25, 1986, a half-mile-thick asteroid missed the earth by about 3 million miles. According to a study done by the National Aeronautics and Space Administration, there is only one chance in 1,000 that an asteroid of about that size would smash into earth within the next 100 years. If one did hit, the impact could release energy equal to the detonation of 10,000 megatons of TNT —the equivalent of 10,000 average strategic nuclear weapons.

"By good fortune," said geologist Joseph V. Smith of the University of Chicago, "the earth has not suffered catastrophic loss from an impact by a comet or an asteroid during historic time."

YOUR PERSONAL STAR

You have a personal star. It is called the sun. Without this star you could not wiggle a little finger, walk one step, or read this print.

You can feel the effects of this star in your life this very moment. Simply place your hand on the side of your face. The warmth of your body, the warmth of your blood, is a gift to you from our nearest star. It is the daytime star we call the sun.

THE CORONA

During times of total solar eclipse, astronomers love to look at one of the most delightful sights in the heavens—the sun's corona.

"Corona" is a Latin word meaning "crown." The sun's crowning glory is a thin, extremely hot outer atmosphere. The corona is not a solid thing like a gold crown. It is continually flowing out from the sun. It is made of particles shot out from the sun.

SOLAR PROMINENCES

Tongues of gushing gas and vapor leap up from the surface of the sun. They lash out over a million miles in space. They are particularly visible when the sun is in eclipse. Some leap up like coiled springs and swiftly vanish. Others quiver weirdly through long days. Such streamers of gas are known as solar prominences. They are huge red clouds of hydrogen gas.

SUNSPOTS

Dark spots often appear on the sun's surface. They are called sunspots. They were discovered in 1611 by Galileo. Sunspots are seething oceans of gases that swirl in giant circles 5,000 to 50,000 miles in diameter. Our earth could easily vanish into a large sunspot. Individual sunspots remain visible for periods ranging from a few days to several months. Whence they came and how they go is not known. Clusters of sunspots are often detected, especially at intervals of about 11 years.

THE MILKY WAY GALAXY

Our sun is but one of some 200 billion stars arranged in space like a huge wagon wheel or dinner plate. We call this island of stars the Milky Way galaxy. This collection of hundreds of millions of stars is some 100,000 light-years from rim to rim and 10,000 light-years thick. In other words, a light beam that travels from the sun to the earth in 8 minutes takes 100,000 years to go from edge to edge of the Milky Way.

Our earth and the entire solar system are located toward the outside "rim" of this "wheel" or "dinner plate." Our entire solar system, in fact, is merely a speck. It is about 2/3 of the distance from the center of the "wheel" or "plate."

When we look up we see stars so distant they appear as a hazy, white band encircling the sky overhead. This broad, faint band of light extends like a veil across the vastness of space. It may remind you of a road or lane across the heavens. This is what ancient people thought it to be—a milk-white road, the Milky Way. The word "galaxy" is a Greek word meaning "circle of milk."

ACTIVITIES

1. DAY AND NIGHT

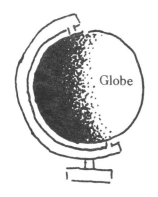

Activity 1

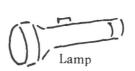

Lamp

Use a desk lamp, spotlight, or strong flashlight to represent the sun. Use a globe of the earth. If a globe is not available, a basketball or grapefruit will do.

Place the globe about five feet from the light. Darken the room. Spin the globe slowly. Notice how much of the "earth" is always in darkness.

Attach a piece of stiff paper to the globe to represent a tall building. Spin or rotate the globe slowly. Watch how "sunrise" hits the top of your "skyscraper" first, then slowly reaches the "ground."

You will also be able to demonstrate how the last rays of sunset continue to illuminate the top of a tall building. This happens even after the ground is in shadows.

Move the globe to within two feet of the lamp. Put your hand over the part of the globe that represents your state. First hold the globe so the sun's rays hit your hand directly, at an angle of 90°. Notice the amount of heat. Now tilt the globe so that the rays hit your hand at a low angle. What happens to the heat now? Why?

2. MAKE YOUR OWN MOON!

Use a desk lamp or spotlight for the sun. Use a globe or a basketball to represent the earth. Use an apple tied to a string to represent the moon.

Darken the room and direct the light from the spotlight or lamp onto the "earth." Hold the apple by the string and let this "moon" move around the "earth" at the equator. Note that when the moon is between the earth and the sun, it throws a shadow on the earth. This gives us a solar eclipse. When the moon is on the side of the earth away from the sun, the moon is lost in the shadow cast by the earth. This gives us a lunar eclipse.

Notice that we get one solar eclipse and one lunar eclipse with every turn of our apple "moon" around the earth. We would enjoy this sight every month if the moon circled the earth continuously in this manner. Alas, the moon does not always go around the earth like the belt around your waist, so eclipses don't happen that often.

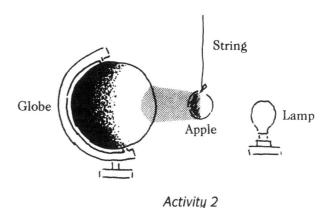

Activity 2

Now hold the apple between the basketball and the lamp but high enough so its shadow does not fall on the earth. When this happens, the dark side of the moon faces the earth. We have a "new" moon. When the moon is high in the heavens on the opposite side of the earth from the sun we see a full moon. To demonstrate this phase of the moon, hold the apple on the far side of the basketball and high enough so the light from the lamp hits it. What do you notice?

3. FOLLOW THE MOON   Home

If you live where the skies are fairly clear, you will find it interesting to "follow the moon" for one month. Make a little drawing each evening on your calendar to show how the moon looks.

Note how many days it takes to go from quarter moon to full moon.

How many nights out of a month is the moon "full"?

How many nights out of a month can you expect to see a moon in the sky?

Note how many nights of the month lack the magic touch of the moon in the sky.

4. OUR NEIGHBOR WORLD

There is a captivating article in *National Geographic* magazine for February, 1958. Try to find this old issue. You will find the pictures on pages 282 to 288 especially interesting. On the pages on the left-hand side are photos of the moon as taken through powerful telescopes. On the facing pages are maps of the same areas giving the names of all the features.

5. *A FANTASTIC VOYAGE*

An article in the *National Geographic*, for May 1969 tells the story of Apollo 8's meeting with the moon. This issue contains the most beautiful and overwhelming photo of the moon I have ever seen. It is a foldout picture on page 596. It allows you to see the surface of the moon as the Apollo 8 astronauts saw it from the window of their spacecraft. The surface of the moon is about 80 miles beneath the spacecraft. Far in the distance, 240,000 miles away, is the earth. It is floating like an ornament in the Christmas sky of 1968.

Pictures on pages 614 and 615 show how delicate and small our earth appears when seen from distant space.

On page 616 you can see why Astronaut Frank Borman called the moon "vast, lonely, forbidding." Astronaut James Lovell said that the moon was "very, very stark."

On page 619 you will see why Astronaut William Anders referred to the far side of the moon as looking like "a sandpile my kids have been playing in."

6. *BUILD YOUR OWN "SOLAR SYSTEM"*   Home

Use a grapefruit to represent the sun, grapes for the smaller planets, an apple for Jupiter, and two walnuts for Uranus and Neptune. A big plum with a paper ring attached around its middle can represent Saturn.

Please note that your "planet salad" only suggests the comparative sizes. It is not exact. Arrange your "planets" so they are in their correct order in relation to the sun.

7. *SPOT THE PLANETS*   Home

See how many planets you can observe in the evening sky. Some city newspapers publish charts every month that will help you identify any planets that may be visible.

8. *A SOLAR MAP*

If at all possible, look at a copy of *National Geographic* magazine for July 1981. Its foldout map of the solar system is up-to-date, accurate, and complete. You will enjoy the beautiful illustrations showing the planets and their moons. Especially interesting is the drawing of Jupiter with its recently discovered ring. Remember to look at Uranus with its thin, delicate rings.

9. **COUNT SHOOTING STARS**   *Home*

If you live where there are clear skies, mark your calendar to remind yourself of the dates of the various meteor showers. From August 10 to 12, for example, you may wish to watch the Perseid showers. Keep track of how many shooting stars you see in one hour.

10. **WALK INTO A CRATER**

Someday, perhaps, you may have the good luck to visit the state of Arizona. If possible, try to get to the great meteorite crater 40 miles east of Flagstaff. This hole or crater was punched into the earth some 20,000 years ago by a monster rock or pile of rocks from space. Traveling at a speed of 33,000 miles per hour, this meteoric mass struck the earth. The crater is 4,150 feet from rim to rim. It is more than three miles in circumference. It is deeper than the Washington Monument is tall.

11. **WATCH THAT HELIOTROPE!**

The word "heliotrope" is a Greek one that means "to turn with the sun." One of the most interesting heliotropes to watch is the sunflower. It turns so as to keep its face toward the sun all day.

12. **VISIT A PLANETARIUM**

Many people live in huge cities where smoke, smog, and city lights make it very difficult, if not impossible, to see the stars at night. Fortunately, many cities today have planetariums. The planetarium is a projector or machine that throws images of the stars on a curved, domed ceiling. So accurate and lifelike are the images of the stars glittering high overhead that many people gasp with astonishment when they first see the beauty of the evening sky.

Many planetariums change their programs with the seasons. In December, for example, a favorite presentation is "The Star of Bethlehem."

13. STAR CHARTS

For a number of years I lived in the country. At night, when there were no clouds, it was a thrill to look up at the sparkling stars. With the aid of a star chart I learned the names of different groups of stars. My star chart had a dial that could be turned to correspond to the time of the year and the hour of the night. It also showed how certain constellations or groups of stars vanish from the sky during some months of the year, only to appear later on.

You will find a star and planet locator easy to use. You will be delighted to find yourself at home among the stars. Various types of star charts and locaters are offered for sale by:

Edmund Scientific
101 East Gloucester Pike
Barrington, New Jersey 08007

HIGHLIGHTS OF THIS CHAPTER

- Our spaceship, the earth, spins like a top. It whirls at the speed of approximately 1,000 mph at the equator.

- Our planet is also galloping around the sun at the rate of almost 65,000 mph. The reason our planet does not run away from the sun is that the gravitational pull of the sun holds onto the earth.

- The diameter of the moon is 2,160 miles. It does not quite match the width of the United States.

- The average distance of the moon from the earth is about 240,000 miles.

- The time it takes the moon to circle once around the earth is called a lunar month. It is a period of about 29½ days.

- A total eclipse of the sun takes place when the moon seems to cover the entire surface of the sun.

- When the earth's shadow swallows up the moon, we have a lunar eclipse.

- The lights that wander across the skies are called planets.

- Mercury is the closest planet to the sun. It is the "speedy" planet. It has to have a high forward speed to avoid being pulled in by the sun's powerful gravity.

- The twin of the earth is Venus. Both planets are about the same size. Venus is the third brightest object in the sky. Mars is the fourth planet from the sun.

- Jupiter is the king of all the planets. It is 1,300 times the size of the earth.

- The glory of Saturn is its system of sparkling rings.

- Neptune and Uranus are considered to be "twins." They are both about the same size.

- Pluto was discovered in 1930.

- "Comet" is a Greek word meaning "hairy one" or "long-haired."

- Shooting stars are not stars. They are small bits of matter that plunge into our atmosphere at a height of about 50 miles. Friction with the air makes them glow white hot.

- A meteorite is a rock from space that has lived through its long plunge through the air and has landed on the earth.

- There are some 50,000 small planets called asteroids.

- Our personal star is the sun. Our sun is but one of some 200 billion stars that make up the Milky Way galaxy.

Multiple-Choice Questions

1. In the northern hemisphere, where we live, it is colder in the winter than in the summer because:
    a. the earth is a lot farther away from the sun then.
    b. the sun's rays do not hit us head-on in winter.
    c. the earth slows down in winter.
    d. the earth spins faster in winter.

2. The point at which the moon is closest to the earth is called the moon's:
    a. perigee.
    b. apogee.
    c. umbra.
    d. penumbra.

3. The moon goes around the earth:
    a. once a week.
    b. once a day.
    c. once a year.
    d. once a month.

4. A meteoroid is:
    a. a shooting star.
    b. a hot rock from space plunging through the earth's atmosphere.
    c. a rock from space that has landed on earth.
    d. a small solid body traveling in the solar system.

5. If you are in Chicago, you are:
    a. standing still.
    b. being pulled toward the equator.
    c. moving eastward constantly.
    d. moving westward constantly.

True or False Questions

1. The sun does not rise or set.

2. Moonlight is "bounced" sunlight.

3. Saturn is the only planet with rings.

4. If a rock is seen falling from space and then is picked up, it is called a "find."

5. "Fireball" is another name for a comet.

Appendix A

THE METRIC SYSTEM

Now I'd like to show you that the metric system is as easy as dollars and cents. The truth is that you have been using the metric system all your past life—when it came to dollars and cents. The metric system uses decimals; we in the United States use decimals in our money system.

The Dollar is the Unit of Our Money

It is divided as follows:

DIME - this word is from the Latin word "decimus," meaning one tenth. The Latin prefix "deci" means one tenth ($1/10$ or .1). The next time you ask a pal to loan you a dime, ask, instead, for a deci-dollar.

CENT - is another Latin word. The Latin prefix "centi" means one hundredth. We rightly call a penny a cent, for that is what it is, namely, one hundredth ($1/100$ or .01) of a dollar.

MILL - is another Latin word. The Latin prefix "milli" means one thousandth ($1/1000$ or .001). I still have a mill left over from the days when I lived in St. Louis in the 1930s. The city had a sales tax based on mills. You got 10 mills for a penny.

We can sum up what we have learned in the following outline:

.1 of a DOLLAR is a dime.
.01 of a DOLLAR is a cent.
.001 of a DOLLAR is a mill.

The Meter is the Unit of Length in the Metric System

When the French adopted the metric system, the meter was intended to be, and very nearly is, a ten-millionth part of the distance from the north pole to the equator when measured along a line through Paris.

The meter is slightly longer than our yard, measuring 39.37 inches.

The meter is broken up into decimals, just like our dollar.

.1 of a meter is a decimeter.

A decimeter is to the meter as a dime is to a dollar.

.01 of a meter is a centimeter.

A centimeter is to a meter as a cent is to a dollar.

.001 of a meter is a millimeter.

A millimeter is to a meter as a mill is to a dollar.

We now have the following comparison:

DOLLAR

.1 of a DOLLAR is a dime.

.01 of a DOLLAR is a cent.

.001 of a DOLLAR is a mill.

METER

.1 of a METER is a decimeter.

.01 of a METER is a centimeter.

.001 of a METER is a millimeter.

The Gram is a Unit of Mass and Weight in the Metric System

A gram is defined as being the mass of one cubic centimeter of pure water taken at a temperature of 4° centigrade.

.1 of a gram is a decigram.

.01 of a gram is a centigram.

.001 of a gram is a milligram.

We now combine all our comparisons:

DOLLAR

.1 of a DOLLAR is a dime.

.01 of a DOLLAR is a cent.

.001 of a DOLLAR is a mill.

METER

.1 of a METER is a decimeter.

.01 of a METER is a centimeter.

.001 of a METER is a millimeter.

GRAM

.1 of a GRAM is a decigram.

.01 of a GRAM is a centigram.

.001 of a GRAM is a milligram.

We have divided the dollar, meter, and gram into smaller parts; namely, one tenth, one hundredth, and one thousandth.

Go Big! Think Greek!

We can also multiply our units by ten ("deka"), one hundred ("hecto"), and one thousand ("kilo"). The prefixes indicating these measurements all come from Greek.

Appendix B

THE SCIENTIFIC METHOD

Science starts with curiosity. Curiosity is wanting to know.

People were curious about what was beneath the great layer of ice that covers the North Pole, so scientists made a submarine with special underwater searchlights. On August 3, 1958, the *Nautilus* became the first submarine to pass under the North Pole on her history-making voyage under the polar ice cap. As the powerful searchlights of the *Nautilus* swept across the under side of the 12-foot-thick ice, people had their first look at this strange, cold world at the top of the earth.

People looked up into the midnight skies and wondered what was out there in space, so they devised the first primitive telescopes centuries ago. Gradually these have developed into such advanced examples as the Hale telescope at Palomar Observatory in California. The 200-inch glass mirror this telescope possesses can collect 640,000 times as much light as the human eye. Telescopes that use mirrors to collect the light are known as reflecting telescopes.

When people first began to ask questions about the universe in which we live, they called their study "physics"—a word that means the study or science of nature. Many historians consider physics the oldest of all the sciences. Physics deal with the world of things around us that do not have life.

Today physics is but one of the many sciences. As time went on, people acquired new knowledge. Sometimes this new knowledge was given a different name. That's why we have today many branches of this tree of knowledge. It is the custom now to divide the sciences into three main groups, or classes: physical sciences, life sciences, and social sciences.

How Scientists Work

Scientists learn about nature by observation and experimentation. Observation is looking at or taking notice. Experimentation is testing or demonstrating.

When you worked the experiments with the pendulum in Chapter 5, you found out how one scientist went about his work. You used what is called the scientific method—the method, or way, to solve a problem:

1. First there was a problem: "What determines the time needed for a pendulum to make one complete swing?"

2. Perhaps you made a number of guesses. The time might depend on the arc, the weight of the bob, or its length.

3. You collected data, or facts. You did this by letting the bob swing through small and big arcs. You used different weights for bobs. You varied the length of the pendulums.

4. You concluded that the time depends only on the length of the pendulum. The speed of the falling body (the bob) does not depend on its weight.

5. To be sure that your conclusions were correct, you repeated the experiments and checked for any mistakes, or errors.

6. As an added proof that the speed of a falling body does not depend on its weight, you experimented with marbles rolling down an inclined plane.

Joseph Priestley

Sometimes scientists have to be quite clever to think of an experiment that will prove their point.

Do you know how Joseph Priestley, an eighteenth-century chemist, discovered that plants give out oxygen? (Oxygen is the part of the air you breathe that keeps you alive.) He put mice in a sealed jar in which there were plants. The mice lived. When he placed mice in a sealed jar without plants, the mice died.

Louis Pasteur

Sometimes a scientist carries on experiments only at the risk of death!

At the peril of his own life, Louis Pasteur used a glass tube to suck saliva, or spit, from the foaming mouths of dogs that had the disease known as rabies. Then he injected this saliva into rabbits.

When the rabbits developed the disease, he took out the rabbits' spinal cords. This is the main place the deadly rabies poison attacks. Pasteur hung the deadly cords up to dry, hoping this would weaken the virus, or poison, to a point where it would not be deadly any more. After the cords had been drying for 14 days, they were ground up and mixed with a liquid. This mixture was injected into animals. Pasteur's hunch was right. The mixture did not give rabies to the research animals.

The big question, however, was not yet answered. Would the mixture, called a vaccine, protect human beings? On July 6, 1885, Pasteur had a terrible opportunity to find the answer.

At this time in history, rabies was always fatal. No person had ever been known to live after being bitten by an animal that had it. A nine-year-old boy, Joseph Meister, had been bitten 14 times by a dog with rabies. Joseph was almost certain to die. Yet Pasteur knew that if he gave the boy his vaccine and it failed, his medical enemies might charge him with murder!

With worry and doubt, Pasteur shot vaccine made from the 14-day rabbit cord into the sick boy.

The boy lived.

The good news spread. Dozens of bitten people crowded into Pasteur's tiny laboratory to be given the vaccine.

Different Methods

By now you see that different scientists discover new things by different methods. Galileo used exact measurements and mathematics to reach his conclusion about pendulums. Louis Pasteur had no mathematics to guide him. He had to make a leap in the dark, guided only by his own brilliant mind, and at the risk of his life and reputation.

Some writers of history divide scientists into two groups: the data gatherers, who collect facts, and the theory makers, who dream the impossible dream. (A theory may be called a guess or a mental plan of the way to do something.)

The larger group of scientists are data gatherers, who follow more or less closely the scientific method. We become data gatherers when we followed the scientific method and repeated the experiments that led Galileo to his discoveries.

The Theory Makers

The second and much smaller group of scientists are the theory makers, who sometimes may seem like dreamers chasing visions. One such theory maker is Dr. Charles Townes, the Nobel Prize winner who gave us the theory that led to the ruby-red laser, a beam of light so powerful it can burn a hole in a piece of steel—and yet so delicate it can be used in an operation on the human eye.

Dr. Charles Townes tells us that he got his ideas that led to the laser while he was sitting on a park bench, in early spring, in Washington, D.C., looking at some flowers. He says that "the great scientific discoveries, the real leaps, do not usually come from the so-called scientific method, but by revelations which are just as real."

In revelations we are shown things that were not known before.

Other famous scientists who got many of their ideas by revelations are Sir Isaac Newton and Albert Einstein. During an 18-month period in his early twenties, Sir Isaac Newton formulated the law of gravitation, invented calculus, and proposed theories of light and color.

Answer Key

Chapter 1 Activities

1. What happens? The block of wood does not turn with the gallon jar. Why? Because of Newton's First Law of Motion which says, "a body at rest tends to remain at rest."

5. What happens? The moment you jerk on the scale, the indicator will jump to a higher reading. As you continue to pull, the indicator will fall back to a lower reading.

   Why? It takes more force to get something into motion than it does to keep it moving.

7. What happens? The rapidly moving water tends to stay in motion. It whirls around with the wooden block.

   Why? Because of the second part of Newton's First Law, "a body in motion tends to stay in motion."

8. When the skateboard hits the brick, the Cabbage Patch doll will be thrown forward.

9. Newton's First Law of Motion informs us that a body in motion tends to keep in motion in a straight line unless compelled by an external force to change. The yo-yo falls downward until it comes to the end of the string. It is then forced to reverse direction and roll back up the string.

13. What happens? The marble will "climb" up the walls of the glass bowl. Why? A body in circular motion tries to "flee from the center."

14. What happens?

    The amount of the centrifugal force depends on several things:
    a. The WEIGHT—the heavier the weight the greater is the centrifugal force tending to hurl it off the rim.
    b. The DISTANCE FROM THE CENTER—the greater the radius, or the distance of the weight from the center, the greater is the centrifugal force.
    c. The SPEED—the faster the turntable spins, the greater the force tending to throw the weight off the turntable.

17. What happens? As you rotate the pipe faster, the washer will "flee the center" and pull up on the bolt to bring it in contact with the lower rim of the pipe.

Multiple-Choice and True or False Questions

1. c	2. d	3. c	4. c	5. a
1. True	2. True	3. False	4. True	5. True

Chapter 2 Activities

4. What happens? The first time you pull, string #2 breaks.

    Why? The heavy book tends to remain at rest. It absorbs the sudden pull. The second time string #1 breaks. When you pull slowly, the force has time to extend up through the book to string #1. This means that string #1 has to withstand both your pull and the pull of the book.

5. The faster you accelerate, the more force is required.

6. The force required to push three bricks is three times the force required to push one brick. You have proved that the force required to put an object in motion depends on the mass of the object.

Multiple-Choice and True or False Questions

1. d	2. b	3. c	4. c	5. b
1. True	2. False	3. True	4. False	5. True

Chapter 3 Activities

5. When the gas pressure builds up, the cork will pop out. The reaction to the expanding gas will push the bottle backward.

8. The rocket will go much higher due to the additional mass of the water rushing out the exhaust.

9. Throw the coconuts one at a time as hard as you can out the prow of the canoe. The reaction will push the canoe to the shore.

10. Simply sneeze. The reaction will push you to the shore.

12. The freight train has been standing still. As it very slowly begins to move, its cow catcher pushes you to one side.

    The bike is speeding down a steep hill at high speed. Astride it is a 215-lb. man.

Multiple-Choice and True or False Questions

1. b   2. a   3. b   4. d   5. c
1. False   2. True   3. True   4. False   5. True

Chapter 4 Activities

6. You are in such a state of stable equilibrium that you are unable to get out of the chair—unless you become unstable. You can do this by leaning your body forward.

8. The container will rock back and forth until its center of gravity comes to rest in the lowest position possible.

9. Strange as it may seem, the hammer is in stable equilibrium. A slight tipping tends to raise the center of gravity, which is in the head of the hammer.

12. You have an amazing demonstration of stable equilibrium. It is stable because a slight tipping tends to raise the center of gravity, which is in the heavy buckle.

13. When the head of the hammer is in the air, you have unstable equilibrium. A slight tipping tends to lower the center of gravity.

14. The center of gravity gets into the act, as you will find out for yourself.

Multiple-Choice and True or False Questions

1. a   2. d   3. c   4. b   5. b
1. True   2. True   3. True   4. False   5. False

Chapter 5 Activities

1. The results are truly amazing. Like Galileo, you will find that the size of the arc has no influence on the time required for a complete swing of the pendulum. In other words, the period of the pendulum is independent of the size of the arc through which it swings.

2. The results show that the heavy weight takes the same time to make the swing as did the light weight. The time required for a complete swing is independent of the weight of the bob. Truly amazing—the weight has nothing to do with the speed!

4. The results show that the longer the pendulum, the longer the time needed to make the swing. In other words, the period of a pendulum is proportional to

the square root of the length of the pendulum. You no doubt found that the period of the 9-inch pendulum was half that of the 36-inch pendulum.

6. Again you find that the weight of a body has no effect on its speed.

7. It shows that the final speed is determined both by the amount of acceleration and the time the object accelerates. Expressed in a formula:

$$S_f = at$$

S_f = final speed or velocity
a = acceleration
t = time

8. D represents a speed of 60 m.p.h. due east.

12. When the bob reverses direction it "falls" from C to B and "climbs" back toward A again. If it were not for friction, the pendulum would be a perpetual motion machine.

13.
$$D = \tfrac{1}{2} at^2$$
$$1 = \tfrac{1}{2}(32 \times t^2)$$
$$1 = 16\,t^2$$
$$1/\sqrt{16} = t = \tfrac{1}{4}\text{ second}$$

14. A pendulum starting from a given height will reach the same height on the opposite end of its swing. This occurs even when the string hits an intervening object, such as the handle of the broom.

15. The arrow would come down into your hip pocket!

17. The 6-foot pendulum swings back and forth in slow, majestic style, like a king walking in dignity and precision up to his throne.

18. Suppose it takes 4 seconds from the time the baseball leaves your hand until it falls back into your hands. This means that the baseball spent 2 seconds on the way up and 2 seconds on the way down.

To find the final speed, we use this formula:

$$S_f = at$$
$$S_f = 32 \times 2 = 64 \text{ ft. per sec.}$$

This is the same speed with which it left your hand.

To find how high the baseball went we use this formula:

$$D = \tfrac{1}{2} at^2$$
$$D = \tfrac{1}{2}(32 \times 2^2) = 16 \times 4 = 64 \text{ feet}$$

To find the average speed, we use this formula:

$$S_a = \frac{1}{2} S_f$$
$$S_a = \frac{1}{2}(64) = 32 \text{ ft. per sec.}$$

Multiple-Choice and True or False Questions

1. b	2. d	3. c	4. a	5. c
1. True	2. True	3. False	4. True	5. True

Chapter 6 Activities

2. Even though the mouth of the bottle of the flask is not pressed against the bottom of the glass, the water does not all spill out. The pressure of the air on the water in the glass holds the water up inside the bottle.

5. As the air inside the bottle cools, a partial vacuum will result. The atmospheric pressure may force the balloon into the bottle.

6. When the partial vacuum is formed, the grapefruit-size balloon is too large to go entirely into the bottle. Only a portion of the balloon goes inside the bottle.

7. The burning paper consumes oxygen in the bottle. Since oxygen forms about $1/5$ of the air, a partial vacuum is created. In addition, the air inside the bottle cools and shrinks, which increases the partial vacuum. As a result, the air in the room will push water up inside the upside-down bottle. Dramatic proof, indeed, that air does exert pressure.

8. The first thing to notice is how fast the candle flame consumes the oxygen. Then notice how rapidly the water rises in the bottle.

9. The water will rise up in the glass only about 2 centimeters. The air trapped in the glass keeps the water out.

13. The gas compressed in the pop expands and comes to the top.

15. When you blow into the tube, you compress the air inside the bottle. When you remove your mouth, this compressed air forces water up and out the tube. If the bottle is only about ¼ full of water, you can compress more air in the bottle. The greater amount of compressed air will produce a more dynamic "fountain."

11. The air trapped in the bottle keeps the balloon from blowing up.

21. When you release your grip on the squeezed-down bottle, its volume will increase. This lowers its internal pressure. Atmospheric pressure may force smoke down into the bottle.

24. The water stays in the jar. Air pressure pushing up on the lid holds the water in the jar.

Multiple-Choice and True or False Questions

1. b   2. d   3. c   4. b   5. d
1. False 2. True 3. False 4. True 5. False

Chapter 7 Activities

3. To solve this problem, remember that a column of water 1 foot high and with a cross-sectional area of 1 square inch exerts a pressure of approximately ½ pound. If you are 6 feet tall and the pipe has a cross-sectional area of 1 sq. in., the pressure will be 6 × ½, or 3 lbs. per sq. in.

6. The scale beneath the gallon jar gains as much weight as the spring scale in your hand loses.

9. The egg is more dense than fresh water, so it sinks. When salt is added to the water, however, the egg rises to the surface, since it is less dense than salt water.

10. The average human body normally has a density just slightly less than that of water. If you inhale, you increase the volume of your chest by a small amount. You may find that you can float when your lungs are filled with air, but when you exhale, you sink.

    Bones have a greater density than fatty tissue. A person with large bones does not float as easily as an overweight person with a smaller frame.

15. If the carton is tipped on its side as shown here, so the holes are all the same distance from the "bottom," the water pressure at each hole will be the same.

17. The mothballs are heavier than water. They cannot displace their own weight, so they sink to the bottom. Soon, however, hundreds of little gas bubbles cling to the surface of the mothballs. This extra buoyancy enables the mothballs to slowly rise to the surface, where the gas bubbles break away and escape. Deprived of this extra buoyancy, the mothballs sink once more, only to repeat the process again and again. The up-and-down cycle of mothballs demonstrates the fact that if an object becomes lighter than water, it will float to the surface and remain there as long as it can displace its own weight.

22. Their combined weight is $(3 \times 12 \times 3/12) \times 62.4 = 9$ cu. ft. $\times 62.4 = 561.6$ lbs.

23. Density = Mass/Volume = 45.2 gms./8 cc. = 5.65 gms. per cc.

Multiple-Choice and True or False Questions

1. b 2. c 3. a 4. b 5. b
1. True 2. False 3. True 4. True 5. False

Chapter 8 Activities

2. The apples do not fly apart, but come together. The high-velocity air moving between the apples reduces the air pressure between them. The atmospheric pressure of the air on the outside of the apples pushes them together.

5. Air rushing out of straw #1 at "B" reduces the air pressure on the top of straw #2. Atmospheric pressure pushing on the surface of the water in the glass forces water up and out of straw #2. This water is caught in the moving air stream.

6. The paper will rise to flutter in the air stream. By blowing on the top side of the paper you create a high-velocity airstream. This reduces the air pressure on the top side. Atmospheric pressure on the bottom side pushes the paper up.

15. The cork placed in the center of the glass will slowly move to one side due to surface tension. The cork placed on the side of the "haystack" will be pulled to the middle by surface tension.

16. The soap and the oil will reduce the surface tension existing between the toothpicks. The stronger surface tension on the outside of each toothpick will pull them apart. The effect is most dramatic. You may also use a liquid detergent.

17. The steel wool sinks immediately. You have "torpedoed" it by using a detergent to reduce surface tension. You made the water more "wet."

21. The smaller the drops, the more perfect the spheres.

26. The buoyant force of the mixture will counterbalance the downward pull of gravity, so surface tension will have an opportunity to mold the oil drops into near-perfect spheres.

29. This is a vivid way to demonstrate that the rise of water is greater where the capillary tube is thinner. It also illustrates that a capillary tube doesn't have to be a cylinder. It may be any narrow space.

Multiple-Choice and True or False Questions

1. d	2. a	3. b	4. c	5. a
1. False	2. True	3. True	4. False	5. False

Chapter 9 Activities

5. As long as the same two surfaces are in contact, the coefficient of friction remains the same.

7. The greater the area exposed to the wind, the greater the force required.

8. The faster you go, the greater the air resistance.

14. We would have a perpetual motion machine if the pendulum continued to exchange kinetic and potential energy and never lost its energy. Alas, as the pendulum swings through the air, it meets friction. This friction causes a decrease in the amount of energy. As the pendulum swings from A to C, the amount of kinetic energy gained is not quite equal to the potential energy lost. A little more potential energy is lost than kinetic energy is gained. As the pendulum swings from C to E it does not gain back quite all the potential energy it had at A. Some of the pendulum's energy is also lost due to the friction at the place where the string is tied to the rod.

16. Toss a baseball up into the air. As it leaves your fingers, it is all kinetic energy. As it rises, gravity slows it down and changes its kinetic energy into potential energy. When the ball comes to a stop on reaching its maximum height, it is all potential energy. On the way back down, its P.E. is changed into K.E.

17.
At the top
P.E. = 1,200 ft. lbs.
K.E. = 0

¼ way down
P.E. = 900 ft. lbs.
K.E. = 300 ft. lbs.

½ way down
P.E. = 600 ft. lbs.
K.E. = 600 ft. lbs.

¾ way down
P.E. = 300 ft. lbs.
K.E. = 900 ft. lbs.

At the moment you hit water
P.E. = 0
K.E. = 1,200 ft. lbs.

Multiple-Choice and True or False Questions

1. d	2. b	3. c	4. b	5. d
1. True	2. True	3. False	4. True	5. True

Chapter 10 Activities

5. The right hand will tell you that the water is warm. Your left hand will tell you that the water is cold. You can't trust your hands to tell the correct temperature.

8. Copper conducts heat approximately nine times better than iron.

11. The top of the flame does not go through to the top side of the screen. The copper screen conducts heat away so fast that there is not enough heat to ignite the gas that passes through the screen.

12. The iron screen can't carry the heat away as fast as the copper. If the flame is high enough, it may get the iron screen red hot and ignite the gas on the other side.

18. The rising convection currents from the candle warm the air inside the box on the right-hand side. As the air inside this box expands, it becomes less dense. It weighs less than the air in the box on the other side, as the tilting meter stick will indicate.

23. The black cloth, since it absorbs more radiant energy than any of the others, will have melted more snow. Radiant energy will produce heat if it is absorbed. A black body is a good "absorber."

26. As the dry ice turns into vapor, giant-size bubbles of carbon dioxide rise to the surface of the water and break with a bubbling sound. Clouds of carbon dioxide gas tumble out over the top of the bowl and fall to the top of the table. The "clouds" "flow" along the flat surface of the table like a river. When they come to the edge of the table, the "river" of white "smoke" falls to the floor. This is a beautiful demonstration of the behavior of a gas that is heavier than air.

    After a few minutes the intense cold of the block of dry ice will freeze the water in direct contact with it. Thus covered with a layer of thick ice, the carbon dioxide will not be able to escape. The bubbling will stop—but only for a time. Before long, the gas pressure builds up under the layer of ice. With a loud bang, the gas finally breaks open the shell of ice and the process continues.

27. The first thing to notice is that small bubbles of gas seem to mysteriously appear from nowhere. Many of these bubbles cling to the sides of the glass. Heat drives these bubbles of air out from the water in which they were dissolved. The absence of air from freshly boiled water is responsible in part for its flat taste.

   For a brief time the water "rumbles." Finally, bubbles of steam form on the bottom of the flask. They start to rise, but they vanish suddenly. When they bump into colder layers of water above them, they condense back into liquid. As water rushes in to fill the space previously occupied by the bubbles, it makes a humming sound.

   All this time bubbles launch forth bravely from the bottom of the flask. Then they stagger, grow smaller, and vanish as they are condensed by cooler water. Despite their continued defeats, the bubbles slowly succeed in working their way closer and closer to the surface. About this time you will notice thin, gauze-like clouds trailing across the surface of the water. Some of the water vapor escaping from the surface condenses.

   At last, bubbles of steam rising from the bottom of the flask steadily increase in size as they rise to the surface. There they break to produce the turbulent motion we associate with boiling.

29. The current of electricity flowing through the copper wire produces heat in the wire in much the same fashion it does in coils of an electric toaster. As the copper wire becomes warmer, it grows longer and sags. When you turn off the current, the wire will cool in a short time and return to its original length.

Multiple-Choice and True or False Questions

1. c	2. d	3. b	4. a	5. d
1. True	2. False	3. True	4. True	5. False

Chapter 11 Activities

2. The pencils will appear to be bent in different directions.

3. The quarter will appear. The light waves are bent at position B when they pass from the air into the water. The apparent image is at D.

5. Your hand will appear to be very large. The rays of light are bent or refracted in going from the water through the glass and into the air.

8. The focal length depends upon the curve of the lens. The sharper the curve, the shorter is the focal length. In this experiment you use a lens like a camera to produce a small image of the sun. The images formed by convex lenses are called "real."

10. The greater the curvature of the marble, the greater is the magnifying power.

20. You will see a shimmering "parade" of gleaming images that seem to march forever.

21. As you will see, a plane mirror reverses an image. The word STAR becomes RATS.

22. You have made a kaleidoscope. If you can hold it together with a string or rubber bands, use it to look outdoors on a bright day.

29. a. The image is real, inverted, and diminished. You are using the lens as a camera to take a picture of a distant object.

    b. Although the image is bigger than it was before, it is still inverted and diminished. You are using the lens as a camera to take a picture of a not-too-distant object.

    c. The image on the opposite side of the lens will likewise be at twice the focal length. You are using the lens as a copying camera. The image, though inverted, is the same size as the object (the lamp).

    d. The image is inverted and enlarged. You are using the lens as a projector.

    e. There is no image. Instead, you have a blob of light. This represents the setup of automobile headlights. They are arranged to throw a circle of light down the highway, not an image of the filament on the pavement.

    f. You are now using the lens as a microscope. The image is enlarged and is on the same side of the lens as the object. This image cannot be thrown on the screen.

38. a. The bird will appear to be just where it is—straight up. However, since the light beam is moving through water, it is slowed down. The bird will appear to be closer to you than it really is.

    b. You can no longer see the bird at N. When the beam of light leaves the water, it will be bend in the direction D. This means that, even though you are submerged, you will be able to see a bird sitting in the branches of a tree at point D.

c. At point C, where the beam of light hits the under-surface of the lake, draw another normal, N2O2. If the angle between the ray of light and the normal is 48.5°, something strange happens. The beam of light does not leave the water. It is bent through an angle of refraction that is 90°. It moves out across the surface of the lake. You could see a rowboat floating on the lake. The angle of 48.5° is known as the critical angle for water. If a beam of light hits the surface at an angle of 48.5° or more, the light never leaves the water.

d. If you look up at the under surface of the water at an angle greater than 48.5° the light is reflected down to the bottom of the lake. By looking up, you can see down!

Multiple-Choice and True or False Questions

1. d	2. b	3. a	4. a	5. c
1. True	2. True	3. False	4. True	5. True

Chapter 12 Activities

6. The first time you hit the ruler you most likely see the free end moving back and forth, but you won't hear it.
The second time you may be able to both see it move and hear it.

The third time the free end of the ruler will vibrate much faster, and the sound you hear will be higher, or have a higher frequency.

The frequency is the number of times in one second that an object moves back and forth, or vibrates.

The lowest frequencies the human ear can hear vary from 16 to 20 per second. The highest frequencies vary from 16,000 to 20,000 vibrations per second.

Now you know why you can't hear your arms when you move them up and down as fast as you can. You simply cannot move them faster than 20 times a second!

8,9. These experiments will show that the frequency of string instruments—such as the piano, guitar, and violin—depends on three things: the length of the string (or wire); its weight (how thick and heavy the string is), and how tightly it is strung (tension).

10. The pitch or frequency will go up.

11. You may be amazed how clearly the sound travels through the wood.

14. The vibrations are now coming to you by bone conduction. Note, especially, how clear and loud the fork is when you hold the base of the fork on the big bone behind your ear.

Multiple-Choice and True or False Questions

| 1. d | 2. a | 3. c | 4. b | 5. d |
| 1. True | 2. False | 3. True | 4. True | 5. False |

Chapter 13

Multiple-Choice and True or False Questions

| 1. c | 2. d | 3. a | 4. c | 5. a |
| 1. False | 2. True | 3. True | 4. False | 5. True |

Chapter 14 Activities

1. In addition to amoebae, you may see plants that consist of a single cell. They are called thallophytes—from the Greek "thallos," meaning "young shoot," and "phyla," meaning "plants." They have a mass of protoplasm but no roots, stems, or leaves.

2. Most likely the bean plant will emerge through the hole in its search for light.

5. On flat ground trees grow at an angle of 90°, or perpendicular to the ground. If trees grew the same way on the sides of hills, they would be sticking straight out from the steep hills like pins stuck perpendicularly into the sides of a pincushion. The tree would be in unstable equilibrium.

   When a tree grows on a hillside, cells in the tree produce what is called "reaction wood." This forces the trunk into a vertical alignment and thereby keeps the center of gravity in a relatively stable position.

Multiple-Choice and True or False Questions

| 1. c | 2. a | 3. b | 4. d | 5. c |
| 1. True | 2. False | 3. False | 4. True | 5. True |

Chapter 15 Activities

3. At first the charged ruler will attract bits of paper. Now watch closely. You may see that bits of paper cling for a moment to the ruler. Suddenly they jump off and move away. These bits of paper have become negatively charged. They are repelled.

5. The like charges on the two balloons make them repel each other.

6. When both rulers are rubbed in the same manner, they will have like charges so they will repel each other.

   The glass rod with a positive charge will attract the ruler.

14. As you push the ends of the metals into the orange, a current of electricity flows through the coil. The deeper you push the metals into the orange, the more current. The amount of electricity being made depends on the area of the metals in contact with the acid.

15. Among the different acids listed, vinegar gives the greatest amount. The deeper you place the metals in the acid, the more electricity.

Multiple-Choice and True or False Questions

1. c	2. d	3. a	4. a	5. b
1. True	2. False	3. True	4. False	5. False

Chapter 16 Activities

1. The lower the angle, the less the heat. In the winter the earth is closer to the sun than it is in the summer, but the rays of the sun hit it at a glancing angle, not head-on as they do in the summer.

2. When you hold your apple "moon" high enough on the opposite side of the earth so it reflects the light back down to Earth, you have what may be called a "harvest moon" or a "hunter's moon." This full moon is always a delight to see in the heavens.

Multiple-Choice and True or False Questions

1. b	2. a	3. d	4. d	5. c
1. True	2. True	3. False	4. False	5. False